2006 Yearbook of Astronomy

2006 Yearbook of Astronomy

edited by

Patrick Moore

co-editor

John Mason

MACMILLAN

First published 2005 by Macmillan
an imprint of Pan Macmillan Ltd
20 New Wharf Road, London N1 9RR
Basingstoke and Oxford
Associated companies throughout the world
www.panmacmillan.com

ISBN 1 4050 4866 2

9 8 7 6 5 4 3 2 1

A CIP catalogue record for this book is available from the British Library.

Typeset by Rowland Phototypesetting Ltd,
Bury St Edmunds, Suffolk
Printed and bound in Great Britain by
Mackays of Chatham plc, Chatham, Kent

Contents

Editors' Foreword

The *2006 Yearbook* follows the familiar pattern, with the usual wide range of subjects, and articles both from our regular contributors and from some very welcome newcomers. The new style, enlarged star charts for both Northern and Southern Hemispheres, drawn by Wil Tirion, and the expanded section summarizing the events for the year, both of which we introduced last year, seem to have met with readers' approval, and have been retained.

Gordon Taylor has, as always, provided the material for the invaluable monthly notes, and John Isles and Bob Argyle have provided the information on variable stars and double stars respectively.

PATRICK MOORE
JOHN MASON
Selsey, August 2006

Preface

New readers will find that all the information in this *Yearbook* is given in diagrammatic or descriptive form; the positions of the planets may easily be found from the specially designed star charts, while the monthly notes describe the movements of the planets and give details of other astronomical phenomena visible in both the Northern and Southern Hemispheres. Two sets of star charts are provided. The **Northern Charts** (pp. 17 to 41) are designed for use at latitude 52°N, but may be used without alteration throughout the British Isles, and (except in the case of eclipses and occultations) in other countries of similar northerly latitude. The **Southern Charts** (pp. 43 to 67) are drawn for latitude 35°S, and are suitable for use in South Africa, Australia and New Zealand, and other locations in approximately the same southerly latitude. The reader who needs more detailed information will find *Norton's Star Atlas* an invaluable guide, while more precise positions of the planets and their satellites, together with predictions of occultations, meteor showers and periodic comets, may be found in the *Handbook* of the British Astronomical Association. Readers will also find details of forthcoming events given in the American monthly magazine *Sky & Telescope* and the British periodicals *The Sky at Night*, *Astronomy Now* and *Astronomy and Space*.

Important note

The times given on the star charts and in the Monthly Notes are generally given as local times, using the 24-hour clock, the day beginning at midnight. All the dates, and the times of a few events (e.g. eclipses) are given in Greenwich Mean Time (GMT), which is related to local time by the formula

Local Mean Time = GMT – west longitude

In practice, small differences in longitude are ignored, and the observer will use local clock time, which will be the appropriate Standard (or Zone) Time. As the formula indicates, places in west longitude will have a Standard Time slow on GMT, while places in east longitude will have a Standard Time fast on GMT. As examples we have:

Standard Time in	
New Zealand	GMT + 12 hours
Victoria, NSW	GMT + 10 hours
Western Australia	GMT + 8 hours
South Africa	GMT + 2 hours
British Isles	GMT
Eastern ST	GMT – 5 hours
Central ST	GMT – 6 hours, etc.

If Summer Time is in use, the clocks will have been advanced by one hour, and this hour must be subtracted from the clock time to give Standard Time.

Part I

Monthly Charts and Astronomical Phenomena

Notes on the Star Charts

The stars, together with the Sun, Moon and planets, seem to be set on the surface of the celestial sphere, which appears to rotate about the Earth from east to west. Since it is impossible to represent a curved surface accurately on a plane, any kind of star map is bound to contain some form of distortion.

Most of the monthly star charts which appear in the various journals and some national newspapers are drawn in circular form. This is perfectly accurate, but it can make the charts awkward to use. For the star charts in this volume, we have preferred to give two hemispherical maps for each month of the year, one showing the northern aspect of the sky and the other showing the southern aspect. Two sets of monthly charts are provided, one for observers in the Northern Hemisphere and one for those in the Southern Hemisphere.

Unfortunately, the constellations near the overhead point (the zenith) on these hemispherical charts can be rather distorted. This would be a serious drawback for precision charts, but what we have done is to give maps which are best suited to star recognition. We have also refrained from putting in too many stars, so that the main patterns stand out clearly. To help observers with any distortions near the zenith, and the lack of overlap between the charts of each pair, we have also included two circular maps, one showing all the constellations in the northern half of the sky, and one those in the southern half. Incidentally, there is a curious illusion that stars at an altitude of 60° or more are actually overhead, and beginners may often feel that they are leaning over backwards in trying to see them.

The charts show all stars down to the fourth magnitude, together with a number of fainter stars which are necessary to define the shapes of constellations. There is no standard system for representing the outlines of the constellations, and triangles and other simple figures have been used to give outlines which are easy to trace with the naked eye. The names of the constellations are given, together with the proper names of the brighter stars. The apparent magnitudes of the stars are indicated roughly by using different sizes of dot, the larger dots representing the brighter stars.

The two sets of star charts – one each for Northern and Southern Hemisphere observers – are similar in design. At each opening there is a single circular chart which shows all the constellations in that hemisphere of the sky. (These two charts are centred on the North and South Celestial Poles, respectively.) Then there are twelve double-page spreads, showing the northern and southern aspects for each month of the year for observers in that hemisphere. In the **Northern Charts** (drawn for latitude 52°N) the left-hand chart of each spread shows the northern half of the sky (lettered 1N, 2N, 3N . . . 12N), and the corresponding right-hand chart shows the southern half of the sky (lettered 1S, 2S, 3S . . . 12S). The arrangement and lettering of the charts is exactly the same for the **Southern Charts** (drawn for latitude 35°S).

Because the sidereal day is shorter than the solar day, the stars appear to rise and set about four minutes earlier each day, and this amounts to two hours in a month. Hence the twelve pairs of charts in each set are sufficient to give the appearance of the sky throughout the day at intervals of two hours, or at the same time of night at monthly intervals throughout the year. For example, charts 1N and 1S here are drawn for 23 hours on 6 January. The view will also be the same on 6 October at 05 hours; 6 November at 03 hours; 6 December at 01 hours and 6 February at 21 hours. The actual range of dates and times when the stars on the charts are visible is indicated on each page. Each pair of charts is numbered in bold type, and the number to be used for any given month and time may be found from the following table:

Local Time	**18^h**	**20^h**	**22^h**	**0^h**	**2^h**	**4^h**	**6^h**
January	11	12	1	2	3	4	5
February	12	1	2	3	4	5	6
March	1	2	3	4	5	6	7
April	2	3	4	5	6	7	8
May	3	4	5	6	7	8	9
June	4	5	6	7	8	9	10
July	5	6	7	8	9	10	11
August	6	7	8	9	10	11	12
September	7	8	9	10	11	12	1
October	8	9	10	11	12	1	2

Local Time	**18h**	**20h**	**22h**	**0h**	**2h**	**4h**	**6h**
November	9	10	11	12	1	2	3
December	10	11	12	1	2	3	4

On these charts, the ecliptic is drawn as a broken line on which longitude is marked every 10°. The positions of the planets are then easily found by reference to the table on p. 74. It will be noticed that on the **Southern Charts** the ecliptic may reach an altitude in excess of 62.5° on the star charts showing the northern aspect (5N to 9N). The continuations of the broken line will be found on the corresponding charts for the southern aspect (5S, 6S, 8S and 9S).

Northern Star Charts

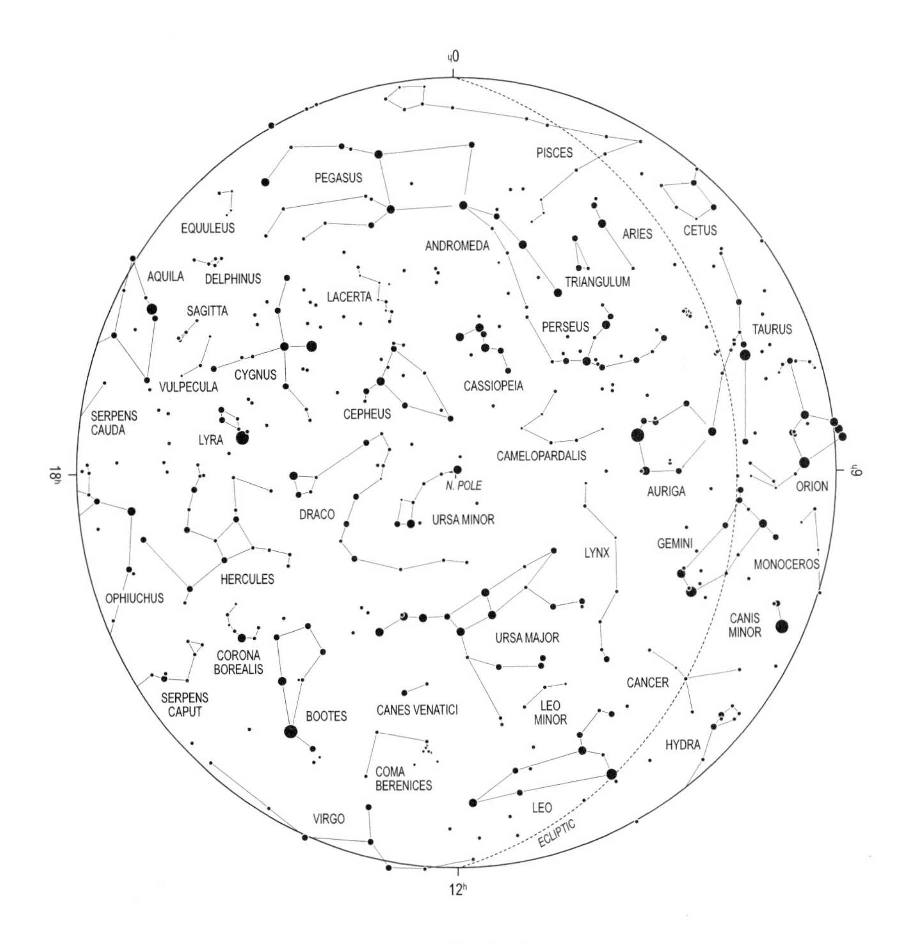

Northern Hemisphere

Note that the markers at 0h, 6h, 12h and 18h indicate hours of Right Ascension.

1N

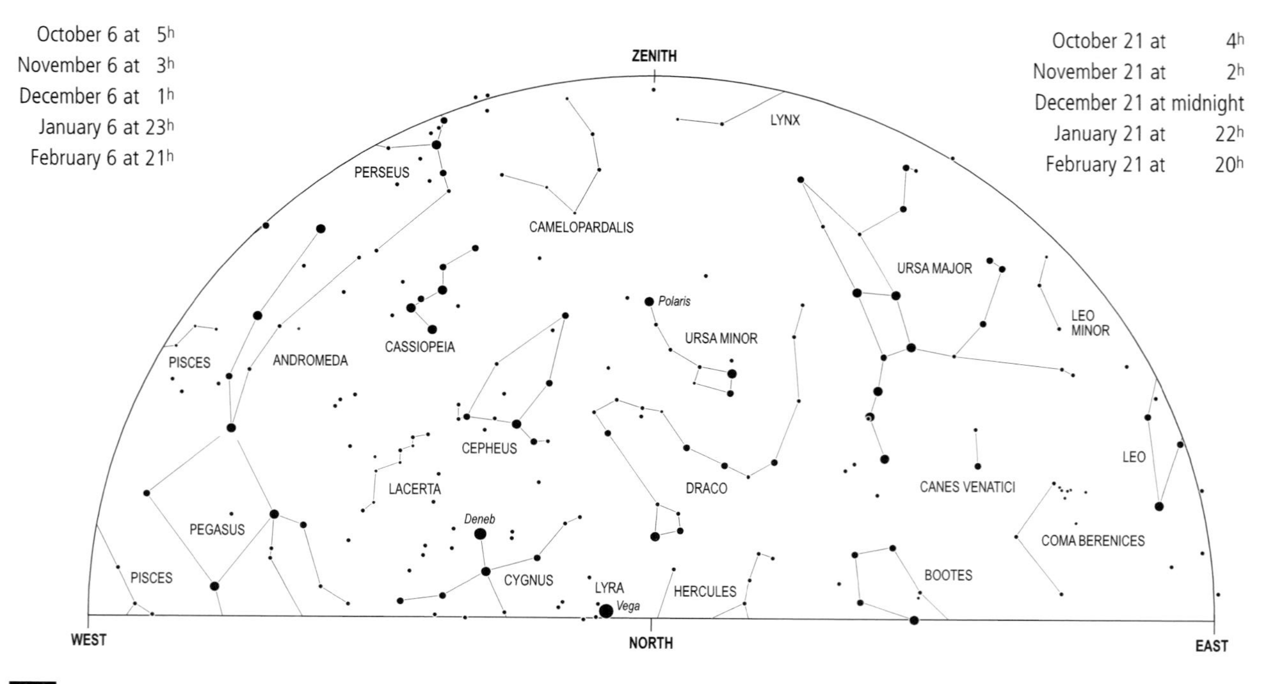

October 6 at 5h
November 6 at 3h
December 6 at 1h
January 6 at 23h
February 6 at 21h
ZENITH
October 21 at 4h
November 21 at 2h
December 21 at midnight
January 21 at 22h
February 21 at 20h
LYNX
PERSEUS
CAMELOPARDALIS
URSA MAJOR
Polaris
CASSIOPEIA
PISCES
ANDROMEDA
URSA MINOR
LEO MINOR
CEPHEUS
LEO
LACERTA
DRACO
CANES VENATICI
Deneb
PEGASUS
COMA BERENICES
PISCES
CYGNUS
LYRA
HERCULES
BOOTES
Vega
WEST
NORTH
EAST

October 6 at 5h	October 21 at 4h
November 6 at 3h	November 21 at 2h
December 6 at 1h	December 21 at midnight
January 6 at 23h	January 21 at 22h
February 6 at 21h	February 21 at 20h

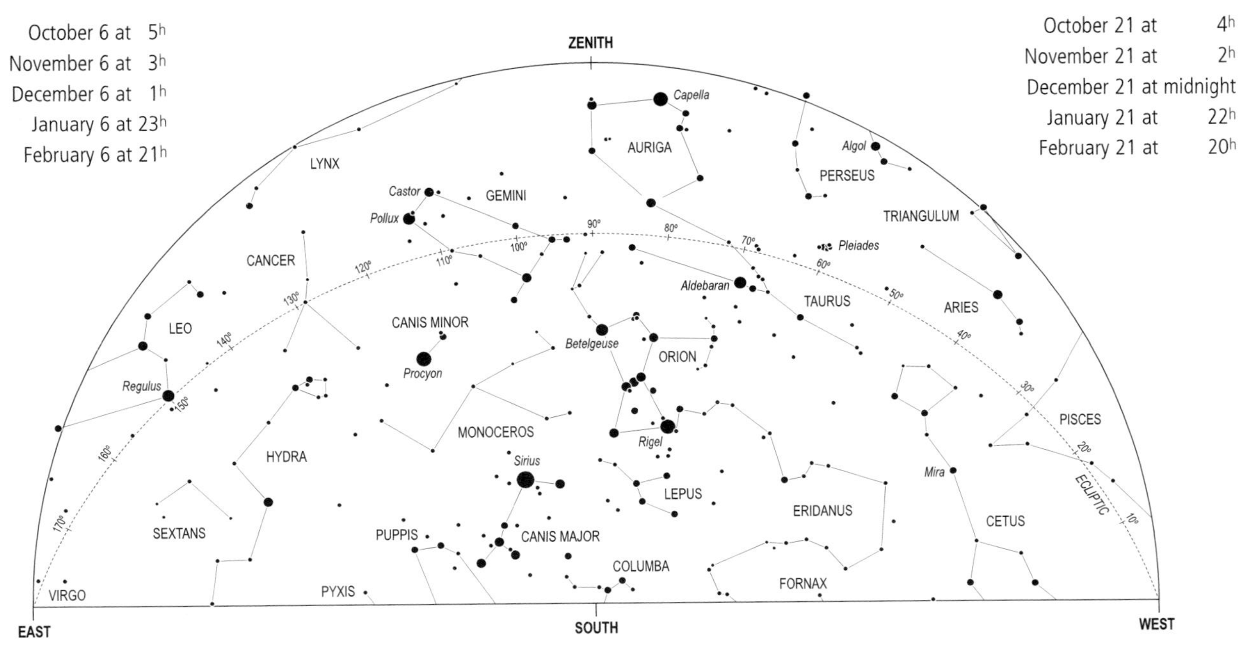

2N

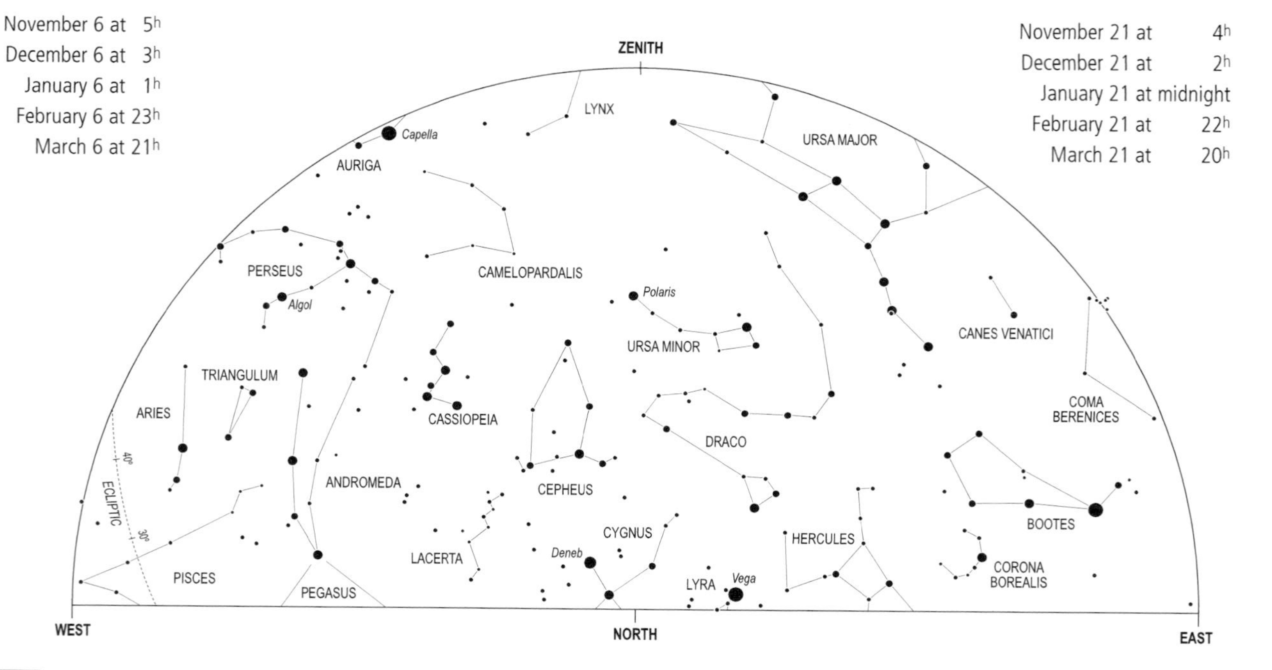
November 6 at 5h
December 6 at 3h
January 6 at 1h
February 6 at 23h
March 6 at 21h
November 21 at 4h
December 21 at 2h
January 21 at midnight
February 21 at 22h
March 21 at 20h
ZENITH
WEST
NORTH
EAST
ECLIPTIC
40°
30°
LYNX
Capella
AURIGA
URSA MAJOR
PERSEUS
Algol
CAMELOPARDALIS
Polaris
URSA MINOR
CANES VENATICI
TRIANGULUM
ARIES
CASSIOPEIA
COMA
BERENICES
DRACO
ANDROMEDA
CEPHEUS
BOOTES
CYGNUS
HERCULES
LACERTA
Deneb
CORONA
BOREALIS
PISCES
PEGASUS
LYRA
Vega

November 6 at 5h
December 6 at 3h
January 6 at 1h
February 6 at 23h
March 6 at 21h

November 21 at 4h
December 21 at 2h
January 21 at midnight
February 21 at 22h
March 21 at 20h

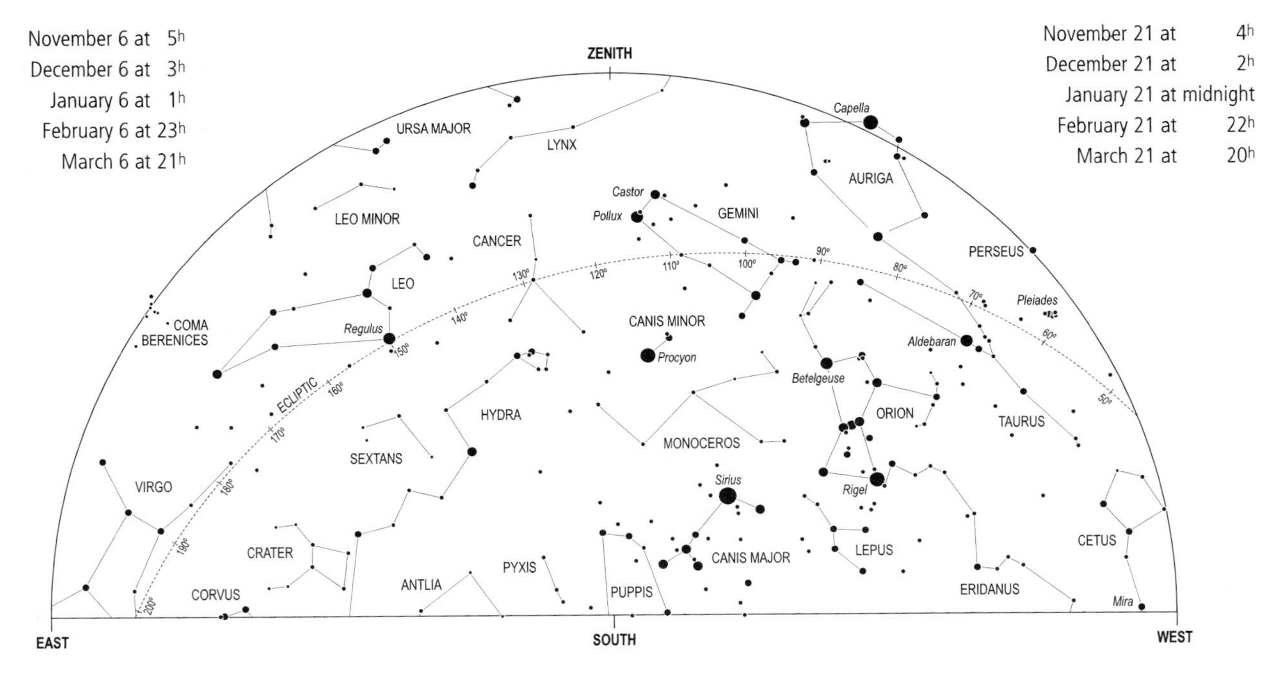

3N

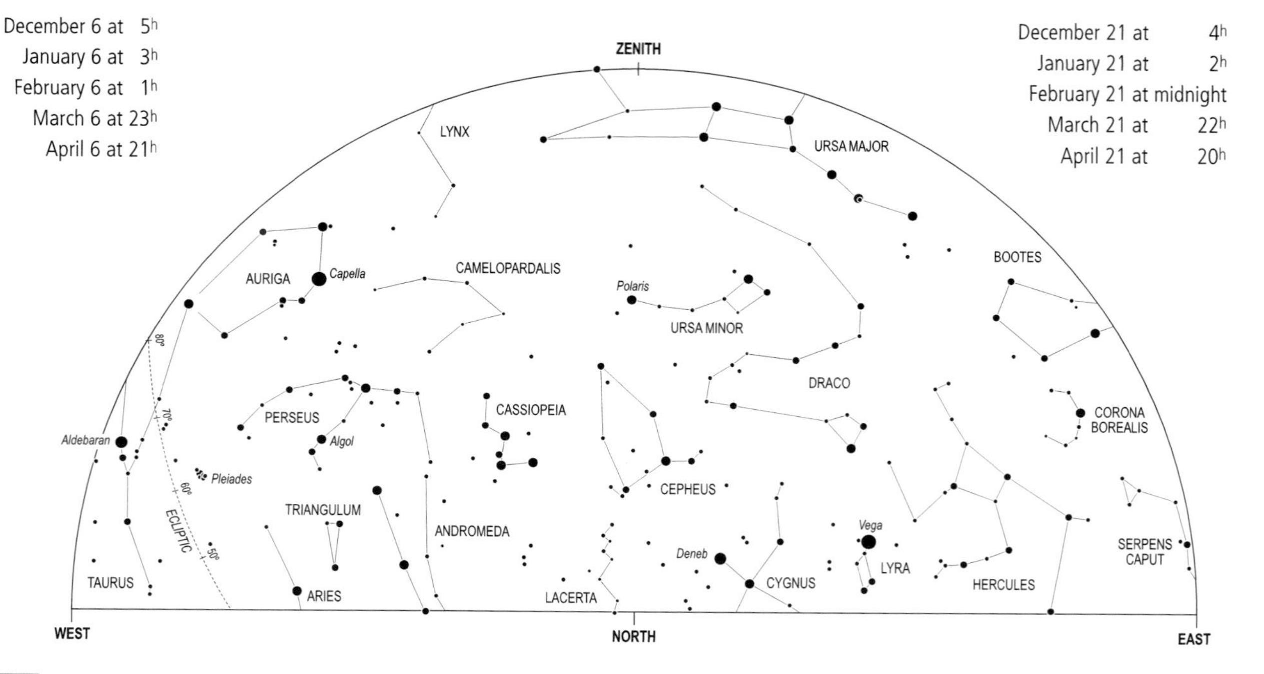
December 6 at 5h
January 6 at 3h
February 6 at 1h
March 6 at 23h
April 6 at 21h
December 21 at 4h
January 21 at 2h
February 21 at midnight
March 21 at 22h
April 21 at 20h
ZENITH
LYNX
URSA MAJOR
AURIGA
Capella
CAMELOPARDALIS
Polaris
URSA MINOR
BOOTES
80°
70°
60°
50°
ECLIPTIC
PERSEUS
Algol
CASSIOPEIA
DRACO
CORONA
BOREALIS
Aldebaran
Pleiades
TRIANGULUM
ANDROMEDA
CEPHEUS
Vega
SERPENS
CAPUT
Deneb
LYRA
TAURUS
ARIES
LACERTA
CYGNUS
HERCULES
WEST
NORTH
EAST

3S

December 6 at 5h
January 6 at 3h
February 6 at 1h
March 6 at 23h
April 6 at 21h

December 21 at 4h
January 21 at 2h
February 21 at midnight
March 21 at 22h
April 21 at 20h

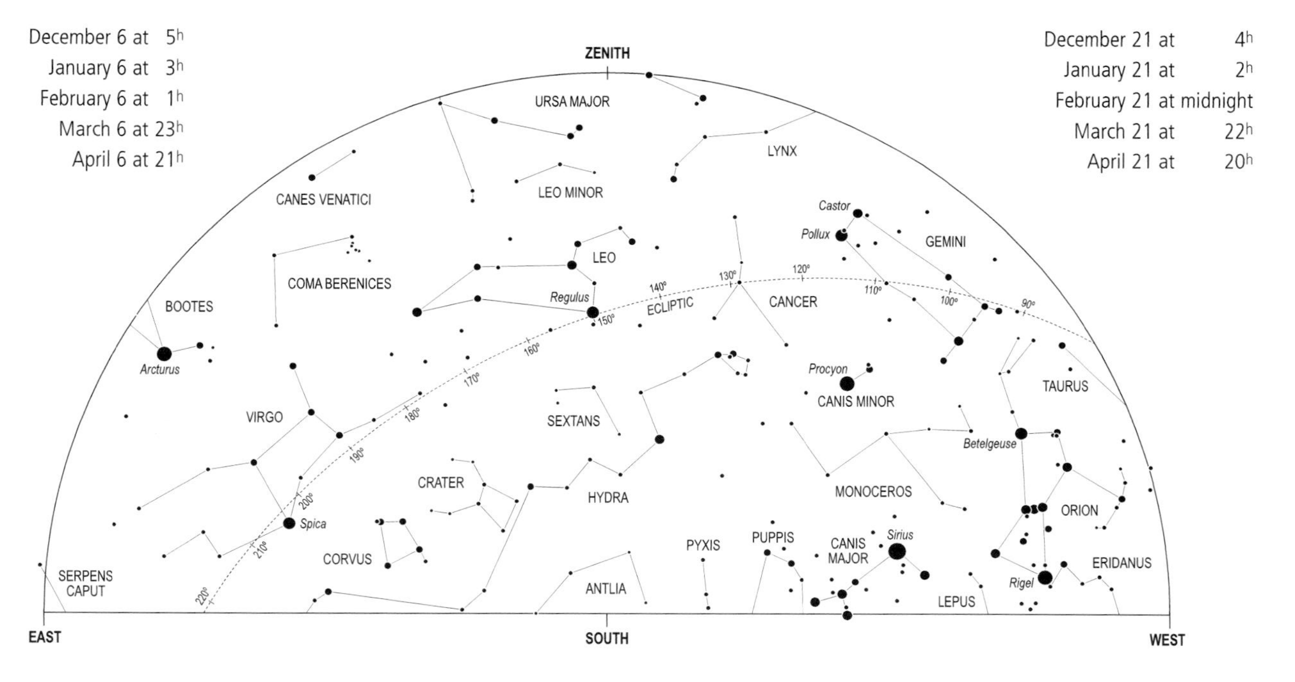

4N

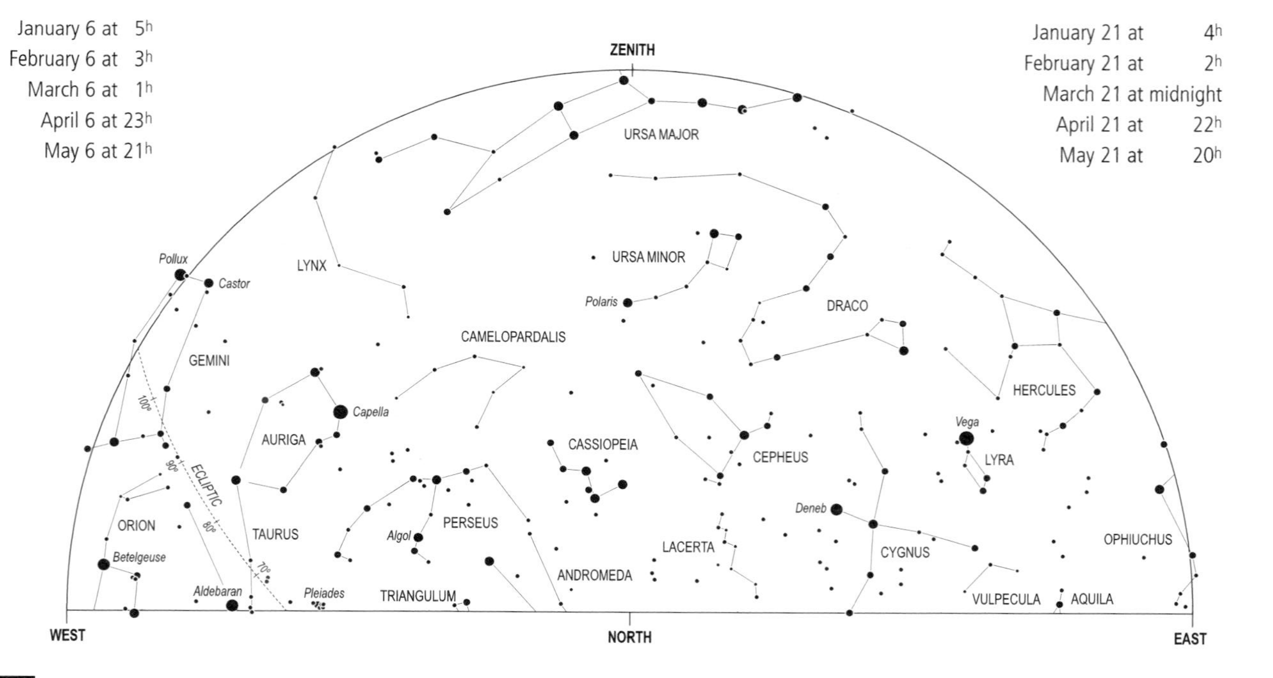
January 6 at 5h
February 6 at 3h
March 6 at 1h
April 6 at 23h
May 6 at 21h
January 21 at 4h
February 21 at 2h
March 21 at midnight
April 21 at 22h
May 21 at 20h
ZENITH
WEST
NORTH
EAST
URSA MAJOR
URSA MINOR
Polaris
LYNX
Pollux
Castor
GEMINI
CAMELOPARDALIS
DRACO
AURIGA
Capella
HERCULES
Vega
LYRA
CASSIOPEIA
CEPHEUS
ECLIPTIC
100°
90°
80°
70°
ORION
Betelgeuse
TAURUS
Aldebaran
Pleiades
PERSEUS
Algol
TRIANGULUM
ANDROMEDA
LACERTA
Deneb
CYGNUS
OPHIUCHUS
VULPECULA
AQUILA

4S

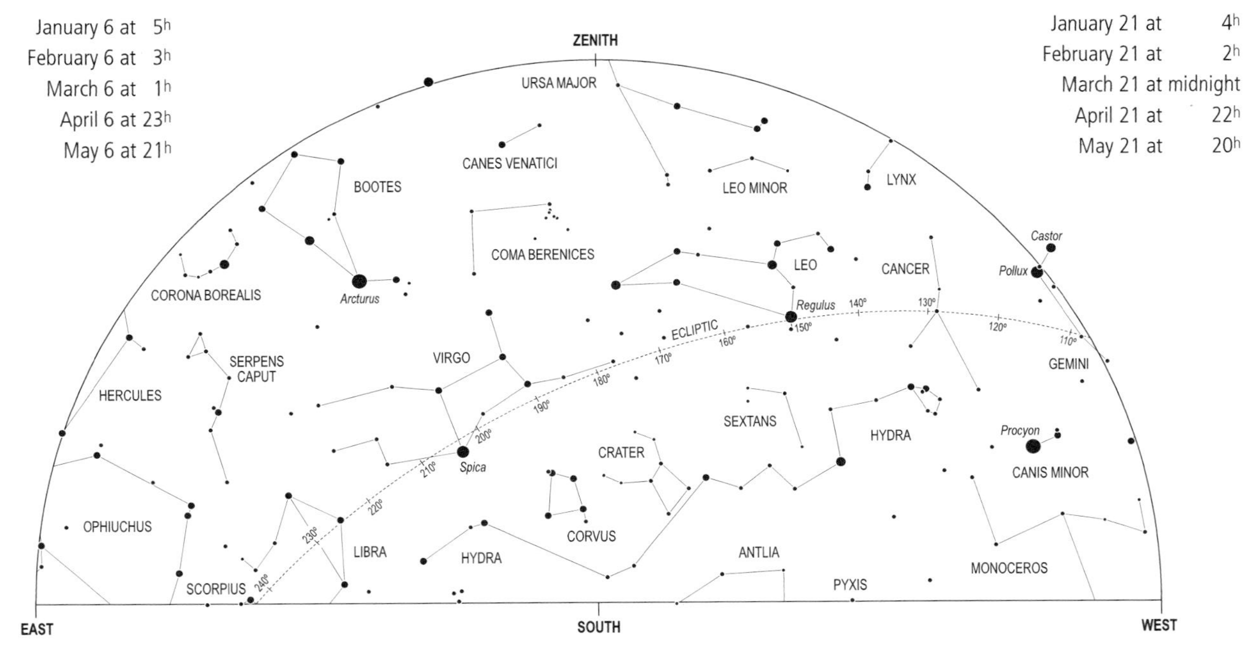
January 6 at 5h
February 6 at 3h
March 6 at 1h
April 6 at 23h
May 6 at 21h
January 21 at 4h
February 21 at 2h
March 21 at midnight
April 21 at 22h
May 21 at 20h
ZENITH
EAST
SOUTH
WEST
URSA MAJOR
CANES VENATICI
BOOTES
LEO MINOR
LYNX
COMA BERENICES
CORONA BOREALIS
Arcturus
LEO
CANCER
Castor
Pollux
Regulus
ECLIPTIC
GEMINI
VIRGO
SERPENS CAPUT
HERCULES
SEXTANS
HYDRA
Procyon
CANIS MINOR
CRATER
Spica
OPHIUCHUS
CORVUS
LIBRA
HYDRA
ANTLIA
MONOCEROS
SCORPIUS
PYXIS

5N

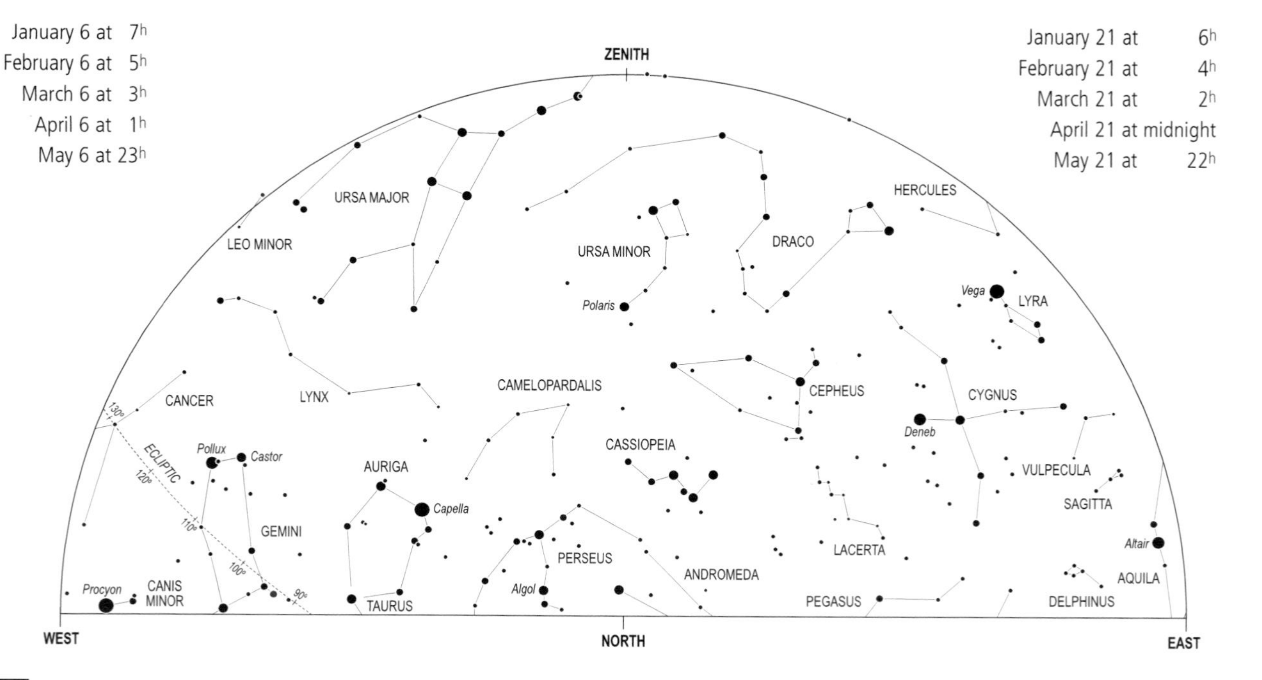
January 6 at 7h
February 6 at 5h
March 6 at 3h
April 6 at 1h
May 6 at 23h
January 21 at 6h
February 21 at 4h
March 21 at 2h
April 21 at midnight
May 21 at 22h
ZENITH
WEST
NORTH
EAST
ECLIPTIC
130°
120°
110°
100°
90°
URSA MAJOR
LEO MINOR
URSA MINOR
Polaris
DRACO
HERCULES
Vega
LYRA
CANCER
LYNX
CAMELOPARDALIS
CEPHEUS
CYGNUS
Deneb
Pollux
Castor
GEMINI
AURIGA
Capella
CASSIOPEIA
VULPECULA
SAGITTA
Altair
AQUILA
PERSEUS
ANDROMEDA
LACERTA
Procyon
CANIS MINOR
TAURUS
Algol
PEGASUS
DELPHINUS

5S

January 6 at 7^h
February 6 at 5^h
March 6 at 3^h
April 6 at 1^h
May 6 at 23^h

January 21 at 6^h
February 21 at 4^h
March 21 at 2^h
April 21 at midnight
May 21 at 22^h

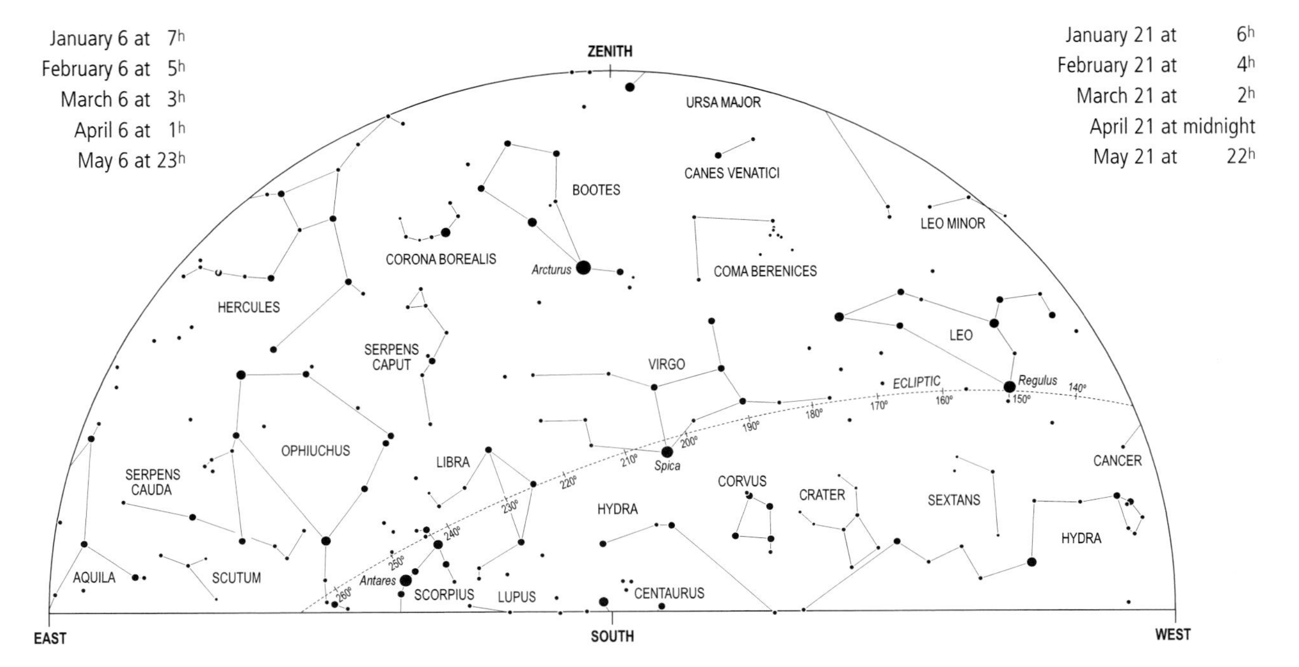

6N

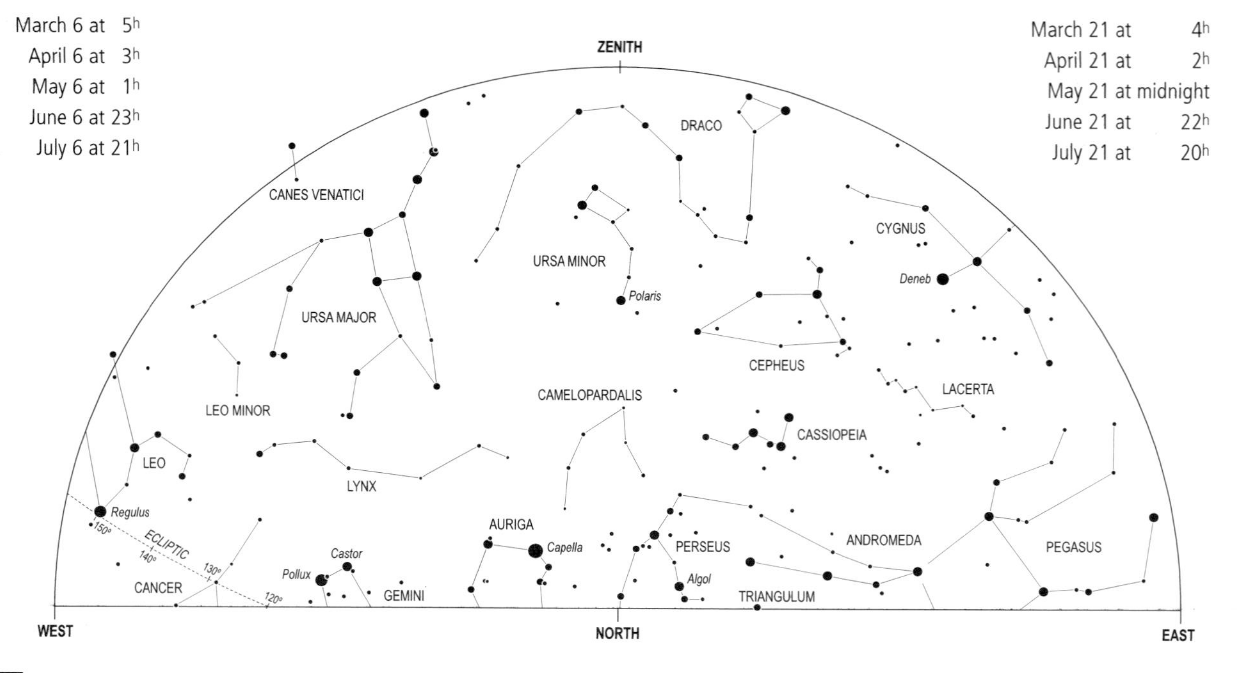
March 6 at 5h
April 6 at 3h
May 6 at 1h
June 6 at 23h
July 6 at 21h
March 21 at 4h
April 21 at 2h
May 21 at midnight
June 21 at 22h
July 21 at 20h
ZENITH
WEST
NORTH
EAST
DRACO
CANES VENATICI
URSA MINOR
Polaris
CYGNUS
Deneb
URSA MAJOR
CEPHEUS
LEO MINOR
CAMELOPARDALIS
LACERTA
CASSIOPEIA
LEO
LYNX
Regulus
150°
ECLIPTIC
140°
130°
120°
CANCER
Castor
Pollux
GEMINI
AURIGA
Capella
PERSEUS
Algol
TRIANGULUM
ANDROMEDA
PEGASUS

March 6 at 5h	March 21 at 4h
April 6 at 3h	April 21 at 2h
May 6 at 1h	May 21 at midnight
June 6 at 23h	June 21 at 22h
July 6 at 21h	July 21 at 20h

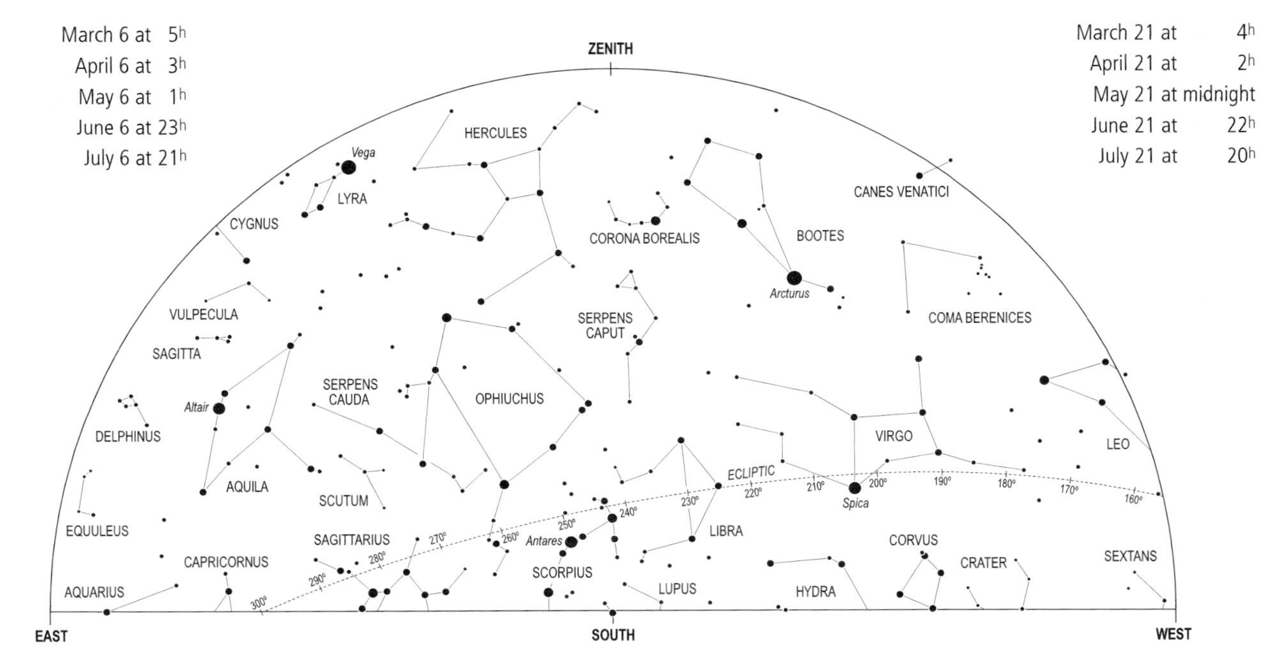

7N

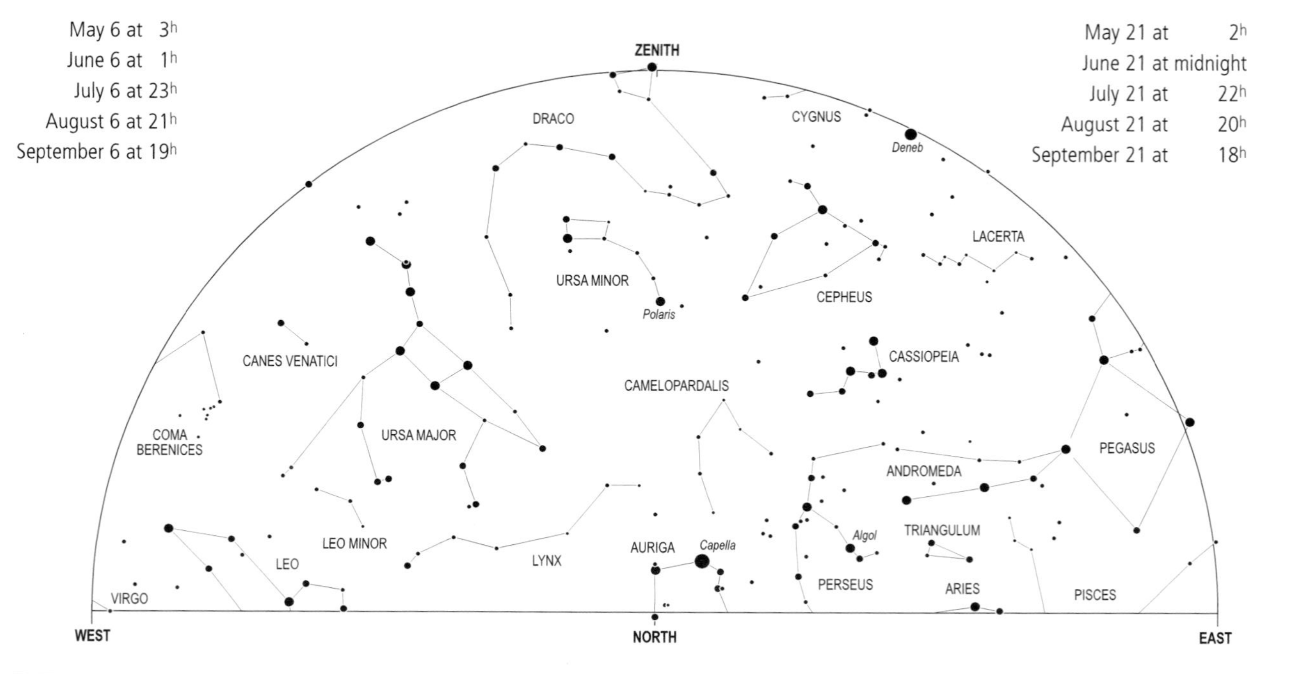
May 6 at 3h
June 6 at 1h
July 6 at 23h
August 6 at 21h
September 6 at 19h
May 21 at 2h
June 21 at midnight
July 21 at 22h
August 21 at 20h
September 21 at 18h
ZENITH
DRACO
CYGNUS
Deneb
URSA MINOR
Polaris
CEPHEUS
LACERTA
CANES VENATICI
CASSIOPEIA
CAMELOPARDALIS
URSA MAJOR
COMA
BERENICES
PEGASUS
ANDROMEDA
LEO MINOR
TRIANGULUM
Algol
AURIGA
Capella
LEO
LYNX
PERSEUS
ARIES
PISCES
VIRGO
WEST
NORTH
EAST

7S

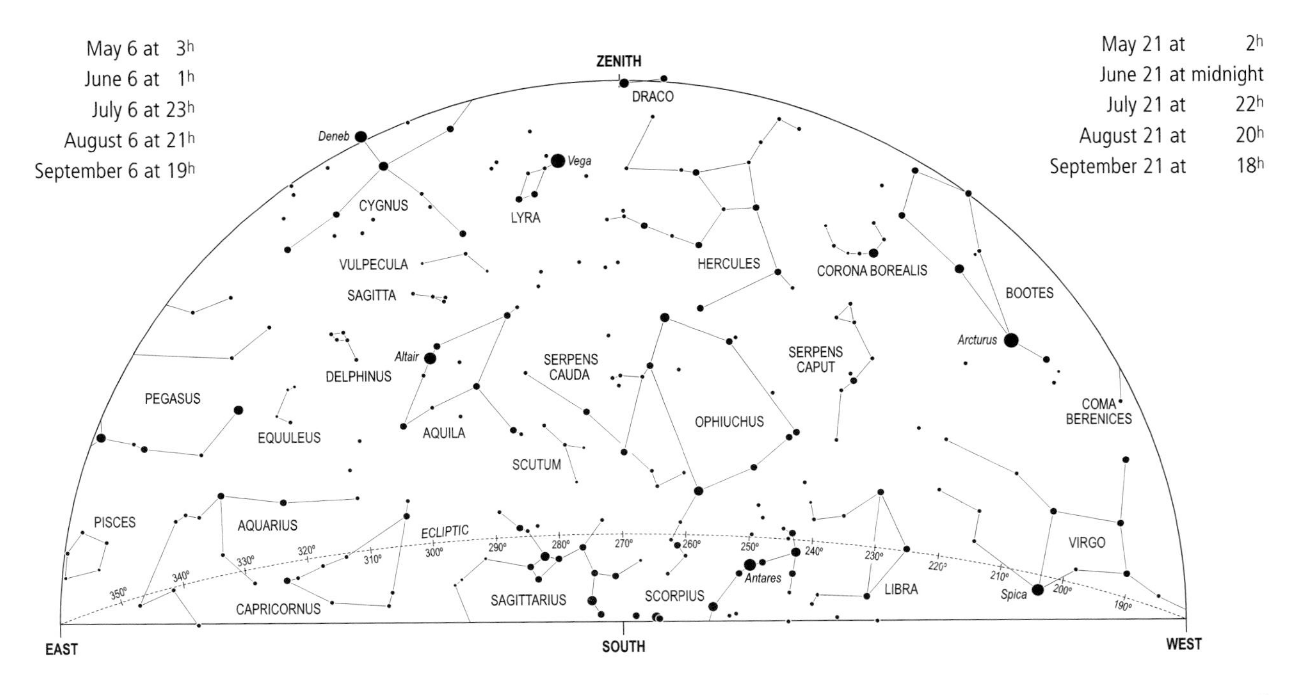
May 6 at 3h
June 6 at 1h
July 6 at 23h
August 6 at 21h
September 6 at 19h
May 21 at 2h
June 21 at midnight
July 21 at 22h
August 21 at 20h
September 21 at 18h
ZENITH
DRACO
Deneb
Vega
CYGNUS
LYRA
HERCULES
CORONA BOREALIS
VULPECULA
SAGITTA
BOOTES
Altair
DELPHINUS
SERPENS CAUDA
SERPENS CAPUT
Arcturus
PEGASUS
COMA BERENICES
EQUULEUS
AQUILA
OPHIUCHUS
SCUTUM
PISCES
AQUARIUS
ECLIPTIC
VIRGO
LIBRA
Antares
Spica
SAGITTARIUS
SCORPIUS
CAPRICORNUS
350°
340°
330°
320°
310°
300°
290°
280°
270°
260°
250°
240°
230°
220°
210°
200°
190°
EAST
SOUTH
WEST

8N

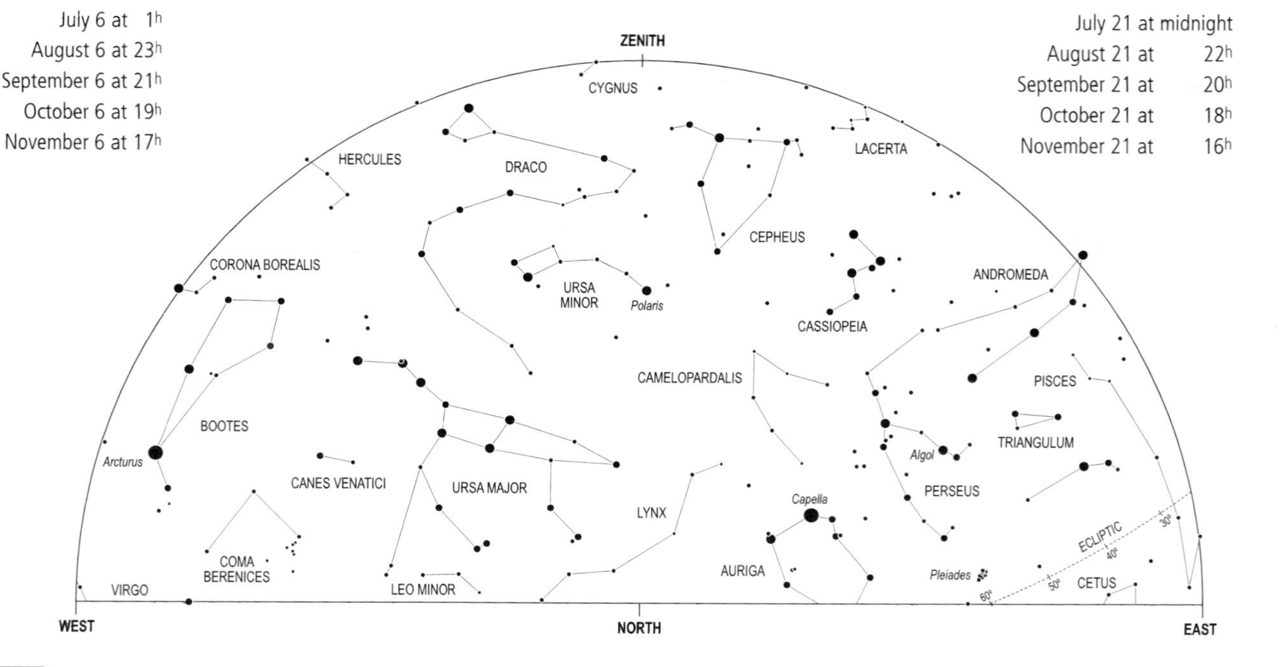
July 6 at 1h
August 6 at 23h
September 6 at 21h
October 6 at 19h
November 6 at 17h
July 21 at midnight
August 21 at 22h
September 21 at 20h
October 21 at 18h
November 21 at 16h
ZENITH
CYGNUS
HERCULES
DRACO
LACERTA
CEPHEUS
CORONA BOREALIS
URSA MINOR
Polaris
ANDROMEDA
CASSIOPEIA
CAMELOPARDALIS
PISCES
BOOTES
Arcturus
CANES VENATICI
URSA MAJOR
Algol
TRIANGULUM
PERSEUS
Capella
LYNX
ECLIPTIC
30°
40°
50°
60°
COMA BERENICES
AURIGA
Pleiades
CETUS
VIRGO
LEO MINOR
WEST
NORTH
EAST

8S

July 6 at 1h
August 6 at 23h
September 6 at 21h
October 6 at 19h
November 6 at 17h

July 21 at midnight
August 21 at 22h
September 21 at 20h
October 21 at 18h
November 21 at 16h

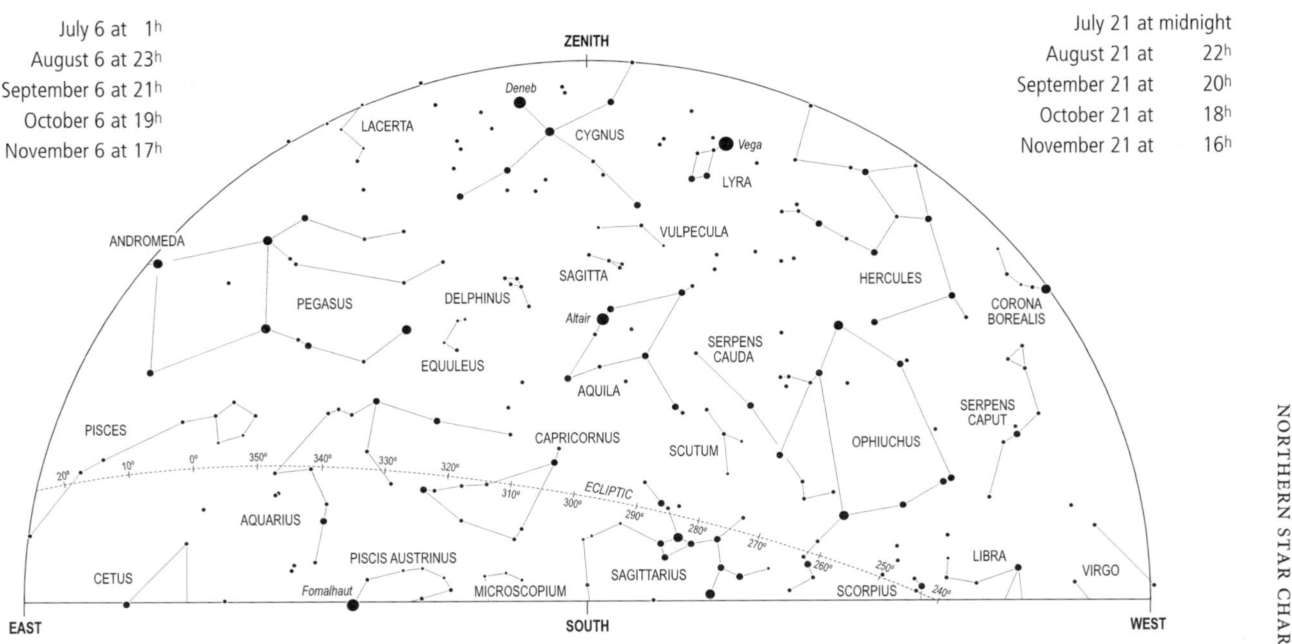

9N

August 6 at 1h
September 6 at 23h
October 6 at 21h
November 6 at 19h
December 6 at 17h

August 21 at midnight
September 21 at 22h
October 21 at 20h
November 21 at 18h
December 21 at 16h

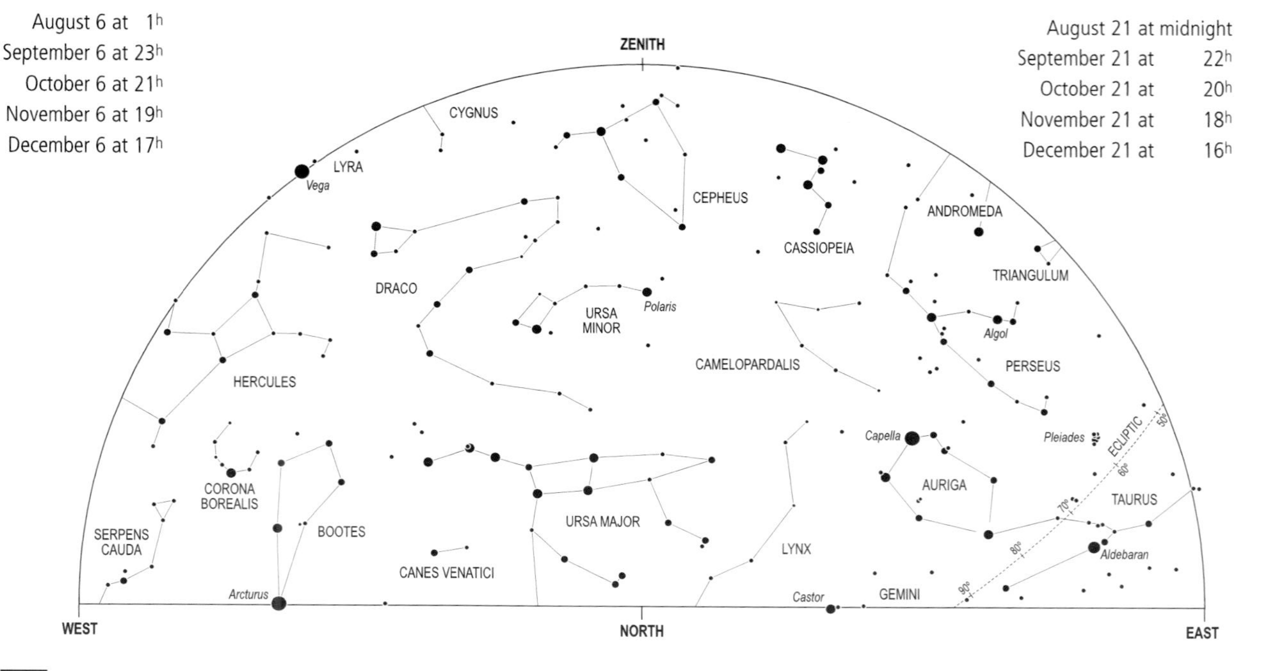

9S

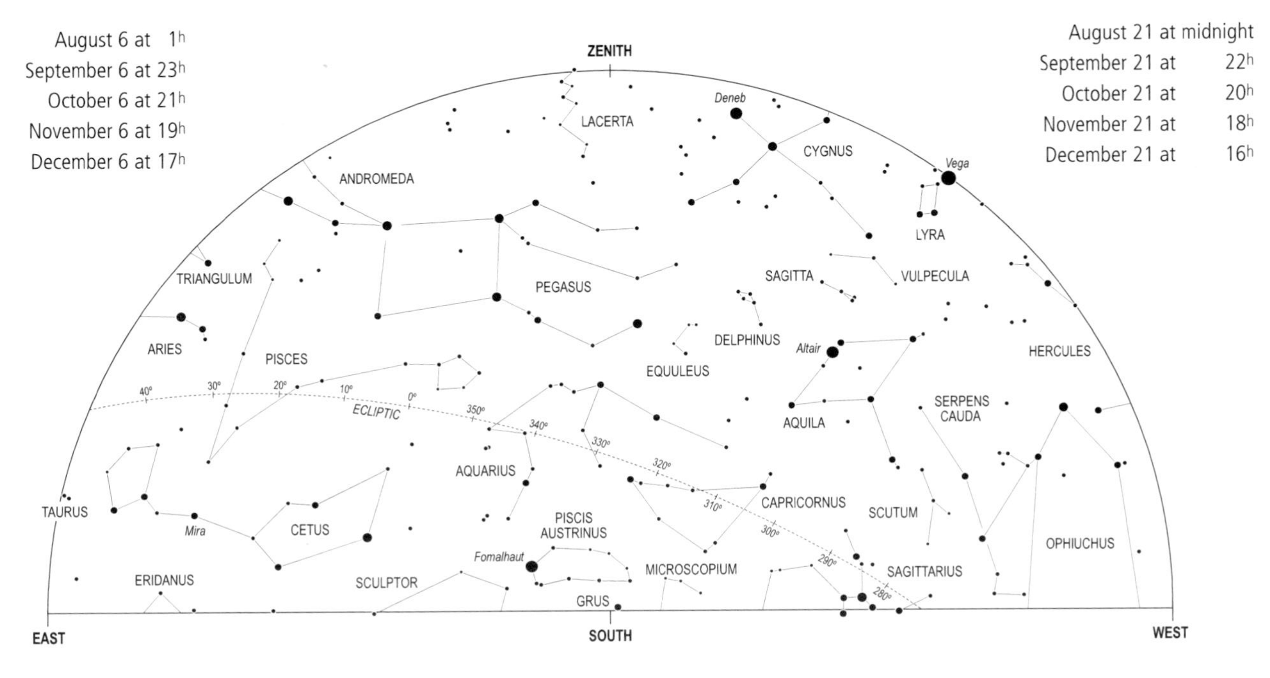
August 6 at 1h
September 6 at 23h
October 6 at 21h
November 6 at 19h
December 6 at 17h
August 21 at midnight
September 21 at 22h
October 21 at 20h
November 21 at 18h
December 21 at 16h
ZENITH
EAST
SOUTH
WEST
LACERTA
Deneb
CYGNUS
Vega
LYRA
ANDROMEDA
TRIANGULUM
PEGASUS
SAGITTA
VULPECULA
ARIES
PISCES
DELPHINUS
Altair
EQUULEUS
HERCULES
40°
30°
20°
10°
0°
350°
340°
330°
320°
310°
300°
290°
280°
ECLIPTIC
AQUILA
SERPENS CAUDA
AQUARIUS
TAURUS
Mira
CETUS
PISCIS AUSTRINUS
CAPRICORNUS
SCUTUM
OPHIUCHUS
Fomalhaut
ERIDANUS
SCULPTOR
MICROSCOPIUM
SAGITTARIUS
GRUS

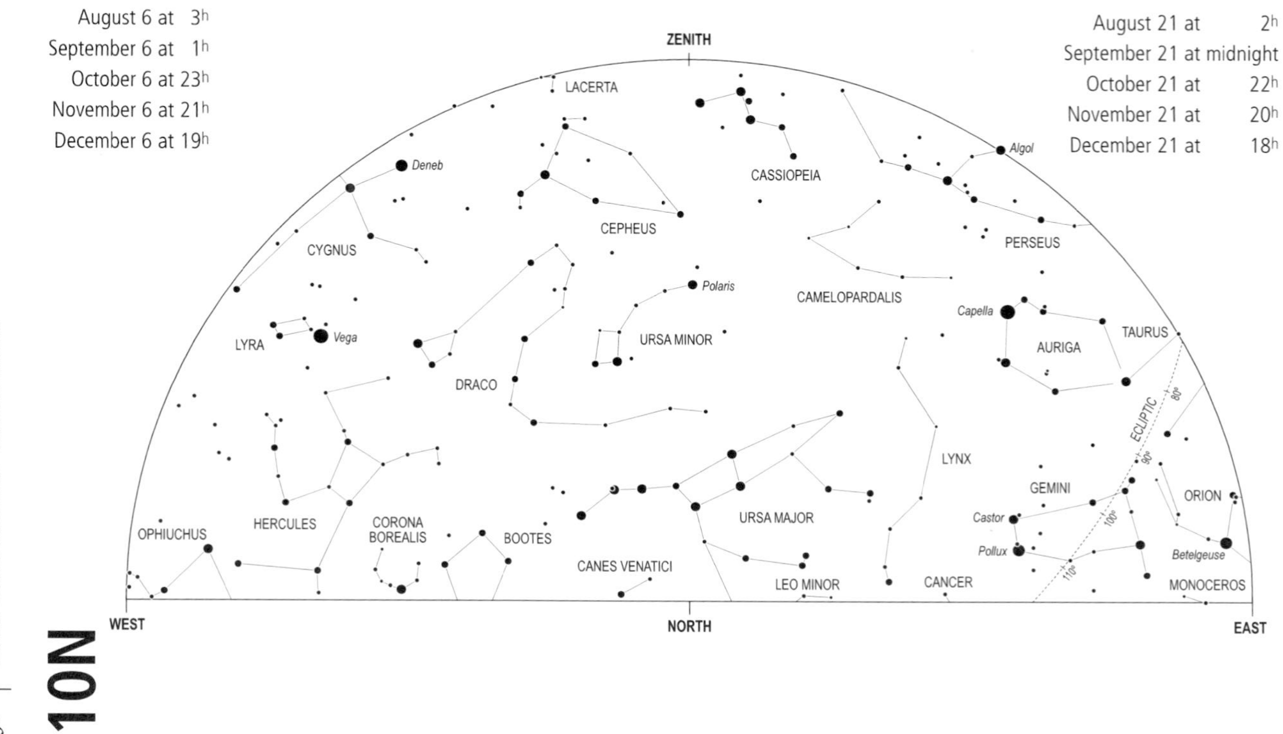
10N
August 6 at 3h
September 6 at 1h
October 6 at 23h
November 6 at 21h
December 6 at 19h
August 21 at 2h
September 21 at midnight
October 21 at 22h
November 21 at 20h
December 21 at 18h
ZENITH
LACERTA
CASSIOPEIA
Algol
Deneb
CEPHEUS
PERSEUS
CYGNUS
Polaris
CAMELOPARDALIS
Capella
TAURUS
LYRA
Vega
URSA MINOR
AURIGA
DRACO
ECLIPTIC
80°
90°
100°
110°
LYNX
GEMINI
ORION
HERCULES
CORONA BOREALIS
BOOTES
URSA MAJOR
Castor
Pollux
Betelgeuse
OPHIUCHUS
CANES VENATICI
LEO MINOR
CANCER
MONOCEROS
WEST
NORTH
EAST

10S

August 6 at 3h
September 6 at 1h
October 6 at 23h
November 6 at 21h
December 6 at 19h

August 21 at 2h
September 21 at midnight
October 21 at 22h
November 21 at 20h
December 21 at 18h

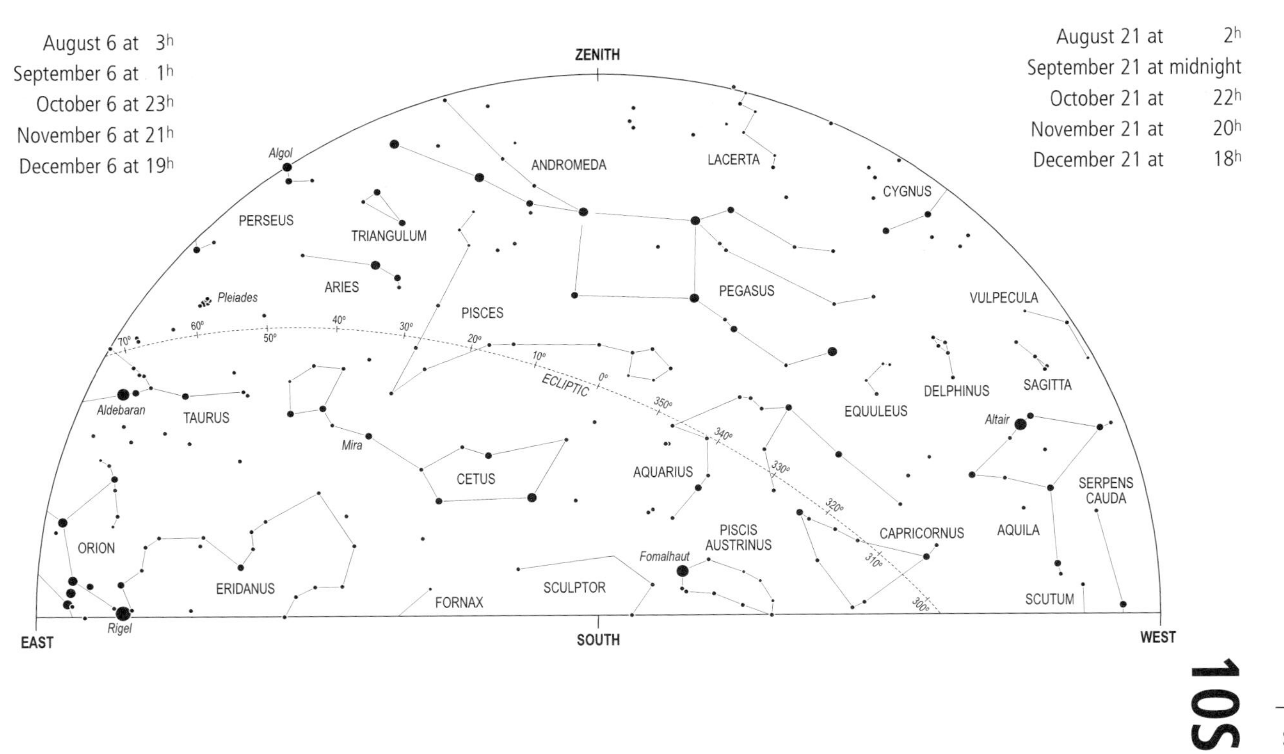

11N

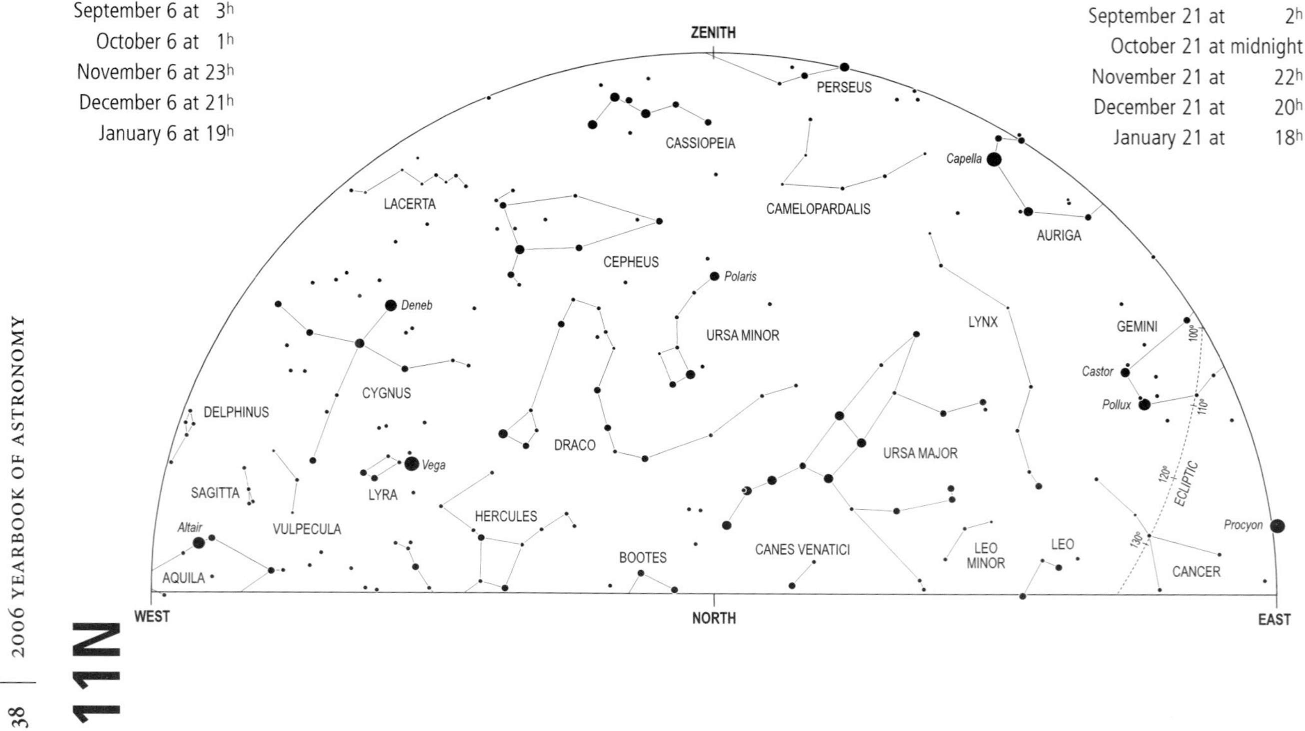
September 6 at 3h
October 6 at 1h
November 6 at 23h
December 6 at 21h
January 6 at 19h
September 21 at 2h
October 21 at midnight
November 21 at 22h
December 21 at 20h
January 21 at 18h
ZENITH
PERSEUS
CASSIOPEIA
Capella
CAMELOPARDALIS
AURIGA
LACERTA
CEPHEUS
Polaris
URSA MINOR
Deneb
LYNX
GEMINI
CYGNUS
Castor
Pollux
DELPHINUS
DRACO
URSA MAJOR
Vega
LYRA
SAGITTA
HERCULES
ECLIPTIC
100°
110°
120°
130°
Altair
VULPECULA
BOOTES
CANES VENATICI
LEO MINOR
LEO
Procyon
AQUILA
CANCER
WEST
NORTH
EAST

11S

September 6 at 3^h
October 6 at 1^h
November 6 at 23^h
December 6 at 21^h
January 6 at 19^h

September 21 at 2^h
October 21 at midnight
November 21 at 22^h
December 21 at 20^h
January 21 at 18^h

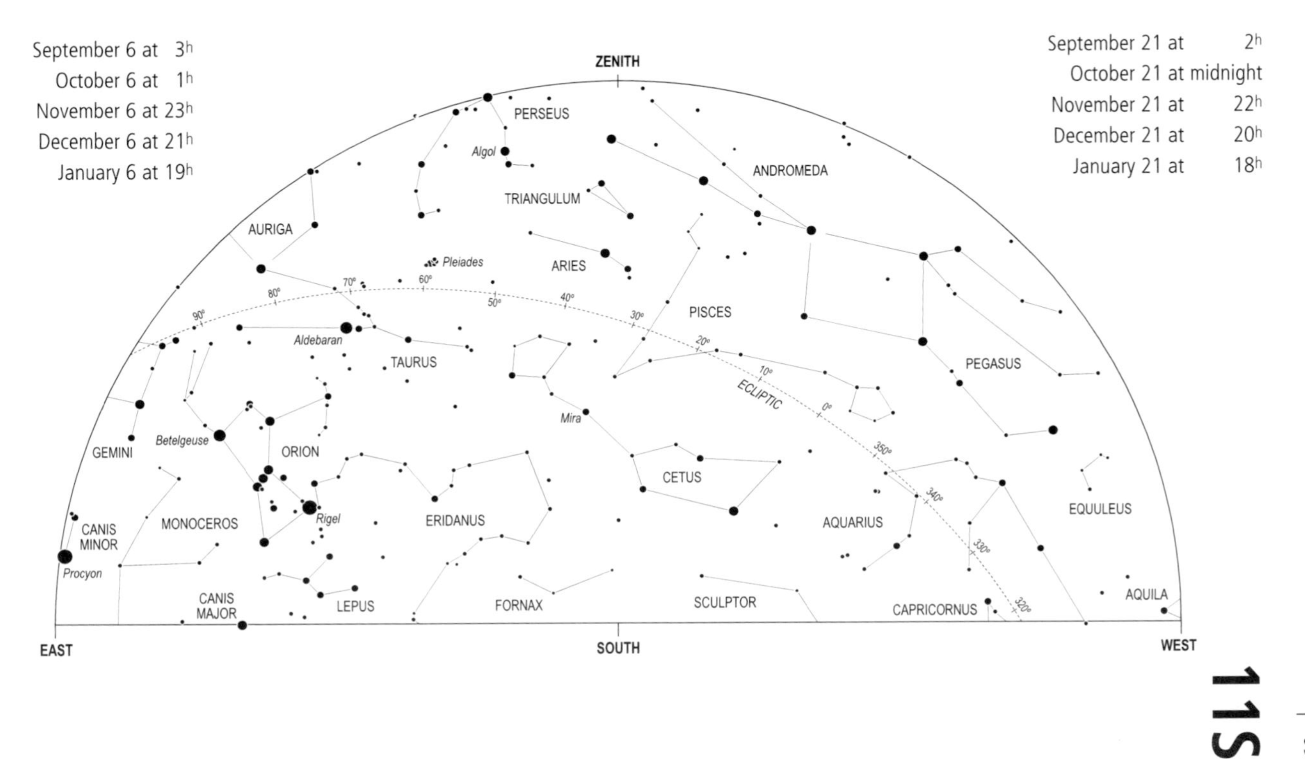

12N

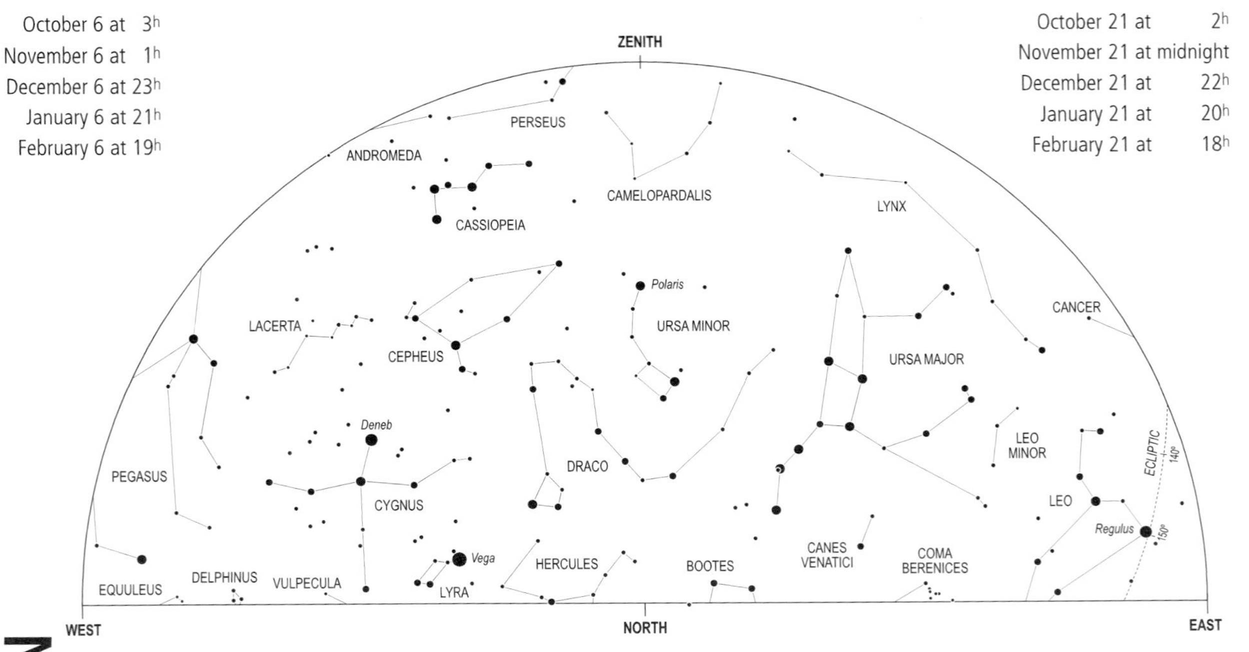
October 6 at 3h
November 6 at 1h
December 6 at 23h
January 6 at 21h
February 6 at 19h
October 21 at 2h
November 21 at midnight
December 21 at 22h
January 21 at 20h
February 21 at 18h
ZENITH
PERSEUS
ANDROMEDA
CAMELOPARDALIS
LYNX
CASSIOPEIA
Polaris
CANCER
LACERTA
URSA MINOR
CEPHEUS
URSA MAJOR
Deneb
LEO MINOR
DRACO
PEGASUS
CYGNUS
ECLIPTIC
140°
LEO
Regulus
150°
Vega
CANES VENATICI
COMA BERENICES
HERCULES
BOOTES
DELPHINUS
VULPECULA
EQUULEUS
LYRA
WEST
NORTH
EAST

12S

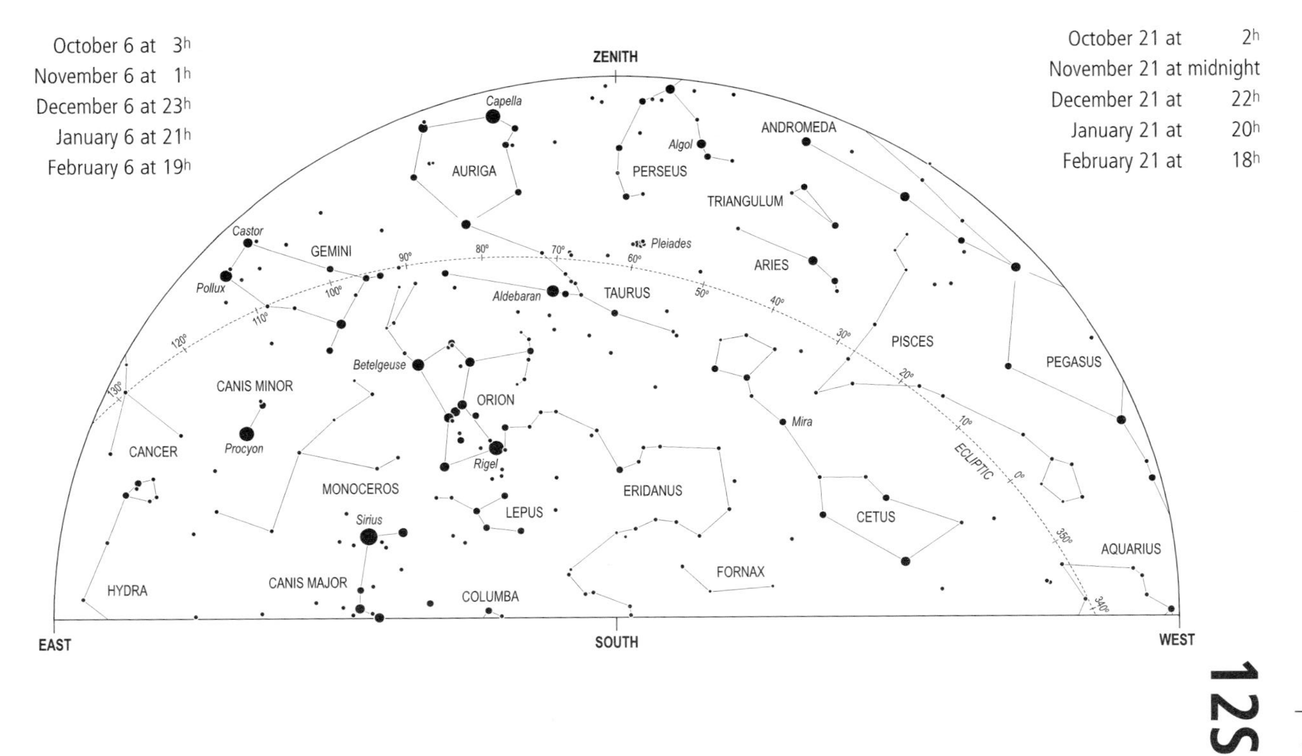
October 6 at 3h
November 6 at 1h
December 6 at 23h
January 6 at 21h
February 6 at 19h
October 21 at 2h
November 21 at midnight
December 21 at 22h
January 21 at 20h
February 21 at 18h
ZENITH
EAST
SOUTH
WEST
Capella
AURIGA
PERSEUS
Algol
ANDROMEDA
TRIANGULUM
Pleiades
ARIES
Castor
GEMINI
Pollux
TAURUS
Aldebaran
PISCES
PEGASUS
CANIS MINOR
Procyon
Betelgeuse
ORION
Rigel
Mira
ECLIPTIC
CANCER
MONOCEROS
ERIDANUS
LEPUS
CETUS
Sirius
AQUARIUS
FORNAX
HYDRA
CANIS MAJOR
COLUMBA
130°
120°
110°
100°
90°
80°
70°
60°
50°
40°
30°
20°
10°
0°
350°
340°

Southern Star Charts

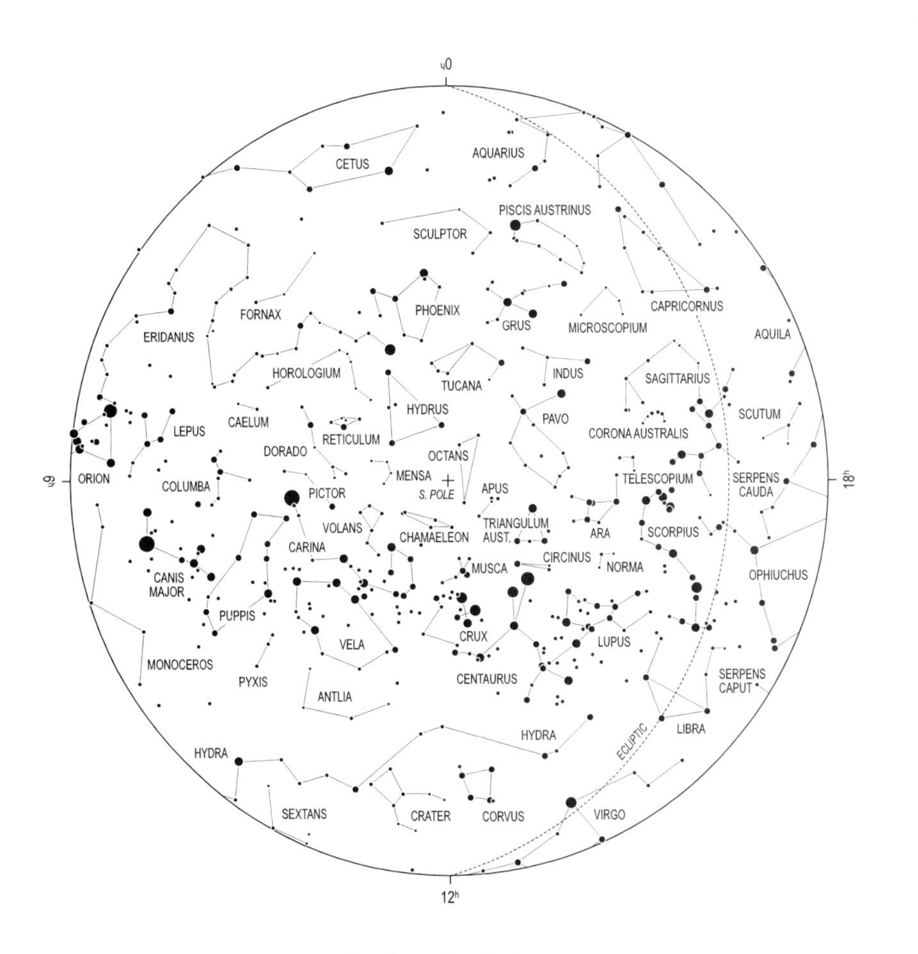

Southern Hemisphere

Note that the markers at 0h, 6h, 12h and 18h indicate hours of Right Ascension.

1N

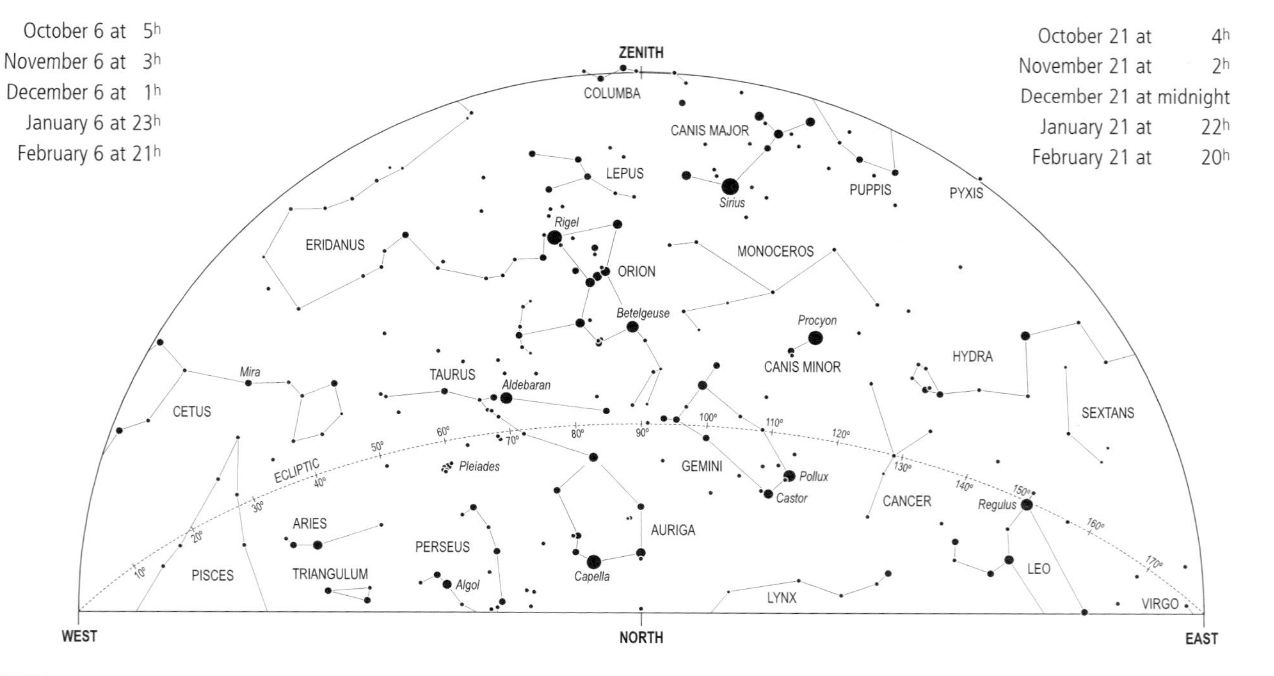
October 6 at 5h
November 6 at 3h
December 6 at 1h
January 6 at 23h
February 6 at 21h
October 21 at 4h
November 21 at 2h
December 21 at midnight
January 21 at 22h
February 21 at 20h
ZENITH
COLUMBA
CANIS MAJOR
LEPUS
Sirius
PUPPIS
PYXIS
Rigel
ERIDANUS
ORION
MONOCEROS
Betelgeuse
Procyon
CANIS MINOR
HYDRA
Mira
TAURUS
Aldebaran
CETUS
SEXTANS
ECLIPTIC
Pleiades
GEMINI
Pollux
Castor
CANCER
Regulus
ARIES
AURIGA
PERSEUS
PISCES
TRIANGULUM
Algol
Capella
LEO
LYNX
VIRGO
WEST
NORTH
EAST

1S

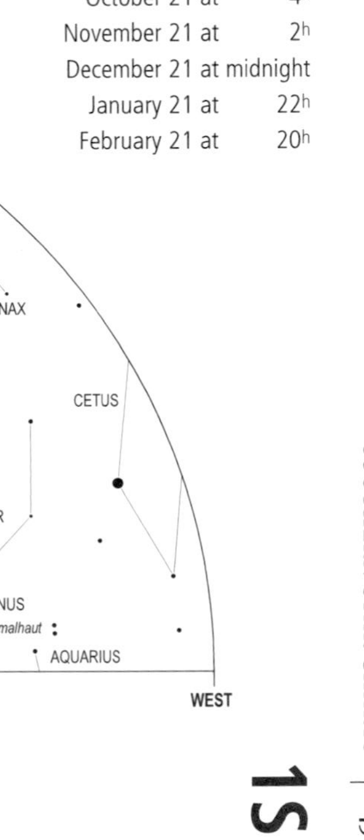
October 21 at 4h
November 21 at 2h
December 21 at midnight
January 21 at 22h
February 21 at 20h

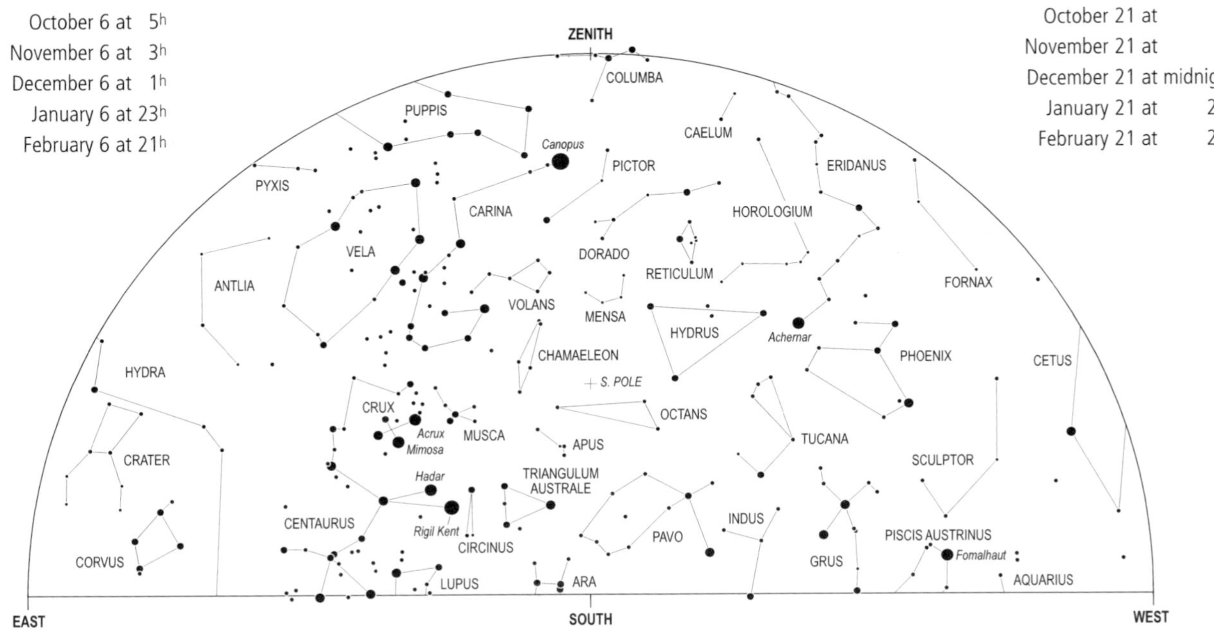
October 6 at 5h
November 6 at 3h
December 6 at 1h
January 6 at 23h
February 6 at 21h
ZENITH
COLUMBA
PUPPIS
Canopus
CAELUM
PICTOR
ERIDANUS
PYXIS
CARINA
HOROLOGIUM
VELA
DORADO
RETICULUM
FORNAX
ANTLIA
VOLANS
MENSA
HYDRUS
Achernar
CHAMAELEON
PHOENIX
CETUS
HYDRA
S. POLE
CRUX
OCTANS
Acrux
Mimosa
MUSCA
APUS
TUCANA
CRATER
SCULPTOR
Hadar
TRIANGULUM AUSTRALE
CENTAURUS
INDUS
Rigil Kent
PAVO
PISCIS AUSTRINUS
CIRCINUS
GRUS
Fomalhaut
CORVUS
LUPUS
ARA
AQUARIUS
EAST
SOUTH
WEST

2N

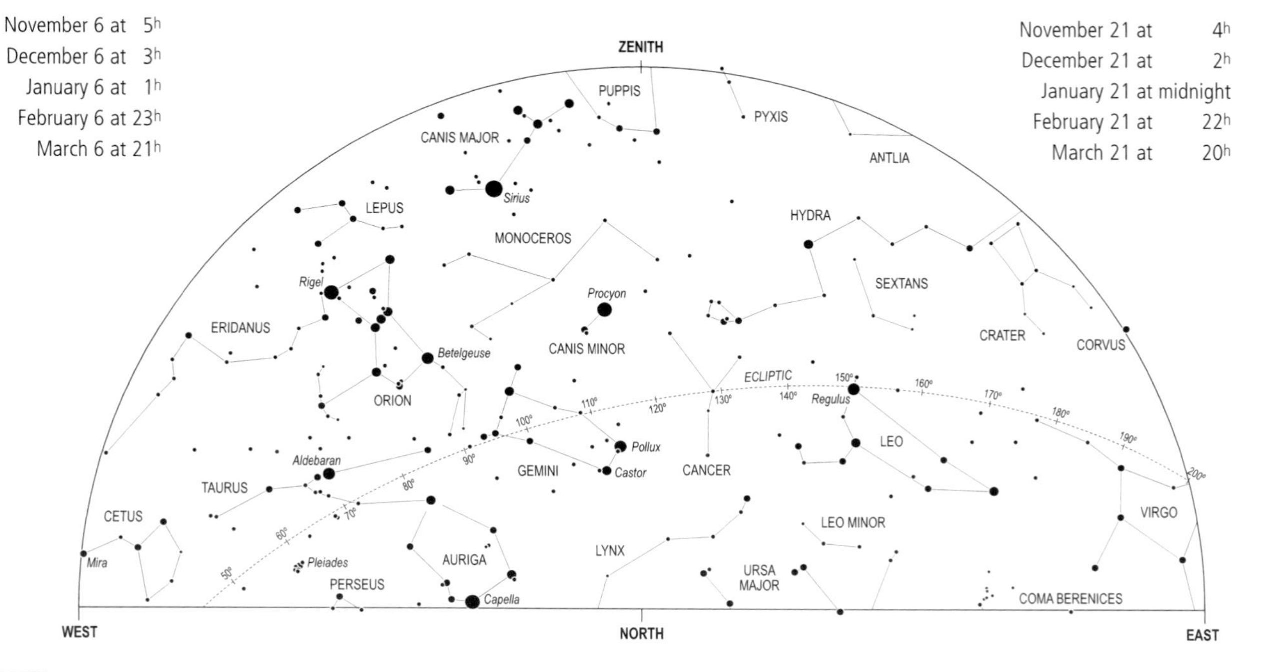
November 6 at 5h
December 6 at 3h
January 6 at 1h
February 6 at 23h
March 6 at 21h
November 21 at 4h
December 21 at 2h
January 21 at midnight
February 21 at 22h
March 21 at 20h
ZENITH
PUPPIS
PYXIS
CANIS MAJOR
ANTLIA
Sirius
LEPUS
HYDRA
MONOCEROS
SEXTANS
Rigel
Procyon
ERIDANUS
CANIS MINOR
CRATER
CORVUS
Betelgeuse
ECLIPTIC
150°
160°
170°
180°
190°
200°
140°
130°
120°
110°
100°
90°
80°
70°
60°
50°
Regulus
ORION
Pollux
Aldebaran
GEMINI
Castor
CANCER
LEO
TAURUS
CETUS
VIRGO
LEO MINOR
LYNX
AURIGA
Mira
Pleiades
URSA MAJOR
PERSEUS
Capella
COMA BERENICES
WEST
NORTH
EAST

2S

November 6 at 5h
December 6 at 3h
January 6 at 1h
February 6 at 23h
March 6 at 21h

November 21 at 4h
December 21 at 2h
January 21 at midnight
February 21 at 22h
March 21 at 20h

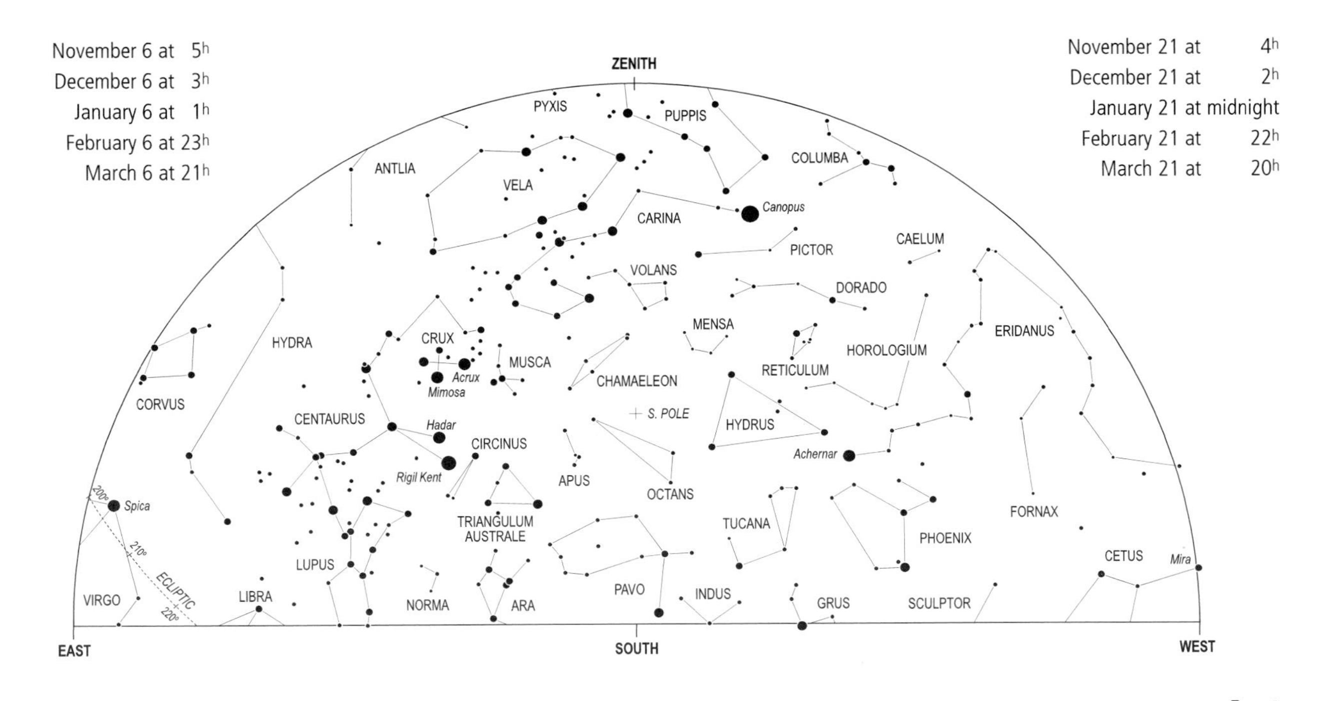

3N

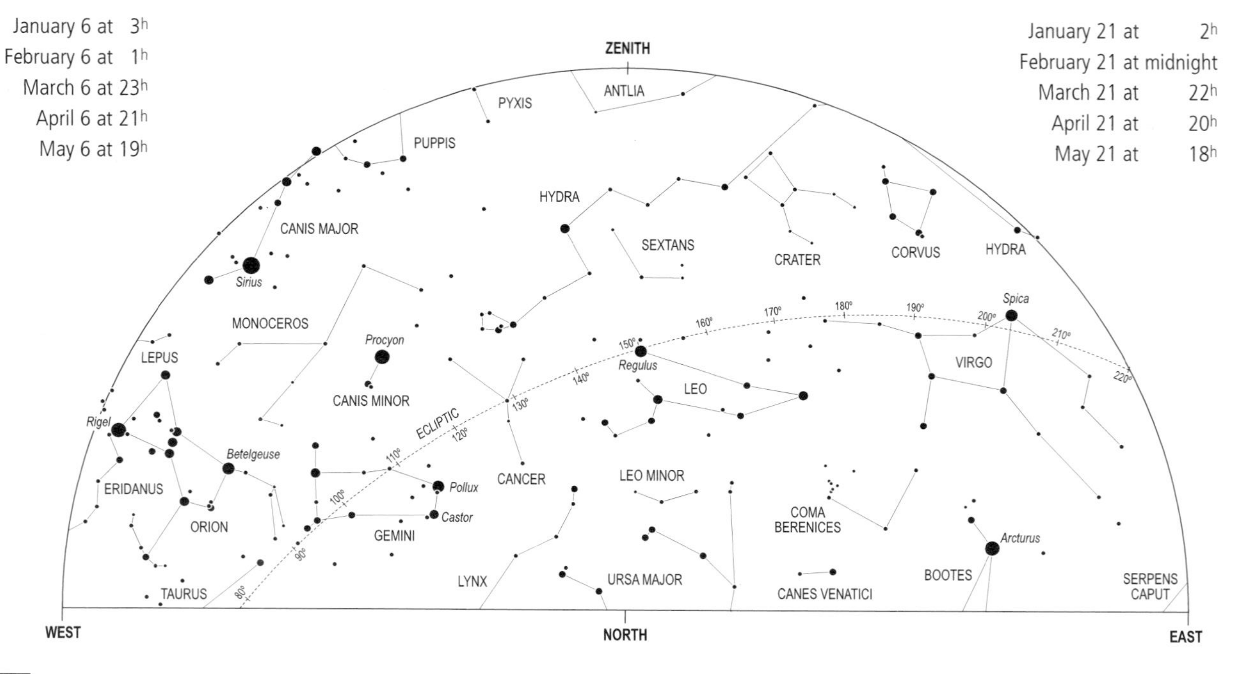

January 6 at 3h
February 6 at 1h
March 6 at 23h
April 6 at 21h
May 6 at 19h
January 21 at 2h
February 21 at midnight
March 21 at 22h
April 21 at 20h
May 21 at 18h
ZENITH
PYXIS
ANTLIA
PUPPIS
HYDRA
CANIS MAJOR
Sirius
SEXTANS
CRATER
CORVUS
HYDRA
Spica
MONOCEROS
Procyon
LEPUS
CANIS MINOR
Regulus
LEO
VIRGO
Rigel
ECLIPTIC
Betelgeuse
ERIDANUS
Pollux
CANCER
LEO MINOR
COMA BERENICES
Castor
ORION
GEMINI
Arcturus
LYNX
URSA MAJOR
BOOTES
TAURUS
CANES VENATICI
SERPENS CAPUT
WEST
NORTH
EAST
80°
90°
100°
110°
120°
130°
140°
150°
160°
170°
180°
190°
200°
210°
220°

3S

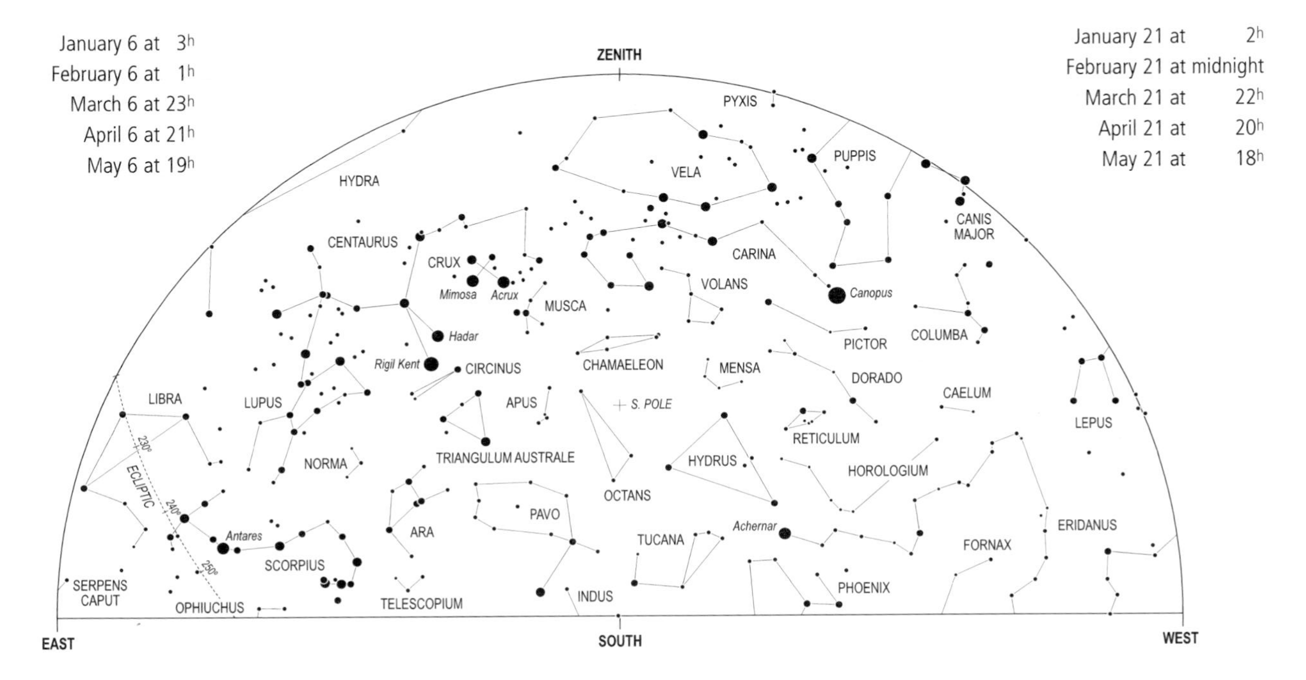
January 6 at 3h
February 6 at 1h
March 6 at 23h
April 6 at 21h
May 6 at 19h
January 21 at 2h
February 21 at midnight
March 21 at 22h
April 21 at 20h
May 21 at 18h
ZENITH
PYXIS
HYDRA
VELA
PUPPIS
CENTAURUS
CRUX
CARINA
CANIS MAJOR
Mimosa
Acrux
MUSCA
VOLANS
Canopus
Hadar
PICTOR
COLUMBA
Rigil Kent
CIRCINUS
CHAMAELEON
MENSA
DORADO
CAELUM
LIBRA
LUPUS
APUS
S. POLE
LEPUS
RETICULUM
230°
NORMA
TRIANGULUM AUSTRALE
HYDRUS
HOROLOGIUM
ECLIPTIC
OCTANS
240°
PAVO
Achernar
ERIDANUS
Antares
ARA
TUCANA
FORNAX
SCORPIUS
250°
PHOENIX
SERPENS CAPUT
OPHIUCHUS
TELESCOPIUM
INDUS
EAST
SOUTH
WEST

4N

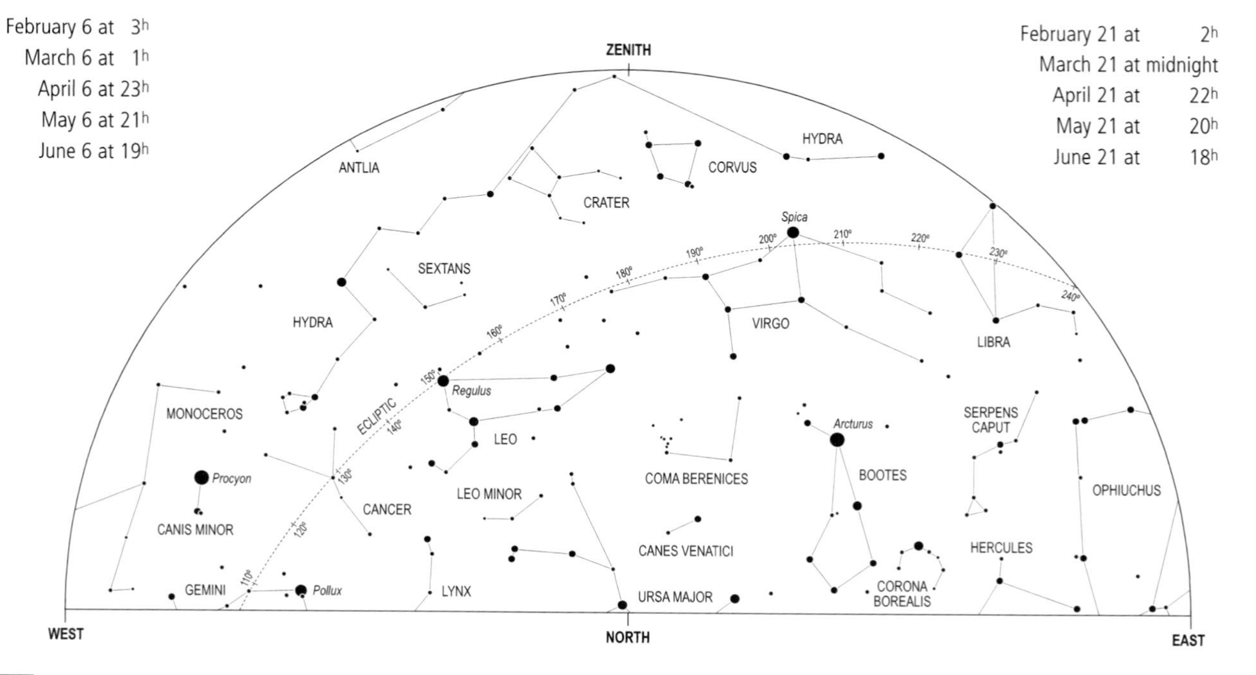
February 6 at 3h
March 6 at 1h
April 6 at 23h
May 6 at 21h
June 6 at 19h
February 21 at 2h
March 21 at midnight
April 21 at 22h
May 21 at 20h
June 21 at 18h
ZENITH
ANTLIA
CRATER
CORVUS
HYDRA
Spica
SEXTANS
HYDRA
VIRGO
LIBRA
ECLIPTIC
Regulus
MONOCEROS
LEO
Arcturus
SERPENS CAPUT
Procyon
COMA BERENICES
BOOTES
CANCER
LEO MINOR
OPHIUCHUS
CANIS MINOR
CANES VENATICI
HERCULES
GEMINI
Pollux
LYNX
URSA MAJOR
CORONA BOREALIS
WEST
NORTH
EAST
110°
120°
130°
140°
150°
160°
170°
180°
190°
200°
210°
220°
230°
240°

February 6 at	3^h
March 6 at	1^h
April 6 at	23^h
May 6 at	21^h
June 6 at	19^h

February 21 at	2^h
March 21 at midnight	
April 21 at	22^h
May 21 at	20^h
June 21 at	18^h

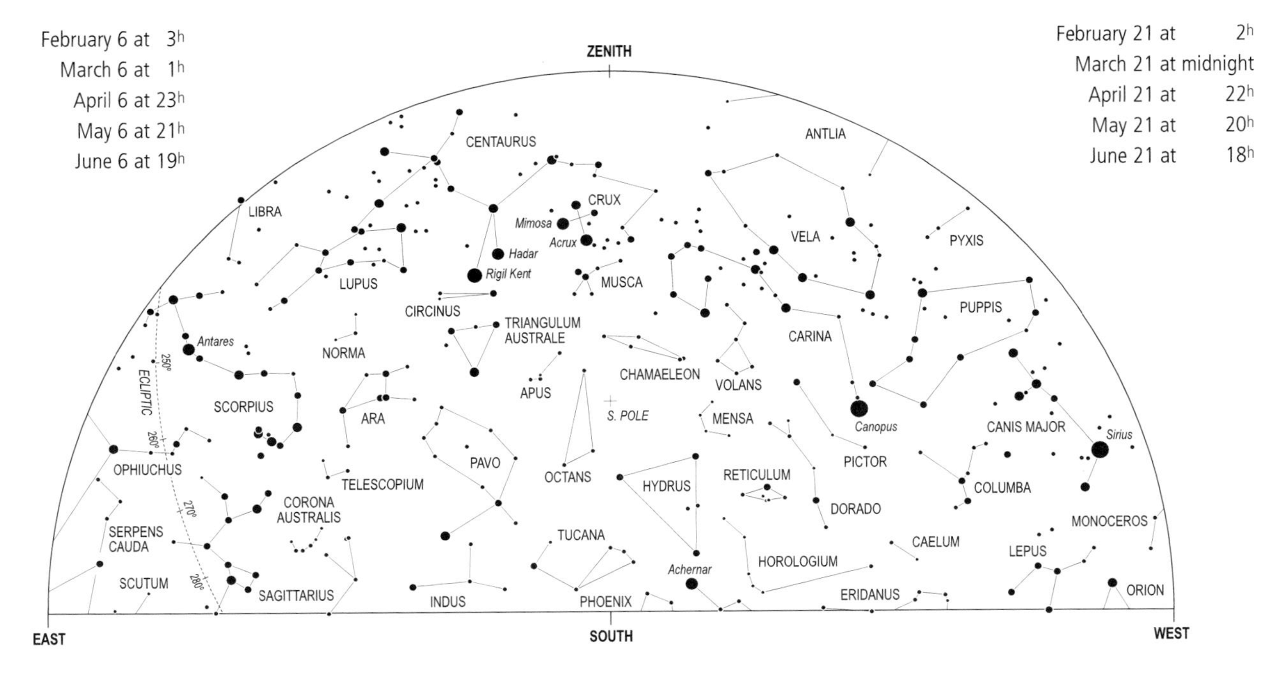

5N

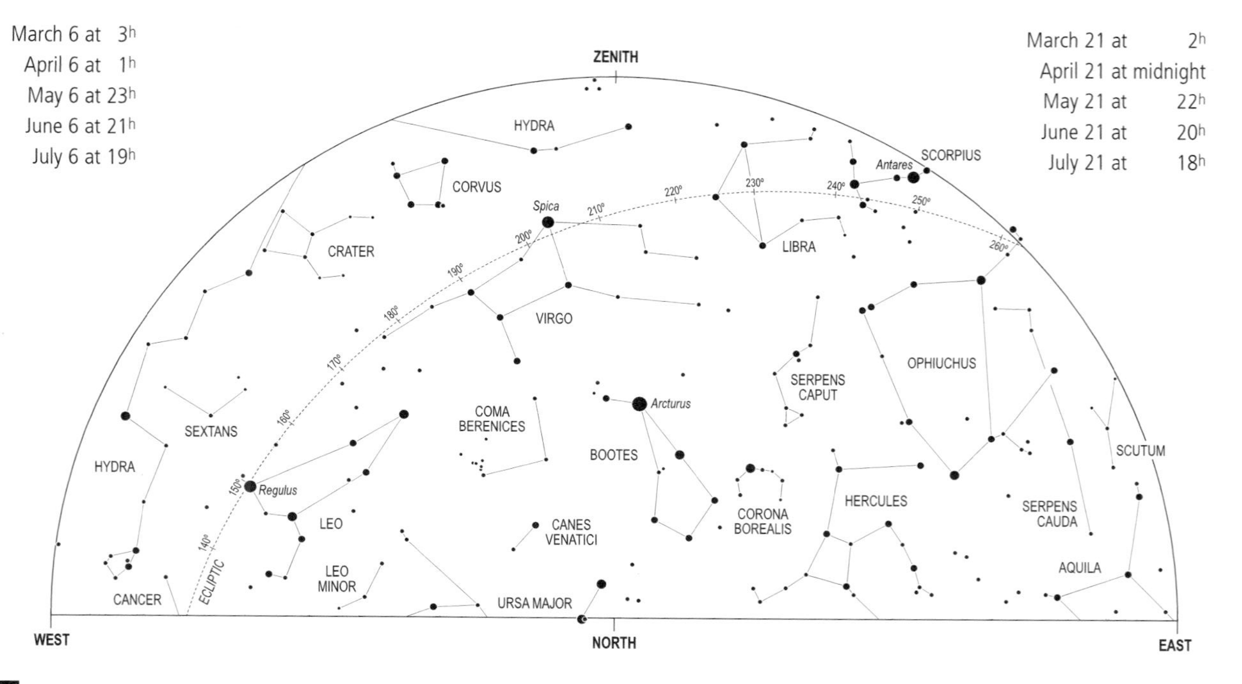
March 6 at 3h
April 6 at 1h
May 6 at 23h
June 6 at 21h
July 6 at 19h
March 21 at 2h
April 21 at midnight
May 21 at 22h
June 21 at 20h
July 21 at 18h
ZENITH
WEST
NORTH
EAST
ECLIPTIC
140°
150°
160°
170°
180°
190°
200°
210°
220°
230°
240°
250°
260°
HYDRA
CORVUS
CRATER
Spica
VIRGO
LIBRA
Antares
SCORPIUS
SEXTANS
HYDRA
Regulus
LEO
LEO MINOR
CANCER
COMA BERENICES
BOOTES
Arcturus
CANES VENATICI
URSA MAJOR
SERPENS CAPUT
OPHIUCHUS
CORONA BOREALIS
HERCULES
SCUTUM
SERPENS CAUDA
AQUILA

5S

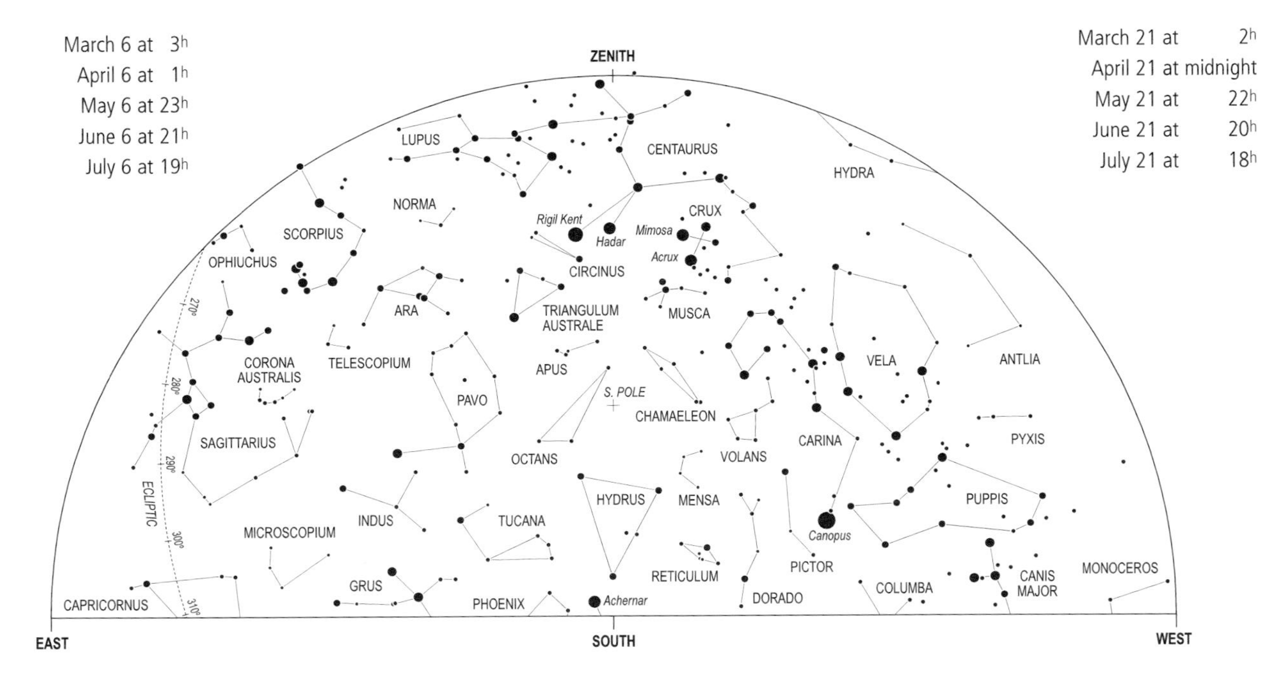
March 6 at 3h
April 6 at 1h
May 6 at 23h
June 6 at 21h
July 6 at 19h
March 21 at 2h
April 21 at midnight
May 21 at 22h
June 21 at 20h
July 21 at 18h
ZENITH
LUPUS
CENTAURUS
HYDRA
NORMA
SCORPIUS
OPHIUCHUS
Rigil Kent
Hadar
Mimosa
CRUX
Acrux
CIRCINUS
ARA
TRIANGULUM AUSTRALE
MUSCA
VELA
ANTLIA
CORONA AUSTRALIS
TELESCOPIUM
APUS
S. POLE
CHAMAELEON
PAVO
SAGITTARIUS
OCTANS
VOLANS
CARINA
PYXIS
PUPPIS
HYDRUS
MENSA
INDUS
TUCANA
MICROSCOPIUM
Canopus
PICTOR
RETICULUM
GRUS
PHOENIX
Achernar
DORADO
COLUMBA
CANIS MAJOR
MONOCEROS
CAPRICORNUS
270°
280°
290°
300°
310°
ECLIPTIC
EAST
SOUTH
WEST

6N

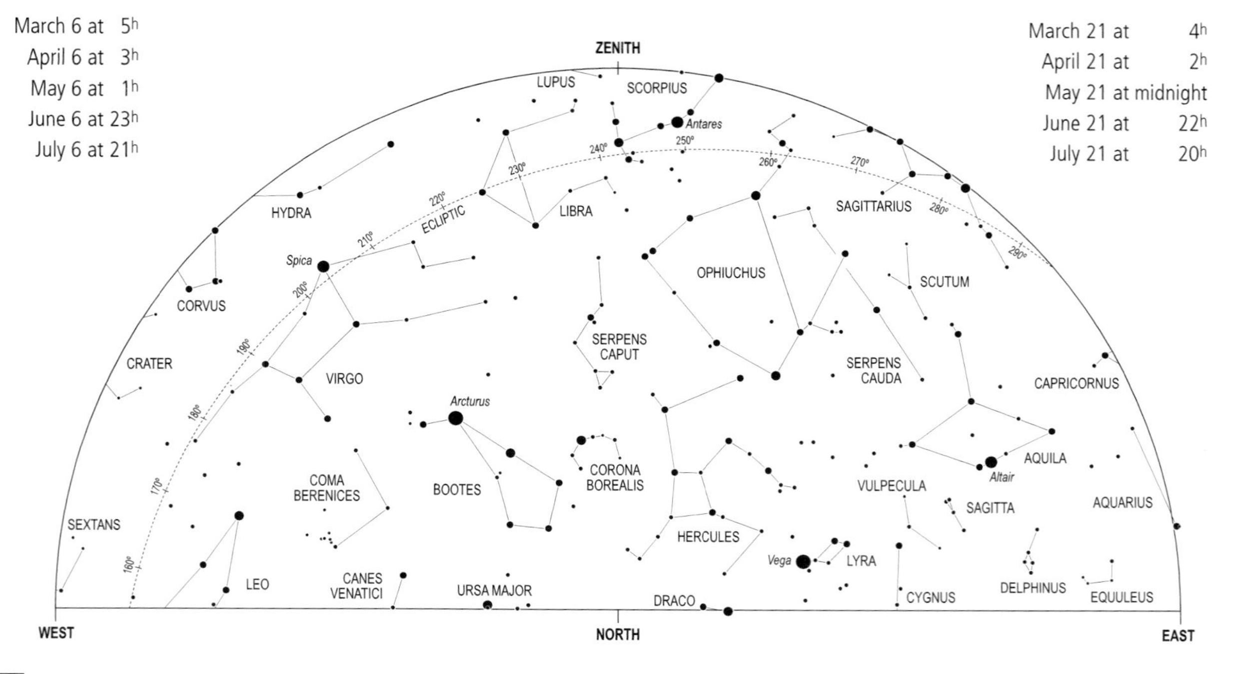
March 6 at 5h
April 6 at 3h
May 6 at 1h
June 6 at 23h
July 6 at 21h
March 21 at 4h
April 21 at 2h
May 21 at midnight
June 21 at 22h
July 21 at 20h
ZENITH
LUPUS
SCORPIUS
Antares
HYDRA
LIBRA
ECLIPTIC
SAGITTARIUS
Spica
OPHIUCHUS
SCUTUM
CORVUS
SERPENS CAPUT
CRATER
VIRGO
SERPENS CAUDA
CAPRICORNUS
Arcturus
AQUILA
Altair
COMA BERENICES
BOOTES
CORONA BOREALIS
VULPECULA
SAGITTA
AQUARIUS
SEXTANS
HERCULES
Vega
LYRA
LEO
CANES VENATICI
URSA MAJOR
DRACO
CYGNUS
DELPHINUS
EQUULEUS
WEST
NORTH
EAST
160°
170°
180°
190°
200°
210°
220°
230°
240°
250°
260°
270°
280°
290°

6S

March 6 at	5^h
April 6 at	3^h
May 6 at	1^h
June 6 at	23^h
July 6 at	21^h

March 21 at	4^h
April 21 at	2^h
May 21 at	midnight
June 21 at	22^h
July 21 at	20^h

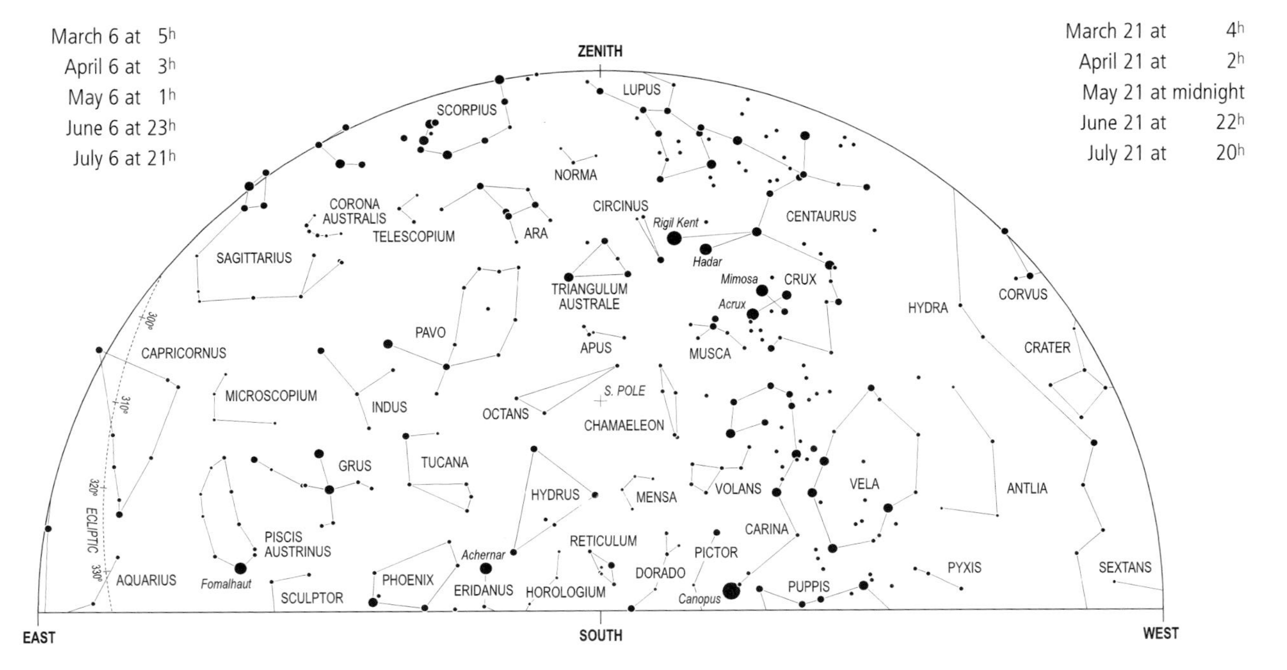

7N

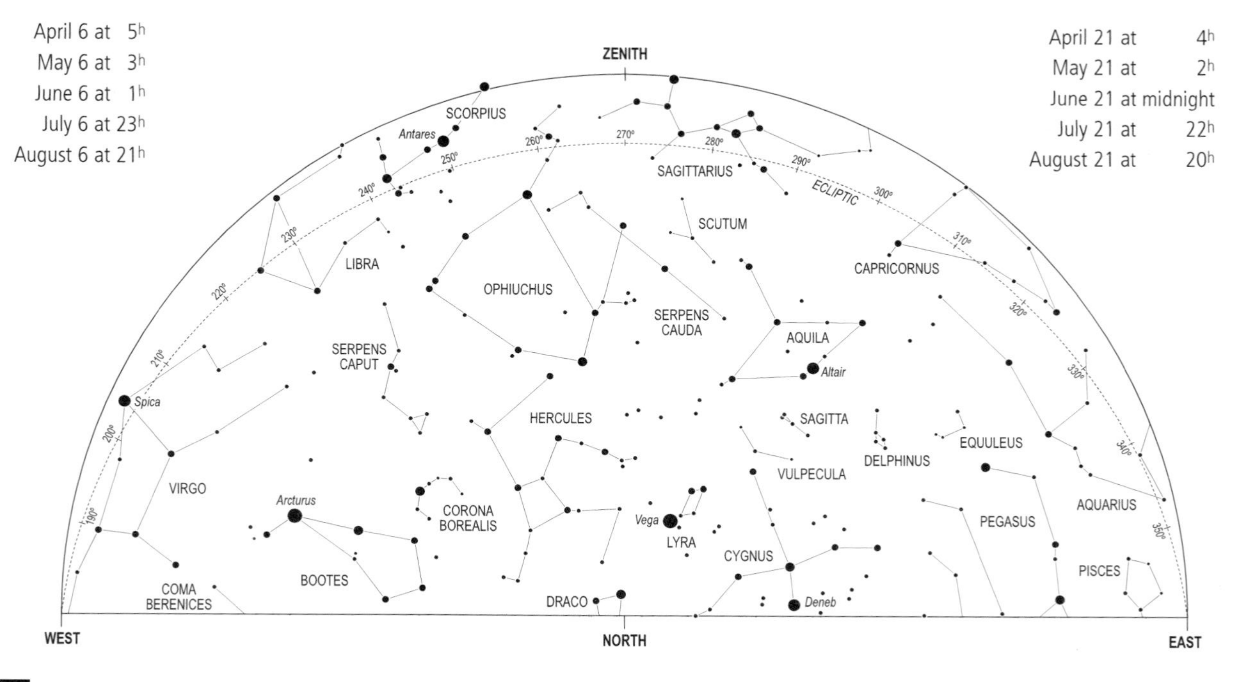
April 6 at 5h
May 6 at 3h
June 6 at 1h
July 6 at 23h
August 6 at 21h
April 21 at 4h
May 21 at 2h
June 21 at midnight
July 21 at 22h
August 21 at 20h
ZENITH
WEST
NORTH
EAST
ECLIPTIC
SCORPIUS
Antares
SAGITTARIUS
SCUTUM
LIBRA
OPHIUCHUS
SERPENS CAUDA
AQUILA
Altair
CAPRICORNUS
SERPENS CAPUT
Spica
HERCULES
SAGITTA
DELPHINUS
EQUULEUS
VIRGO
VULPECULA
Arcturus
CORONA BOREALIS
Vega
LYRA
CYGNUS
PEGASUS
AQUARIUS
BOOTES
COMA BERENICES
DRACO
Deneb
PISCES
190°
200°
210°
220°
230°
240°
250°
260°
270°
280°
290°
300°
310°
320°
330°
340°
350°

April 6 at 5^{h}
May 6 at 3^{h}
June 6 at 1^{h}
July 6 at 23^{h}
August 6 at 21^{h}

April 21 at 4^{h}
May 21 at 2^{h}
June 21 at midnight
July 21 at 22^{h}
August 21 at 20^{h}

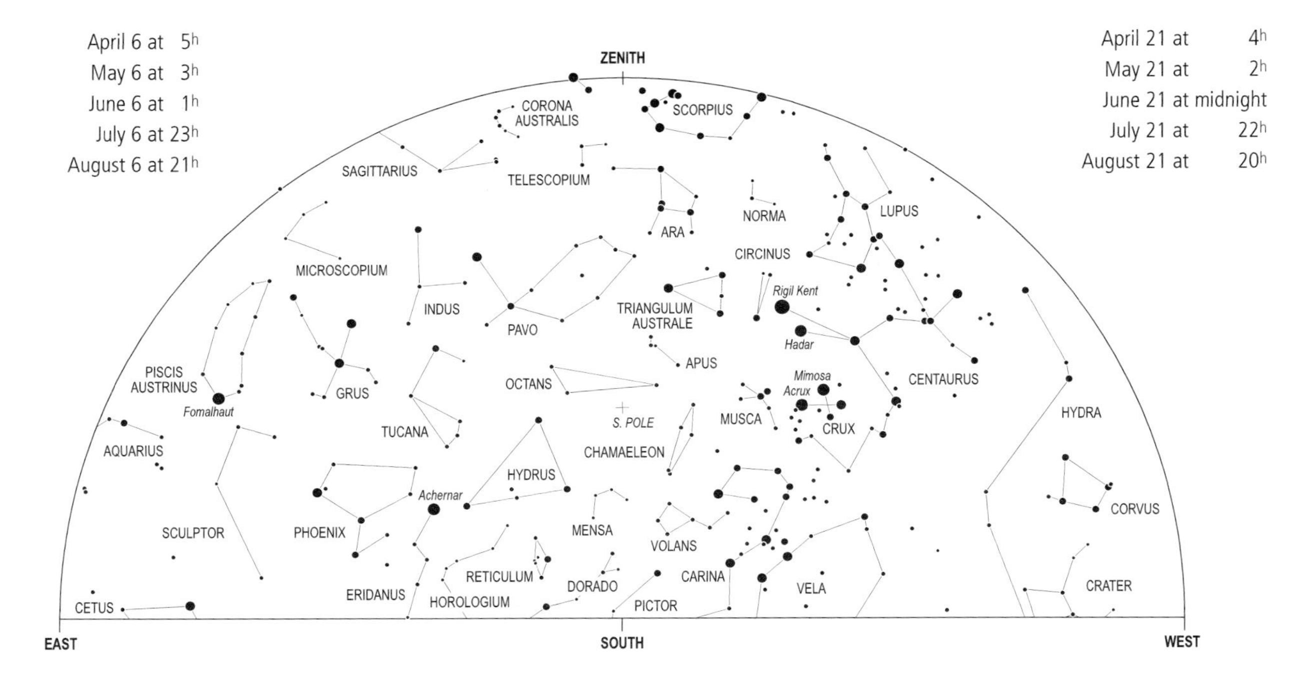

8N

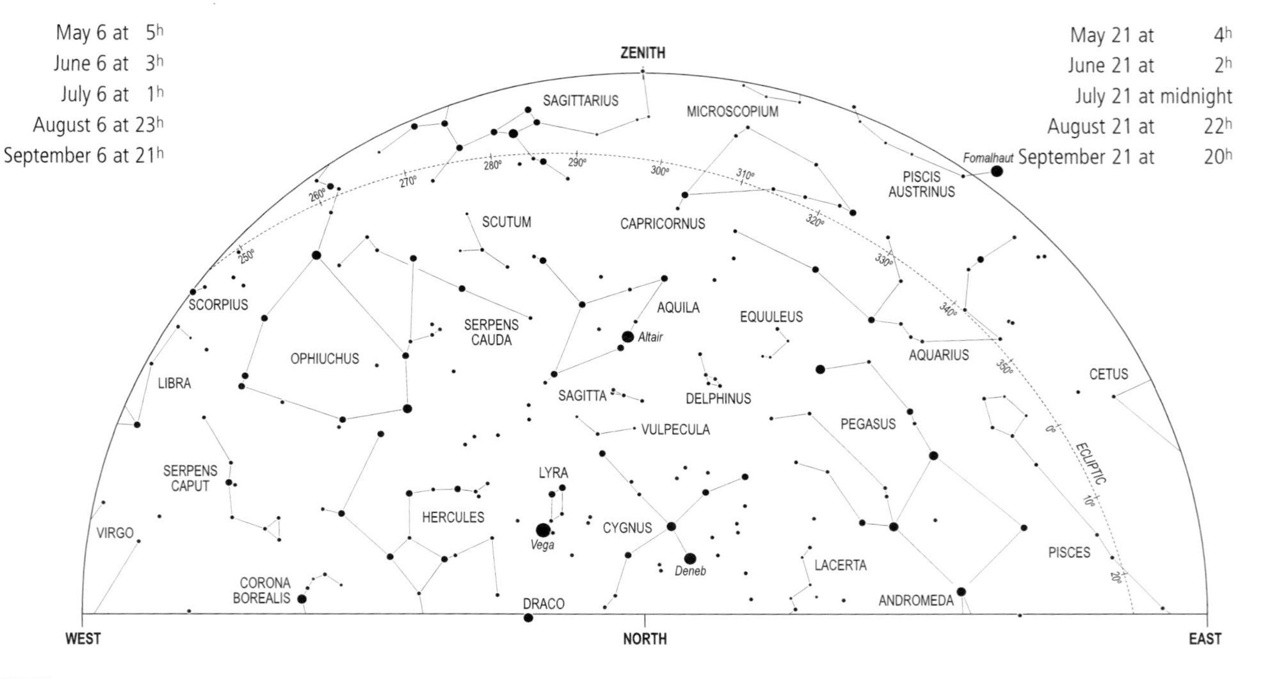

May 6 at 5h
June 6 at 3h
July 6 at 1h
August 6 at 23h
September 6 at 21h
May 21 at 4h
June 21 at 2h
July 21 at midnight
August 21 at 22h
September 21 at 20h
ZENITH
SAGITTARIUS
MICROSCOPIUM
Fomalhaut
PISCIS AUSTRINUS
SCUTUM
CAPRICORNUS
SCORPIUS
SERPENS CAUDA
AQUILA
EQUULEUS
Altair
OPHIUCHUS
AQUARIUS
CETUS
LIBRA
SAGITTA
DELPHINUS
VULPECULA
PEGASUS
ECLIPTIC
SERPENS CAPUT
LYRA
HERCULES
CYGNUS
VIRGO
Vega
Deneb
LACERTA
PISCES
CORONA BOREALIS
DRACO
ANDROMEDA
WEST
NORTH
EAST
250°
260°
270°
280°
290°
300°
310°
320°
330°
340°
350°
0°
10°
20°

8S

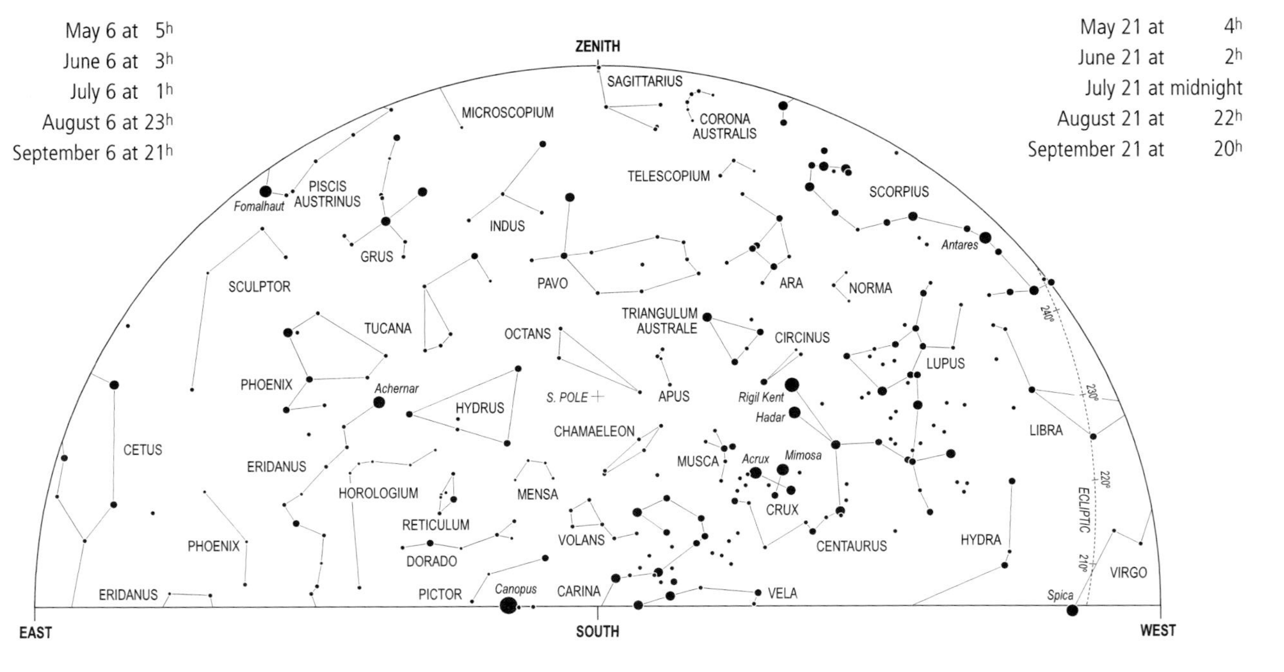
May 6 at 5h
June 6 at 3h
July 6 at 1h
August 6 at 23h
September 6 at 21h
May 21 at 4h
June 21 at 2h
July 21 at midnight
August 21 at 22h
September 21 at 20h
ZENITH
SAGITTARIUS
CORONA AUSTRALIS
MICROSCOPIUM
PISCIS AUSTRINUS
Fomalhaut
TELESCOPIUM
SCORPIUS
INDUS
GRUS
Antares
SCULPTOR
PAVO
ARA
NORMA
TRIANGULUM AUSTRALE
240°
TUCANA
OCTANS
CIRCINUS
LUPUS
PHOENIX
Achernar
S. POLE
APUS
Rigil Kent
230°
HYDRUS
Hadar
LIBRA
CETUS
CHAMAELEON
ERIDANUS
MUSCA
Acrux
Mimosa
220°
HOROLOGIUM
MENSA
CRUX
ECLIPTIC
RETICULUM
PHOENIX
VOLANS
CENTAURUS
HYDRA
210°
DORADO
VIRGO
ERIDANUS
PICTOR
Canopus
CARINA
VELA
Spica
EAST
SOUTH
WEST

9N

June 6 at 5h
July 6 at 3h
August 6 at 1h
September 6 at 23h
October 6 at 21h

June 21 at 4h
July 21 at 2h
August 21 at midnight
September 21 at 22h
October 21 at 20h

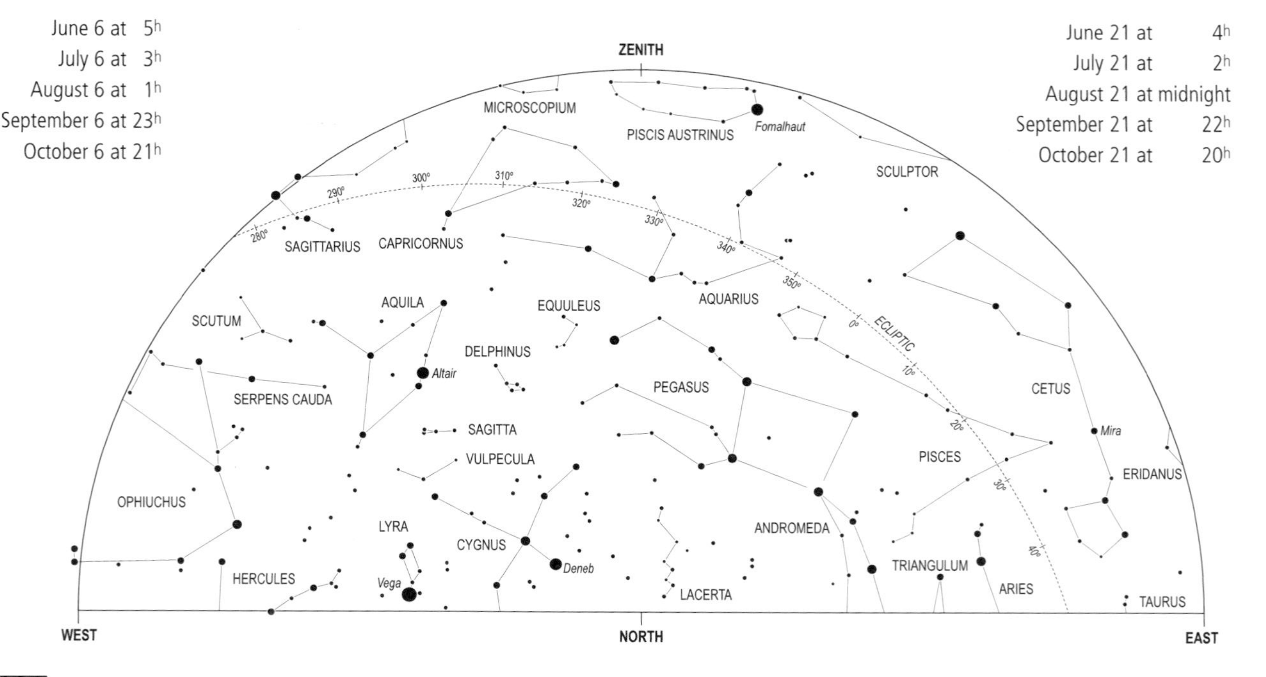

9S

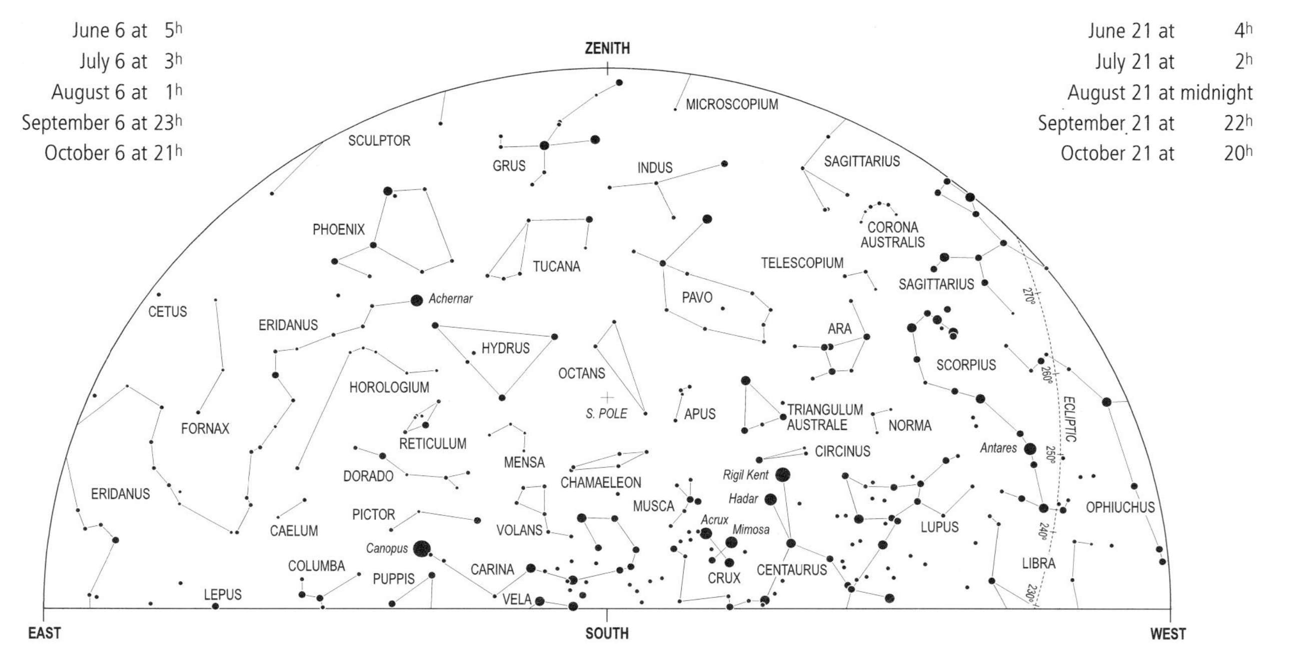
June 6 at 5h
July 6 at 3h
August 6 at 1h
September 6 at 23h
October 6 at 21h
June 21 at 4h
July 21 at 2h
August 21 at midnight
September 21 at 22h
October 21 at 20h
ZENITH
EAST
SOUTH
WEST
MICROSCOPIUM
SCULPTOR
GRUS
INDUS
SAGITTARIUS
PHOENIX
CORONA AUSTRALIS
TUCANA
TELESCOPIUM
SAGITTARIUS
PAVO
Achernar
CETUS
ERIDANUS
ARA
HYDRUS
SCORPIUS
OCTANS
HOROLOGIUM
S. POLE
APUS
TRIANGULUM AUSTRALE
NORMA
ECLIPTIC
270°
260°
250°
240°
230°
FORNAX
RETICULUM
CIRCINUS
Antares
MENSA
DORADO
CHAMAELEON
Rigil Kent
ERIDANUS
Hadar
MUSCA
OPHIUCHUS
PICTOR
Acrux
Mimosa
LUPUS
CAELUM
VOLANS
Canopus
LIBRA
COLUMBA
CARINA
CENTAURUS
PUPPIS
CRUX
LEPUS
VELA

10N

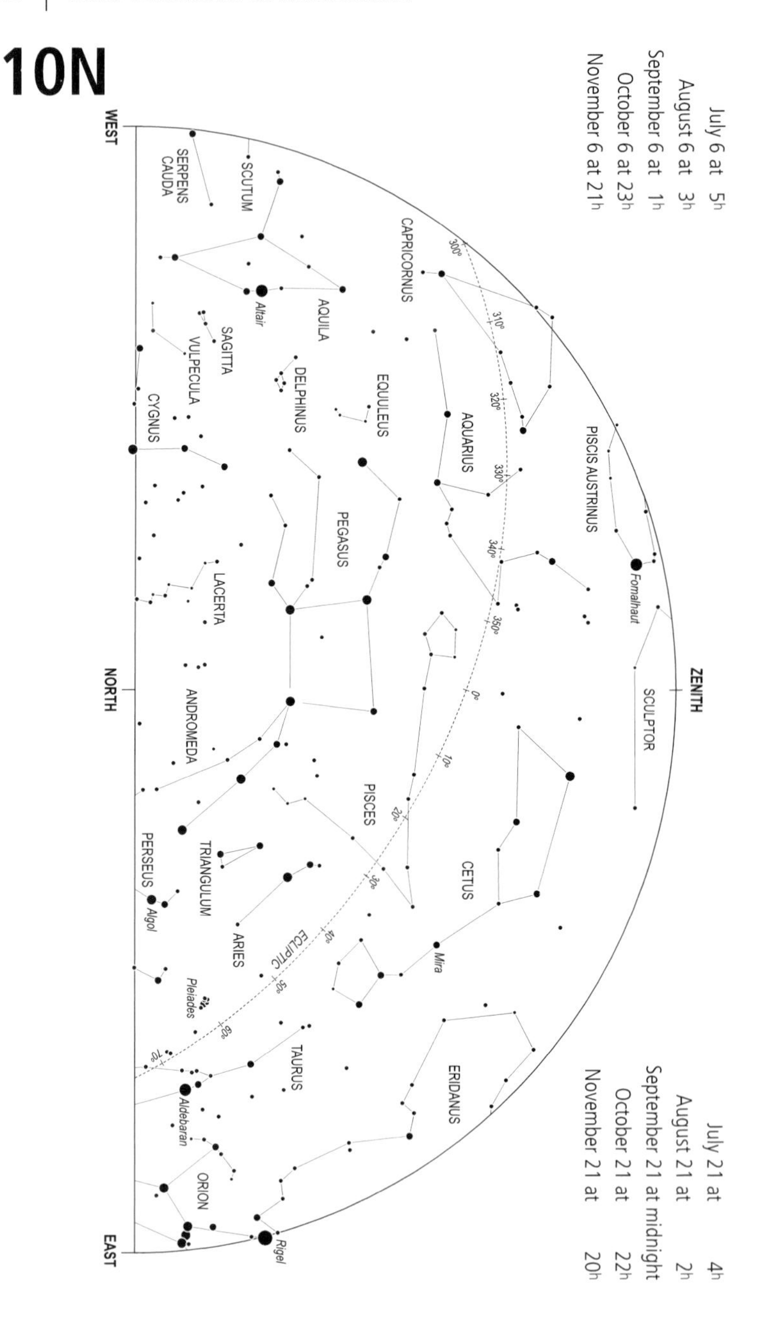
July 6 at 5h
August 6 at 3h
September 6 at 1h
October 6 at 23h
November 6 at 21h
July 21 at 4h
August 21 at 2h
September 21 at midnight
October 21 at 22h
November 21 at 20h
WEST
NORTH
EAST
ZENITH
SERPENS CAUDA
SCUTUM
CAPRICORNUS
AQUILA
Altair
SAGITTA
VULPECULA
CYGNUS
DELPHINUS
EQUULEUS
AQUARIUS
PISCIS AUSTRINUS
Fomalhaut
PEGASUS
LACERTA
ANDROMEDA
SCULPTOR
PISCES
CETUS
Mira
PERSEUS
Algol
TRIANGULUM
ARIES
ECLIPTIC
Pleiades
TAURUS
Aldebaran
ERIDANUS
ORION
Rigel
300°
310°
320°
330°
340°
350°
0°
10°
20°
30°
40°
50°
60°
70°

10S

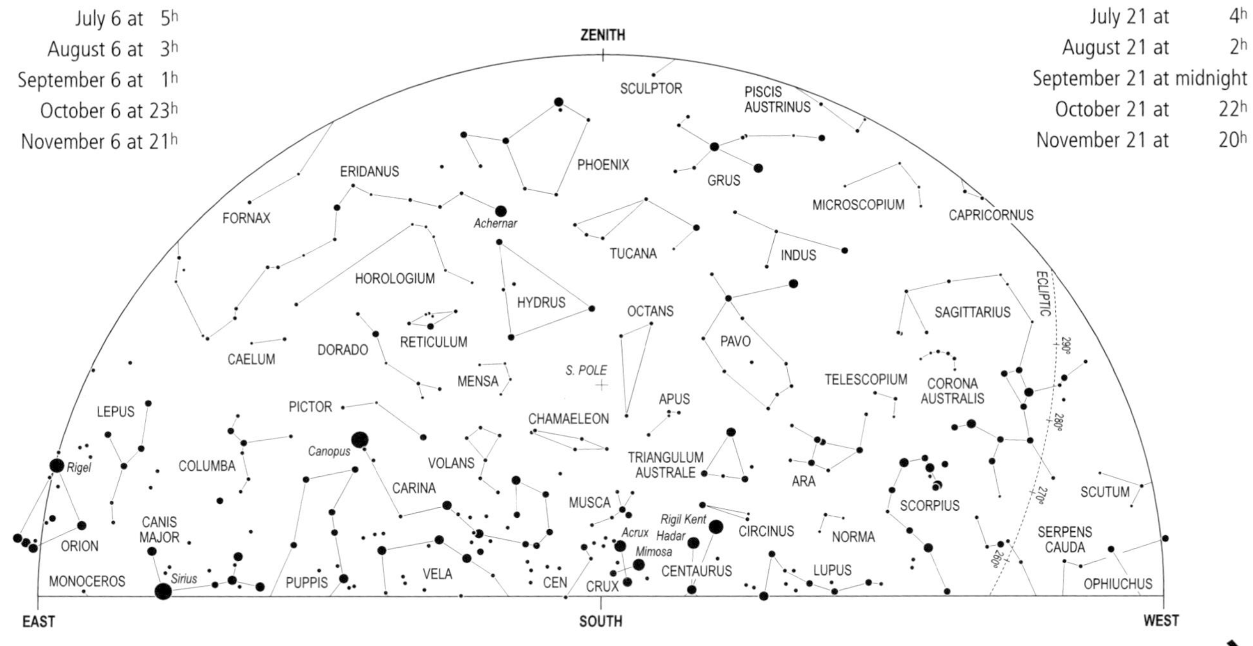
July 6 at 5h
August 6 at 3h
September 6 at 1h
October 6 at 23h
November 6 at 21h
July 21 at 4h
August 21 at 2h
September 21 at midnight
October 21 at 22h
November 21 at 20h
ZENITH
EAST
SOUTH
WEST
SCULPTOR
PISCIS AUSTRINUS
PHOENIX
GRUS
ERIDANUS
MICROSCOPIUM
CAPRICORNUS
FORNAX
Achernar
TUCANA
INDUS
HOROLOGIUM
ECLIPTIC
HYDRUS
OCTANS
SAGITTARIUS
RETICULUM
PAVO
CAELUM
DORADO
290°
MENSA
S. POLE
TELESCOPIUM
CORONA AUSTRALIS
APUS
LEPUS
PICTOR
CHAMAELEON
280°
Canopus
TRIANGULUM AUSTRALE
Rigel
COLUMBA
VOLANS
ARA
CARINA
270°
SCUTUM
SCORPIUS
MUSCA
Rigil Kent
CANIS MAJOR
CIRCINUS
Acrux
Hadar
NORMA
SERPENS CAUDA
ORION
Mimosa
260°
CENTAURUS
LUPUS
Sirius
VELA
MONOCEROS
PUPPIS
CEN
CRUX
OPHIUCHUS

11N

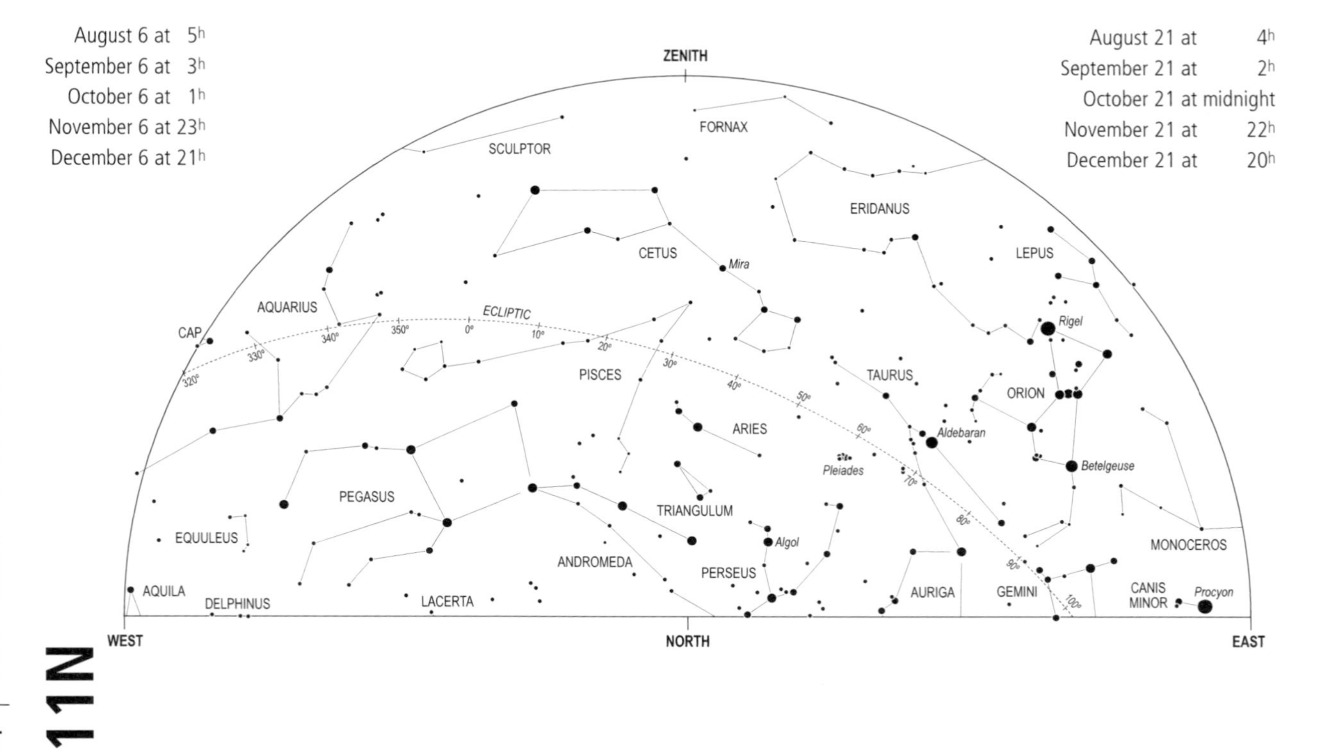
August 6 at 5h
September 6 at 3h
October 6 at 1h
November 6 at 23h
December 6 at 21h
August 21 at 4h
September 21 at 2h
October 21 at midnight
November 21 at 22h
December 21 at 20h
ZENITH
WEST
NORTH
EAST
SCULPTOR
FORNAX
ERIDANUS
CETUS
Mira
LEPUS
AQUARIUS
CAP
ECLIPTIC
320°
330°
340°
350°
0°
10°
20°
30°
40°
50°
60°
70°
80°
90°
100°
PISCES
TAURUS
Rigel
ORION
ARIES
Aldebaran
Pleiades
Betelgeuse
PEGASUS
TRIANGULUM
Algol
EQUULEUS
ANDROMEDA
PERSEUS
MONOCEROS
AQUILA
DELPHINUS
LACERTA
AURIGA
GEMINI
CANIS MINOR
Procyon

11S

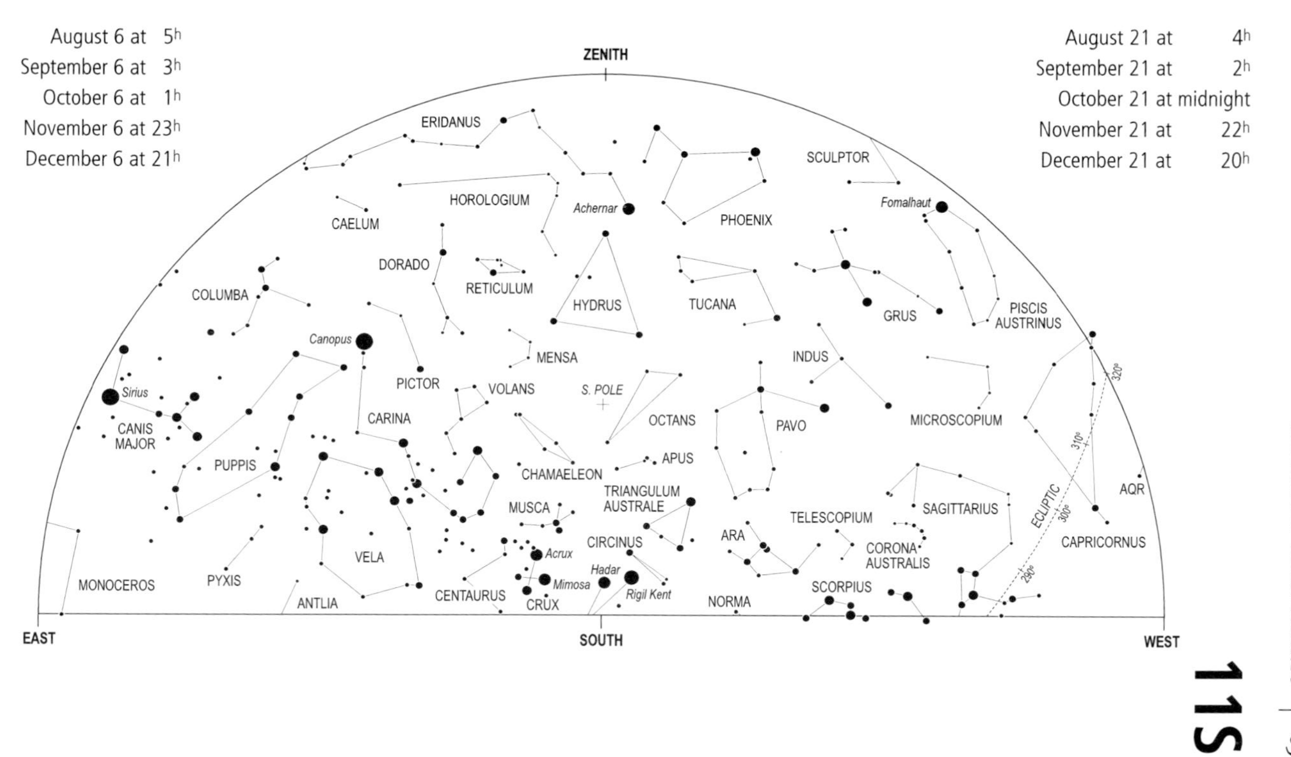
August 6 at 5h
September 6 at 3h
October 6 at 1h
November 6 at 23h
December 6 at 21h
August 21 at 4h
September 21 at 2h
October 21 at midnight
November 21 at 22h
December 21 at 20h
ZENITH
ERIDANUS
SCULPTOR
HOROLOGIUM
Achernar
PHOENIX
Fomalhaut
CAELUM
DORADO
RETICULUM
HYDRUS
TUCANA
GRUS
PISCIS AUSTRINUS
COLUMBA
Canopus
MENSA
INDUS
320°
PICTOR
VOLANS
S. POLE
OCTANS
PAVO
MICROSCOPIUM
Sirius
CANIS MAJOR
CARINA
APUS
310°
PUPPIS
CHAMAELEON
TRIANGULUM AUSTRALE
SAGITTARIUS
ECLIPTIC
300°
AQR
MUSCA
TELESCOPIUM
CAPRICORNUS
ARA
CIRCINUS
CORONA AUSTRALIS
VELA
Acrux
290°
Hadar
MONOCEROS
PYXIS
Mimosa
SCORPIUS
Rigil Kent
ANTLIA
CENTAURUS
CRUX
NORMA
EAST
SOUTH
WEST

12N

September 6 at 5h
October 6 at 3h
November 6 at 1h
December 6 at 23h
January 6 at 21h

September 21 at 4h
October 21 at 2h
November 21 at midnight
December 21 at 22h
January 21 at 20h

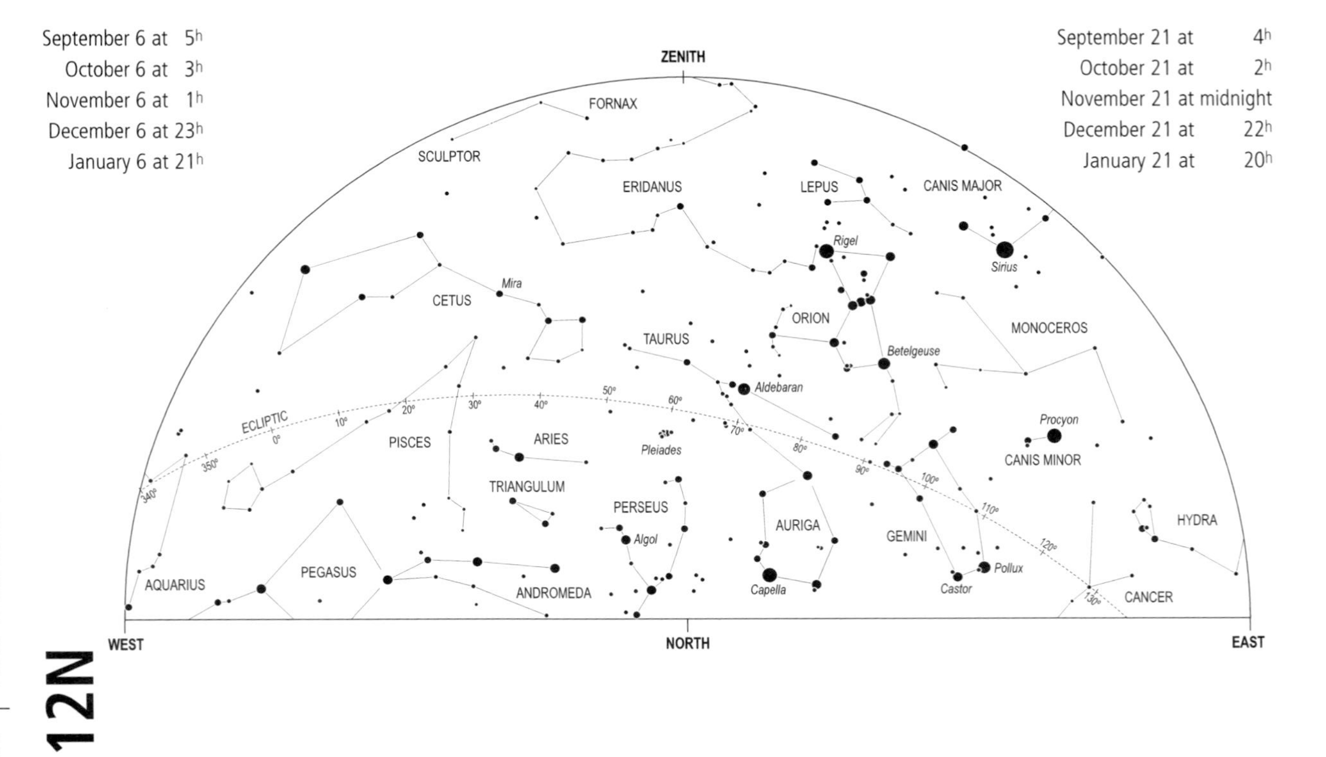

12S

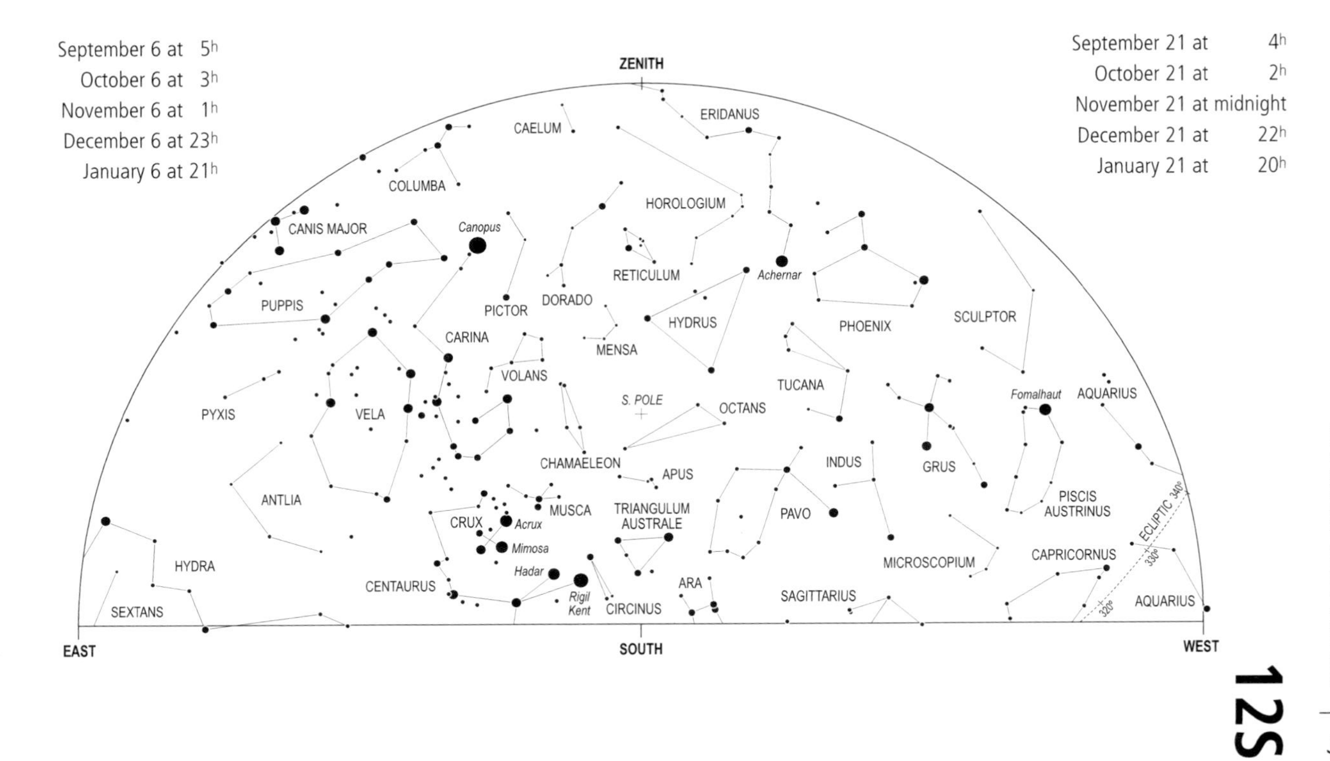
September 6 at 5h
October 6 at 3h
November 6 at 1h
December 6 at 23h
January 6 at 21h
September 21 at 4h
October 21 at 2h
November 21 at midnight
December 21 at 22h
January 21 at 20h
ZENITH
EAST
SOUTH
WEST
CAELUM
ERIDANUS
COLUMBA
HOROLOGIUM
CANIS MAJOR
Canopus
RETICULUM
Achernar
PUPPIS
PICTOR
DORADO
HYDRUS
PHOENIX
SCULPTOR
CARINA
MENSA
VOLANS
TUCANA
PYXIS
VELA
S. POLE
OCTANS
Fomalhaut
AQUARIUS
CHAMAELEON
APUS
INDUS
GRUS
ANTLIA
MUSCA
TRIANGULUM AUSTRALE
PAVO
PISCIS AUSTRINUS
CRUX
Acrux
Mimosa
ECLIPTIC 340°
330°
320°
HYDRA
Hadar
MICROSCOPIUM
CAPRICORNUS
CENTAURUS
Rigil Kent
ARA
CIRCINUS
SAGITTARIUS
SEXTANS
AQUARIUS

The Planets and the Ecliptic

The paths of the planets about the Sun all lie close to the plane of the ecliptic, which is marked for us in the sky by the apparent path of the Sun among the stars, and is shown on the star charts by a broken line. The Moon and naked-eye planets will always be found close to this line, never departing from it by more than about 7°. Thus the planets are most favourably placed for observation when the ecliptic is well displayed, and this means that it should be as high in the sky as possible. This avoids the difficulty of finding a clear horizon, and also overcomes the problem of atmospheric absorption, which greatly reduces the light of the stars. Thus a star at an altitude of 10° suffers a loss of 60 per cent of its light, which corresponds to a whole magnitude; at an altitude of only 4°, the loss may amount to two magnitudes.

The position of the ecliptic in the sky is therefore of great importance, and since it is tilted at about 23.5° to the Equator, it is only at certain times of the day or year that it is displayed to the best advantage. It will be realized that the Sun (and therefore the ecliptic) is at its highest in the sky at noon in midsummer, and at its lowest at noon in midwinter. Allowing for the daily motion of the sky, it follows that the ecliptic is highest at midnight in winter, at sunset in the spring, at noon in summer and at sunrise in the autumn. Hence these are the best times to see the planets. Thus, if Venus is an evening object in the western sky after sunset, it will be seen to best advantage if this occurs in the spring, when the ecliptic is high in the sky and slopes down steeply to the horizon. This means that the planet is not only higher in the sky, but will remain for a much longer period above the horizon. For similar reasons, a morning object will be seen at its best on autumn mornings before sunrise, when the ecliptic is high in the east. The outer planets, which can come to opposition (i.e. opposite the Sun), are best seen when opposition occurs in the winter months, when the ecliptic is high in the sky at midnight.

The seasons are reversed in the Southern Hemisphere, spring beginning at the September Equinox, when the Sun crosses the Equator on its way south, summer beginning at the December Solstice, when the

Sun is highest in the southern sky, and so on. Thus, the times when the ecliptic is highest in the sky, and therefore best placed for observing the planets, may be summarized as follows:

	Midnight	**Sunrise**	**Noon**	**Sunset**
Northern latitudes	December	September	June	March
Southern latitudes	June	March	December	September

In addition to the daily rotation of the celestial sphere from east to west, the planets have a motion of their own among the stars. The apparent movement is generally *direct*, i.e. to the east, in the direction of increasing longitude, but for a certain period (which depends on the distance of the planet) this apparent motion is reversed. With the outer planets this *retrograde* motion occurs about the time of opposition. Owing to the different inclination of the orbits of these planets, the actual effect is to cause the apparent path to form a loop, or sometimes an S-shaped curve. The same effect is present in the motion of the inferior planets, Mercury and Venus, but it is not so obvious, since it always occurs at the time of inferior conjunction.

The *inferior planets*, Mercury and Venus, move in smaller orbits than that of the Earth, and so are always seen near the Sun. They are most obvious at the times of greatest angular distance from the Sun (greatest elongation), which may reach 28° for Mercury, and 47° for Venus. They are seen as evening objects in the western sky after sunset (at eastern elongations) or as morning objects in the eastern sky before sunrise (at western elongations). The succession of phenomena, conjunctions and elongations, always follows the same order, but the intervals between them are not equal. Thus, if either planet is moving round the far side of its orbit its motion will be to the east, in the same direction in which the Sun appears to be moving. It therefore takes much longer for the planet to overtake the Sun – that is, to come to superior conjunction – than it does when moving round to inferior conjunction, between Sun and Earth. The intervals given in the following table are average values; they remain fairly constant in the case of Venus, which travels in an almost circular orbit. In the case of Mercury, however, conditions vary widely because of the great eccentricity and inclination of the planet's orbit.

		Mercury	Venus
Inferior Conjunction	to Elongation West	22 days	72 days
Elongation West	to Superior Conjunction	36 days	220 days
Superior Conjunction	to Elongation East	35 days	220 days
Elongation East	to Inferior Conjunction	22 days	72 days

The greatest brilliancy of Venus always occurs about 36 days before or after inferior conjunction. This will be about a month after greatest eastern elongation (as an evening object), or a month before greatest western elongation (as a morning object). No such rule can be given for Mercury, because its distances from the Earth and the Sun can vary over a wide range.

Mercury is not likely to be seen unless a clear horizon is available. It is seldom as much as 10° above the horizon in the twilight sky in northern temperate latitudes, but this figure is often exceeded in the Southern Hemisphere. This favourable condition arises because the maximum elongation of 28° can occur only when the planet is at aphelion (furthest from the Sun), and it then lies well south of the Equator. Northern observers must be content with smaller elongations, which may be as little as 18° at perihelion (closest to the Sun). In general, it may be said that the most favourable times for seeing Mercury as an evening object will be in spring, some days before greatest eastern elongation; in autumn, it may be seen as a morning object some days after greatest western elongation.

Venus is the brightest of the planets and may be seen on occasions in broad daylight. Like Mercury, it is alternately a morning and an evening object, and it will be highest in the sky when it is a morning object in autumn, or an evening object in spring. Venus is to be seen at its best as an evening object in northern latitudes when eastern elongation occurs in June. The planet is then well north of the Sun in the preceding spring months, and is a brilliant object in the evening sky over a long period. In the Southern Hemisphere a November elongation is best. For similar reasons, Venus gives a prolonged display as a morning object in the months following western elongation in October (in northern latitudes) or in June (in the Southern Hemisphere).

The *superior planets*, which travel in orbits larger than that of the Earth, differ from Mercury and Venus in that they can be seen opposite the Sun in the sky. The superior planets are morning objects after conjunction with the Sun, rising earlier each day until they come to opposition. They will then be nearest to the Earth (and therefore at their brightest), and will be on the meridian at midnight, due south in northern latitudes, but due north in the Southern Hemisphere. After opposition they are evening objects, setting earlier each evening until they set in the west with the Sun at the next conjunction. The difference in brightness from one opposition to another is most noticeable in the case of Mars, whose distance from Earth can vary considerably and rapidly. The other superior planets are at such great distances that there is very little change in brightness from one opposition to the next. The effect of altitude is, however, of some importance, for at a December opposition in northern latitudes the planets will be among the stars of Taurus or Gemini, and can then be at an altitude of more than 60° in southern England. At a summer opposition, when the planet is in Sagittarius, it may only rise to about 15° above the southern horizon, and so makes a less impressive appearance. In the Southern Hemisphere the reverse conditions apply, a June opposition being the best, with the planet in Sagittarius at an altitude which can reach 80° above the northern horizon for observers in South Africa.

Mars, whose orbit is appreciably eccentric, comes nearest to the Earth at oppositions at the end of August. It may then be brighter even than Jupiter, but rather low in the sky in Aquarius for northern observers, though very well placed for those in southern latitudes. These favourable oppositions occur every fifteen or seventeen years (e.g. in 1988, 2003 and 2018). In the Northern Hemisphere the planet is probably better seen at oppositions in the autumn or winter months, when it is higher in the sky – such as in 2005 when opposition was in early November. Oppositions of Mars occur at an average interval of 780 days, and during this time the planet makes a complete circuit of the sky.

Jupiter is always a bright planet, and comes to opposition a month later each year, having moved, roughly speaking, from one Zodiacal constellation to the next.

Saturn moves much more slowly than Jupiter, and may remain in the same constellation for several years. The brightness of Saturn depends on the aspects of its rings, as well as on the distance from Earth and Sun. The Earth passed through the plane of Saturn's rings in 1995 and 1996, when they appeared edge-on; we saw them at maximum opening, and Saturn at its brightest, in 2002. The rings will next appear edge-on in 2009.

Uranus and *Neptune* are both visible with binoculars or a small telescope, but you will need a finder chart to help locate them (such as those reproduced in this *Yearbook* on pages 123 and 129), while *Pluto* is hardly likely to attract the attention of observers without adequate telescopes.

Phases of the Moon in 2006

New Moon				First Quarter				Full Moon				Last Quarter			
	d	h	m		d	h	m		d	h	m		d	h	m
				Jan	6	18	56	Jan	14	09	48	Jan	22	15	14
Jan	29	14	15	Feb	5	06	29	Feb	13	04	44	Feb	21	07	17
Feb	28	00	31	Mar	6	20	16	Mar	14	23	35	Mar	22	19	10
Mar	29	10	15	Apr	5	12	01	Apr	13	16	40	Apr	21	03	28
Apr	27	19	44	May	5	05	13	May	13	06	51	May	20	09	21
May	27	05	26	June	3	23	06	June	11	18	03	June	18	14	08
June	25	16	05	July	3	16	37	July	11	03	02	July	17	19	13
July	25	04	31	Aug	2	08	46	Aug	9	10	54	Aug	16	01	51
Aug	23	19	10	Aug	31	22	56	Sept	7	18	42	Sept	14	11	15
Sept	22	11	45	Sept	30	11	04	Oct	7	03	13	Oct	14	00	26
Oct	22	05	14	Oct	29	21	25	Nov	5	12	58	Nov	12	17	45
Nov	20	22	18	Nov	28	06	29	Dec	5	00	25	Dec	12	14	32
Dec	20	14	01	Dec	27	14	48								

All times are GMT

Longitudes of the Sun, Moon and Planets in 2006

Date		Sun	Moon	Venus	Mars	Jupiter	Saturn
		°	°	°	°	°	°
January	6	286	5	298	42	224	130
	21	301	193	290	48	226	128
February	6	317	56	286	54	228	127
	21	332	239	291	62	229	126
March	6	345	65	301	68	229	125
	21	0	248	314	76	228	125
April	6	16	112	330	85	227	124
	21	31	299	346	94	226	125
May	6	45	144	3	103	224	125
	21	60	338	20	112	222	126
June	6	75	187	39	121	220	128
	21	90	31	56	130	219	129
July	6	104	220	74	140	219	131
	21	118	69	92	149	219	133
August	6	133	267	112	159	220	135
	21	148	117	130	168	222	137
September	6	163	318	150	179	224	139
	21	178	162	168	188	227	140
October	6	193	356	187	198	229	142
	21	207	194	206	208	233	143
November	6	223	50	226	219	236	144
	21	239	239	245	229	239	145
December	6	254	87	263	240	243	145
	21	269	274	282	251	246	145

Longitude of *Uranus* 342°
Neptune 318°

Moon: Longitude of ascending node
Jan 1: 9° Dec 31: 350°

Mercury moves so quickly among the stars that it is not possible to indicate its position on the star charts at convenient intervals. The Monthly Notes must be consulted for the best times at which the planet may be seen.

The positions of the other planets are given in the table on p. 74. This gives the apparent longitudes on dates which correspond to those of the star charts, and the position of the planet may at once be found near the ecliptic at the given longitude.

EXAMPLES

In the Southern Hemisphere two planets are seen in the evening for several hours after sunset, low in the north-western sky early in June. Identify them.

> The southern chart 4N shows the southern sky for 6 June at 19^h, and shows longitudes 110° to 240° along the ecliptic. Reference to the table on p. 74 gives the longitude of Mars as 121° and that of Saturn as 128°, Mars being lower down in the sky than Saturn, and also fainter than Saturn.

The positions of the Sun and Moon can be plotted on the star maps in the same manner as for the planets. The average daily motion of the Sun is 1°, and of the Moon 13°. For the Moon, an indication of its position relative to the ecliptic may be obtained from a consideration of its longitude relative to that of the ascending node. The latter changes only slowly during the year, as will be seen from the values given on p. 74. Let us denote by d the difference in longitude between the Moon and its ascending node. Then if d = 0°, 180° or 360°, the Moon is on the ecliptic. If d = 90° the Moon is 5° north of the ecliptic, and if d = 270° the Moon is 5° south of the ecliptic.

On 6 August the Moon's longitude is given in the table on p. 74 as 267° and the longitude of the node is found by interpolation to be about 358°. Thus d = 269° and the Moon is about 5° south of the ecliptic. Its position may be plotted on northern star charts 6S, 7S, 8S, and on southern star charts 6N, 7N, 8N.

Some Events in 2006

Jan	4	*Earth* at Perihelion
	13	*Venus* at Inferior Conjunction
	14	Full Moon
	26	*Mercury* at Superior Conjunction
	27	*Saturn* at Opposition in Cancer
	29	New Moon
Feb	6	*Neptune* in Conjunction with Sun
	13	Full Moon
	24	*Mercury* at Greatest Eastern Elongation (18°)
	28	New Moon
Mar	1	*Uranus* in Conjunction with Sun
	12	*Mercury* at Inferior Conjunction
	14	Full Moon
	14	Penumbral Eclipse of Moon
	20	Equinox (Spring Equinox in Northern Hemisphere)
	25	*Venus* at Greatest Western Elongation (47°)
	29	New Moon
	29	Total Eclipse of Sun
Apr	8	*Mercury* at Greatest Western Elongation (28°)
	13	Full Moon
	27	New Moon
May	4	*Jupiter* at Opposition in Libra
	13	Full Moon
	18	*Mercury* at Superior Conjunction
	27	New Moon
Jun	11	Full Moon
	16	*Pluto* at Opposition in Serpens
	20	*Mercury* at Greatest Eastern Elongation (25°)

	21	Solstice (Summer Solstice in Northern Hemisphere)
	25	New Moon
Jul	3	*Earth* at Aphelion
	11	Full Moon
	18	*Mercury* at Inferior Conjunction
	25	New Moon
Aug	7	*Mercury* at Greatest Western Elongation (19°)
	7	*Saturn* in Conjunction with Sun
	9	Full Moon
	11	*Neptune* at Opposition in Capricornus
	23	New Moon
Sep	1	*Mercury* at Superior Conjunction
	5	*Uranus* at Opposition in Aquarius
	7	Full Moon
	7	Partial Eclipse of Moon
	22	New Moon
	22	Annular Eclipse of Sun
	23	Equinox (Autumnal Equinox in Northern Hemisphere)
Oct	7	Full Moon
	17	*Mercury* at Greatest Eastern Elongation (25°)
	22	New Moon
	23	*Mars* in Conjunction with Sun
	27	*Venus* at Superior Conjunction
Nov	5	Full Moon
	8	*Mercury* at Inferior Conjunction
	8	Transit of *Mercury*
	20	New Moon
	21	*Jupiter* in Conjunction with Sun
	25	*Mercury* at Greatest Western Elongation (20°)
Dec	5	Full Moon
	20	New Moon
	22	Solstice (Winter Solstice in Northern Hemisphere)

Monthly Notes 2006

January

New Moon: 29 January *Full Moon:* 14 January

EARTH is at perihelion (nearest to the Sun) on 4 January at a distance of 147 million kilometres (91 million miles).

MERCURY, magnitude −0.5, may be seen very low above the east-south-eastern horizon for a very short while around the beginning of morning civil twilight, by observers in tropical and southern latitudes, but only for the first few days of the month. For observers in the latitudes of the British Isles it is unsuitably placed for observation. Mercury goes through superior conjunction on 26 January.

VENUS, magnitude −4.3, is a brilliant object low in the south-western sky in the early evenings just after sunset at the beginning of the month. For observers in the latitudes of the United Kingdom this apparition will last for about ten days, but in southern latitudes Venus will only be visible for the first few days of the month. The planet passes rapidly through inferior conjunction on 13 January when it is 5.5° north of the ecliptic. On the following morning the planet becomes visible again to northern hemisphere observers, low in the south-eastern sky shortly before sunrise. For the last ten days of the month it is also visible in the mornings to those in the southern hemisphere.

Observers in the latitudes of the United Kingdom may be able to detect it telescopically just before and after inferior conjunction. On the evening of the 10th, just after sunset, optical aid should show Venus as an incredibly thin sliver of light (only 0.7 per cent illuminated) with an apparent diameter of 62.4 arcseconds). Again, on the morning of the 14th, just before sunrise, a similar phenomenon will occur with Venus only 0.4 per cent illuminated and with an apparent diameter of 62.6 arcseconds. Since the Earth is not far from perihelion and Venus's orbit is nearly circular, the planet must subtend almost the maximum apparent diameter that is possible.

The Mercury and Venus Section of the British Astronomical

Association notes that: 'near inferior conjunction, given good observing conditions, the planet's cusps may be seen to extend beyond a half circle. The cusps are the north and south parts of the disk – the horns of the crescent phase. Cusp extension is a twilight effect caused by diffused sunlight in the planet's atmosphere. When close to inferior conjunction observers sometimes see Venus completely encircled by this twilight arc.' WARNING – Inferior conjunction is for experienced observers only. Do not attempt these observations unless you use setting circles on the telescope to find Venus, because of the danger of accidentally getting the Sun in the field of view and of irreparably damaging your eyesight. In any event you must exercise the very greatest care.

MARS, its magnitude fading from −0.6 to +0.2, is an evening object, visible in the south-western sky for several hours after sunset, and for observers in the latitudes of the United Kingdom, for well after midnight. Mars is moving eastwards in the constellation of Aries.

JUPITER, magnitude −1.9, is a brilliant object in the morning sky before dawn in the constellation of Libra. Around 10–12 January it passes within 0.8° north of the wide naked-eye double star Alpha Librae: the two stars (magnitudes 5.15 and 2.75) are nearly 4 arcminutes apart.

SATURN, magnitude −0.2, is moving slowly retrograde in the constellation of Cancer, in the direction of the Beehive Cluster, Praesepe. It reaches opposition on 27 January and is therefore visible throughout the hours of darkness, crossing the meridian at midnight. The rings are now closing and, as a result, the planet is not quite as bright as it was in the previous two oppositions. The south pole is tilted towards the Earth, but the far side of the rings no longer appears clear of the body of the planet. Figure 1 shows the path of Saturn against the constellations during the year.

Saturn's Satellites. It is a year now since the European Huygens spacecraft made a controlled landing on the surface of Titan, the largest satellite of Saturn. This is a great triumph – the first landing by a spacecraft on the moon of another planet. But let us not forget Cassini, which carried Huygens during the seven-year journey from Earth.

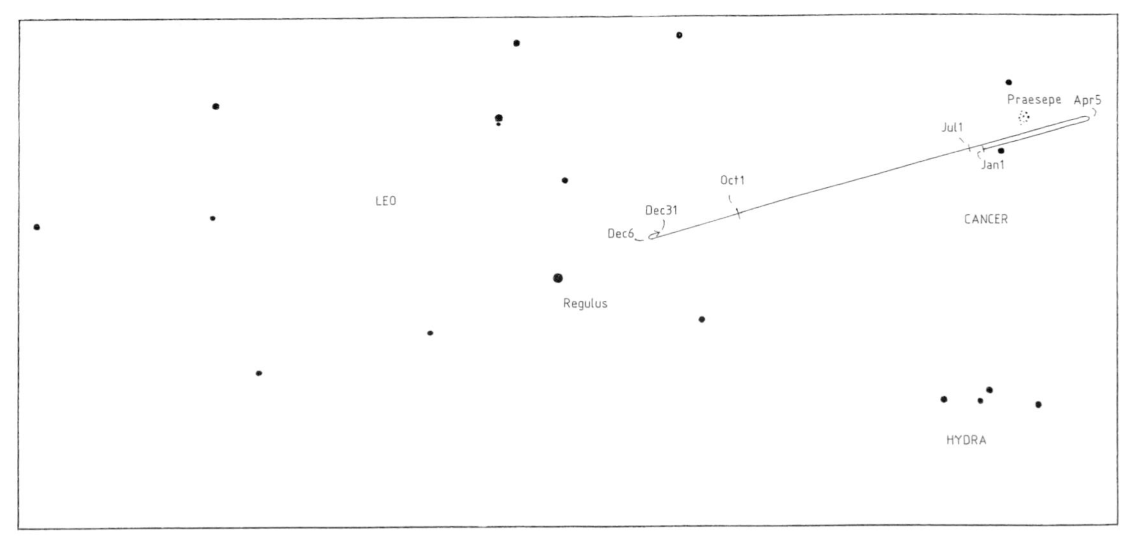

Figure 1. The path of Saturn against the background stars of Cancer and Leo during 2006. The planet passes about 1° south of the Beehive Cluster, Praesepe, in Cancer, early in February and again in early June.

Huygens has now completed its mission, but Cassini has a long programme ahead of it and, provided the spacecraft remains in good health, it will continue to send back data about the planet, its ring system and satellites for several years to come.

With Saturn reaching opposition towards the end of the month, this is a good time to check on the major satellites. Titan (magnitude 8.3) is, of course, easy in a small telescope, and is even within the range of good binoculars. The rest are much fainter. The satellites within the range of very modest telescopes are Rhea (magnitude 9.7), Iapetus (variable; 10.2 at its best), and Tethys and Dione (10.2 to 10.4). Then come Enceladus (11.7) and Mimas (12.9), followed by Hyperion (14.2). Phoebe (16.5) is decidedly elusive, and Mimas and Enceladus are inconveniently close to the planet. All the rest are very difficult indeed.

Iapetus, which is 1,436 kilometres (892 miles) in diameter, has one hemisphere which is icy and bright, while the other is extremely dark. At western elongation the bright hemisphere faces us, and Iapetus can reach magnitude 10.2, which is almost as bright as Rhea. At eastern elongation we see the dark side of Iapetus, and its brightness drops to well below magnitude 11. Giovanni Domenico Cassini discovered Iapetus in 1671, and then thought it disappeared completely when east of Saturn.

The spacecraft named after Cassini has shown that the dark, leading hemisphere of Iapetus is dominated by a heavily cratered region, called Cassini Regio (Figure 2). Here, dark deposits with a visual reflectivity of only about 4 per cent coat nearly everything. However, at higher latitudes, the surface changes to bright, icy terrain, where the brightest materials have a reflectivity of over 60 per cent. The large number of impact craters in Cassini Regio indicates that the surface beneath the dark coating is relatively ancient and has not been obliterated by whatever process caused the dark layer. This implies that it is a deposit or coating on the surface rather than dark material that has welled up from the interior and resurfaced Cassini Regio, but its exact origin is still unclear. The most remarkable feature discovered on Iapetus by the Cassini spacecraft is a ridge that coincides almost exactly with the geographic equator. Along the roughly 1,300-kilometre (800-mile) length over which it can be traced in the images, it remains almost exactly parallel to the equator within a couple of degrees. The physical origin of the ridge has yet to be explained.

Another revelation from Cassini is that the well-known, white, wispy

Figure 2. The Cassini spacecraft obtained this mosaic of four images of Saturn's intriguing moon Iapetus on 31 December 2004. The scene is dominated by the dark, heavily cratered region called Cassini Regio. An ancient, 400-kilometre wide impact basin appears just above the centre of the disc. Also shown is the remarkable ridge which runs almost exactly parallel to the equator. (Image courtesy of NASA/JPL/Space Science Institute.)

features on Dione do not consist of thick ice deposits, but are bright ice cliffs created by tectonic fractures. The small satellite Phoebe, imaged earlier as Cassini neared Saturn in June 2004, is heavily cratered (Figure 3), and is probably a captured body rather than a bona-fide satellite. Although one of the darkest known bodies in the Solar System, Phoebe probably has a bright, icy interior coated with a thin layer of dark material. The emerging opinion is that it was once a member of an ancient population of icy, comet-like bodies, many of which now reside in the Kuiper Belt beyond Neptune. Phoebe orbits Saturn in a retrograde or 'wrong way' direction.

Figure 3. Saturn's irregular moon Phoebe is revealed as an ice-rich body coated with a thin layer of dark material in this mosaic of two Cassini spacecraft images acquired on 11 June 2004. Small, bright craters are probably young features. When impactors slammed into Phoebe, the collisions excavated fresh, bright ice beneath the dark surface layer. On some crater walls the darker deposits have slid downwards, exposing bright material. (Image courtesy of NASA/JPL/Space Science Institute.)

New Horizons. There is no doubt that a space mission to Pluto and the Kuiper Belt – the region of the outer Solar System populated by small icy bodies which extends beyond the orbit of Neptune – is long overdue. In the 1990s, NASA planned the Pluto-Kuiper Express, but this was abandoned on financial grounds. Now a new mission to Pluto is planned; it has been given the name New Horizons, and is scheduled to encounter not only Pluto and its satellite, Charon, but also one or two objects in the Kuiper Belt.

If all goes well, New Horizons will blast off atop an Atlas-Centaur booster in early 2006. The primary launch window is between 11 January and 14 February. The fastest journey to Pluto requires a trip past Jupiter because the giant planet's gravity will help to slingshot the spacecraft into the outer Solar System. If the probe lifts off during the first 23 days of the launch window, it will travel to Pluto by way of Jupiter, receiving a massive boost via the gravity-assist technique and shortening its journey to Pluto by up to three years. If the probe doesn't blast off until the last 12 days of the launch window, it will miss the Jupiter swing-by, and instead will travel direct to Pluto. The date of arrival at Pluto therefore depends quite critically on the launch date; arrival via Jupiter gravity-assist will be in 2015–17, whereas the slower direct trajectory to Pluto will delay the probe's arrival until 2018–20.

Obviously, everybody hopes that the probe will blast off as early as possible during the launch window. Lift-off on or shortly after

Figure 4. Artist's concept of the New Horizons spacecraft during its planned encounter with Pluto and its moon, Charon. The spacecraft's most prominent feature is a 2.1-metre dish antenna, through which it will communicate with Earth from as far as 7.5 billion kilometres away. (Image courtesy of Johns Hopkins University Applied Physics Laboratory and Southwest Research Institute.)

11 January 2006, for example, will see the probe passing Jupiter just under 14 months later, in late February or early March 2007. Travelling at an impressive 75,600 kilometres an hour (46,980 mph), New Horizons will fly three to four times closer to Jupiter than the Cassini spacecraft did in December 2000 while en route to Saturn. After an eight-year cruise, New Horizons would arrive at the Pluto/Charon system in July 2015 (Figure 4), and then go on to encounter one or more Kuiper Belt objects in the period from 2016 to 2020.

There are two reasons why scientists would like to reach Pluto and Charon as quickly as possible. Since 1989, Pluto has been moving further from the Sun, and as the planet gets colder its thin atmosphere will 'freeze out', so the earlier the arrival date the greater the chance of observing a 'thicker' atmosphere. In addition, the longer the delay, the more of Pluto and Charon will be shadowed in an 'arctic night', making it harder for the spacecraft to take pictures in the very low light levels.

February

New Moon: 28 February *Full Moon:* 13 February

MERCURY is an evening object after the first 10–12 days of the month, for those in tropical and northern latitudes. For observers in northern temperate latitudes this will be the most favourable evening apparition of the year. Figure 5 shows, for observers in latitude 52°N, the changes in azimuth (true bearing from the north through east, south and west) and altitude of Mercury on successive evenings when the Sun is 6° below the horizon. This condition is known as the end of evening civil

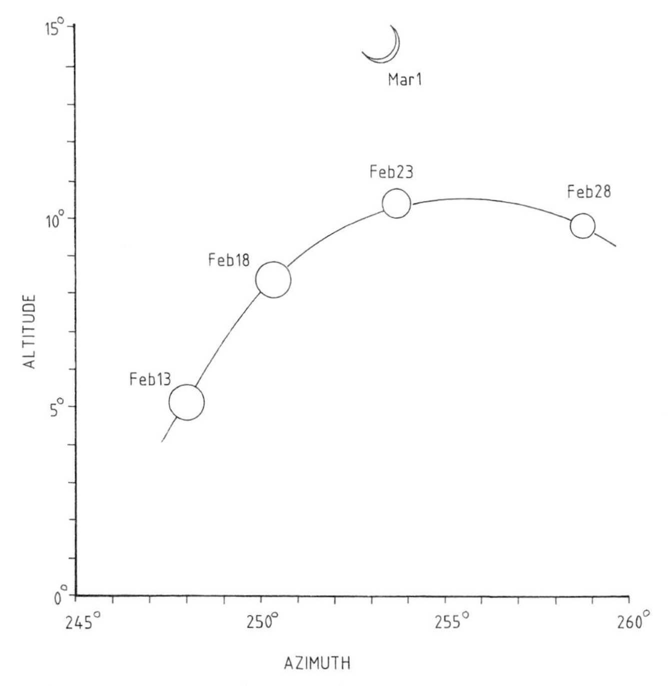

Figure 5. Evening apparition of Mercury, from latitude 52°N. (Angular diameters of Mercury and the crescent Moon not to scale.)

twilight and in this latitude and at this time of year occurs about 35 minutes after sunset. The changes in the brightness of the planet are indicated by the relative sizes of the circles marking Mercury's position at five-day intervals. It will be noticed that Mercury is at its brightest before it reaches greatest eastern elongation (18°) on 24 February. The magnitude of Mercury fades from −1.1 on 11 February to +0.5 by the end of the month.

VENUS is a brilliant object in the early mornings, completely dominating the south-eastern sky before dawn. It attains its greatest brilliancy (magnitude −4.6) on 17 February. It is a beautiful sight in a small telescope around this time, as it exhibits a slender crescent phase. During the month the phase increases noticeably as the apparent diameter decreases. Venus is in the vicinity of the waning crescent Moon on the mornings of 24 and 25 February, giving a good opportunity for it to be detected in the early morning daylight. Closest approach occurs around midday (GMT) on 24 February, though even then the Moon is passing about 10° south of the planet.

MARS continues to be visible as an evening object in the western sky, its magnitude fading from +0.2 to +0.7 during the month. Mars moves eastwards from Aries into Taurus early in February. During the second half of the month the planet will be seen passing between the Pleiades and the Hyades. It is then only very slightly brighter than Aldebaran.

JUPITER continues to be visible as a brilliant object in the morning skies, magnitude is −2.1. The planet remains in the constellation of Libra during February.

SATURN, magnitude −0.2, and just past opposition, continues to be visible as a bright object in Cancer and still available for observation for the greater part of the night. It can now be seen in the eastern sky in the evenings as soon as it gets dark. It is still retrograding slowly in the constellation of Cancer, passing 1° south of the well-known Beehive open cluster, called Praesepe, early in the month. Thus the planet can be used to locate this naked-eye cluster, even in poor conditions. The rings of Saturn present a beautiful spectacle to the observer with a small telescope. The diameter of the minor axis is now 15 arcseconds, rather less than the polar diameter of the planet itself. The rings were last at their maximum opening in 2002. They will next appear edge-on in 2009.

MESSENGER to Mercury. For northern hemisphere observers this month provides the best opportunities for seeing the elusive planet Mercury in the evening sky this year, but it has to be said that ordinary telescopes will show little on it; only the characteristic phase will be obvious. As the closest planet to the Sun, Mercury is always at least 80 million kilometres (50 million miles) from Earth, and is only about 4,880 kilometres (3,030 miles) in diameter – smaller than two of the satellites in the outer part of the Solar System, Ganymede and Titan. Mercury has only a trace of atmosphere, records the greatest extremes of temperature of any planet in the Solar System, and is heavily cratered; to date, it has been visited by only one spacecraft, Mariner 10, which made three active passes in 1974–5 and photographed about 45 per cent of the planet's surface. Since then Mercury has sometimes been called 'the forgotten planet'; the concentration of effort has been first on Venus, and now on Mars.

However, a new spacecraft, called MESSENGER (which stands for MErcury Surface, Space ENvironment, GEochemistry and Ranging) was launched in August 2004 (Figure 6) and is now well on its way. This NASA Discovery mission will conduct the first survey of the planet from an orbit around it. MESSENGER will be in no hurry; its launcher was not powerful enough to send the spacecraft direct to Mercury, and the mission is utilizing the 'gravity-assist' technique, involving a fly-by of Earth (August 2005) and two of Venus (October 2006 and June 2007). There will then be three passes of Mercury itself (in 2008 and 2009) before the spacecraft enters its final orbit round the planet in March 2011. It is hoped to go on collecting data for one Earth year, which covers four Mercurian years or two Mercurian solar days – though probes often last well after their 'sell by' dates, as the two Mars rovers Spirit and Opportunity have shown recently.

Many problems about the planet Mercury remain to be solved. Firstly, 55 per cent of the planet has never been observed by spacecraft, so MESSENGER will map the entire surface and record the surface composition; there is no reason to assume that the newly explored areas will differ from those already seen, but one never knows. Then there is the question, why is Mercury so dense? Although not the densest planet, Mercury's high density implies that it is about two-thirds

Figure 6. The Boeing Delta II rocket with its MESSENGER spacecraft on top breaks through the billows of smoke below as it lifts off on 3 August 2004 from Cape Canaveral Air Force Station, at the start of its circuitous seven-year, 7.9-billion-kilometre journey to the planet Mercury. MESSENGER was built for NASA by the Johns Hopkins University Applied Physics Laboratory in Laurel, Maryland. (Image courtesy of NASA.)

iron metal (the Earth has only half as much), so answering this question is important to our understanding of how the planet is formed. There are also puzzles relating to Mercury's core, which is huge in relation to its size, and the origin of the planet's weak but easily measured magnetic field. For such a small planet, you would expect Mercury's core to be solid, but the presence of a magnetic field implies that the core is liquid. MESSENGER will probe the core by studying Mercury's gravity field. It has also been claimed that there is ice inside some of the craters near Mercury's poles, where the crater-floors are in permanent shadow and remain bitterly cold. Ice seems unlikely to be found anywhere on a world such as Mercury, but MESSENGER should be able to give a definite answer.

Certainly the chances of life on Mercury seem to be effectively nil. Neither is there any prospect of manned flights there in the foreseeable future, though no doubt there will be further unmanned missions as soon as funds become available (one, BepiColumbo, is already being planned by the European Space Agency). Hostile though it may be, Mercury is certainly a fascinating little world.

Eduard Heis and the Pleiades. The German astronomer Eduard Heis was born two hundred years ago, on 18 February 1806, in Cologne. He was educated at Bonn University and, after spending some time as a schoolmaster, was appointed professor of astronomy at Munster (1852). He became a leading authority on all matters concerning meteors, and published a catalogue of 87 radiants; he studied the Zodiacal Light, and made valuable observations of variable stars. In 1872 he published his first star catalogue, and followed it up with a catalogue of 4,943 naked-eye stars, plus an elaborate delineation of the Milky Way. He died on 30 June 1877.

Heis was renowned for his keen eyesight, and is said to have been able to see no less than 19 individual stars in the Pleiades cluster – which seems to be a record. The Pleiades are on view this month, and it is interesting to count the number of stars which can be seen without optical aid. The brightest is Alcyone or Eta Tauri, magnitude 2.9; then follow Atlas (3.6), Electra (3.7), Maia (3.9), Merope (4.2), Taygete (4.3), Pleione (5.1, but variable), Celaeno (5.4) and Asterope (5.6). The cluster is always known by its nickname of the Seven Sisters, but many people are able to see a dozen separate stars. The real total membership of the cluster is around 500 stars, contained in an area about 25 light-years across; there is also nebulosity, which is not easy to see visually but which can be photographed without much trouble.

Estimates of the distance to the cluster do not wholly agree. The Hipparcos astrometric satellite gave 385 light-years, substantially nearer than astronomers had previously supposed; earlier estimates had put the distance of the Pleiades at 410 to 425 light-years. The Pleiades have been known since ancient times and there are many legends about them. The cluster is included in Messiers's Catalogue, as M45.

March

New Moon: **29 March** *Full Moon:* **14 March**

Equinox: 20 March

Summer Time in the United Kingdom commences on 26 March.

MERCURY, magnitude +1, may only be detected very low above the western horizon for a short while around the end of evening civil twilight for the first two days of the month by observers in northern and equatorial latitudes. After passing through inferior conjunction on 12 March it will become visible as a morning object for the last few days of the month to observers in equatorial and southern latitudes, magnitude +1. They should refer to the diagram (Figure 8) given with the notes for April.

VENUS is still a brilliant object in the morning skies, at magnitude −4.5. It is south of the celestial equator, and observers in the latitudes of the United Kingdom will be able to see it only for about an hour before sunrise, low above the east-south-eastern horizon. Observers in the southern hemisphere are more fortunate, enjoying a visibility period of about three hours before dawn. Venus reaches its greatest western elongation (47°) on 25 March.

MARS, its magnitude fading from +0.8 to +1.2, continues to be visible in the south-western quadrant of the sky in the evenings in the constellation of Taurus. On 10 March, Mars passes 7° north of Aldebaran. Figure 7 shows the path of Mars against the constellations during the first eight months of the year.

JUPITER, magnitude −2.3, continues to be visible as a brilliant morning object. By the end of the month it may be seen rising above the east-south-eastern horizon well before midnight. The planet reaches its first stationary point on 4 March, and commences its retrograde motion.

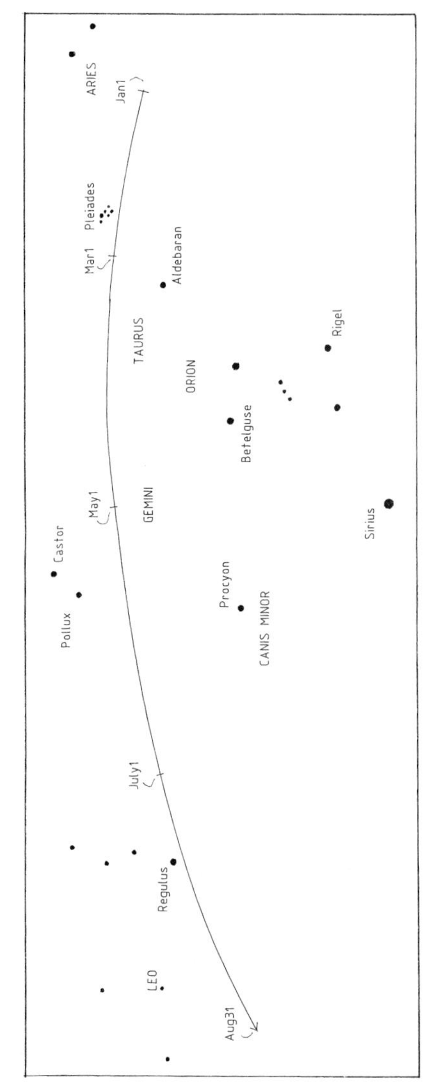

Figure 7. The path of Mars against the stars of Aries, Taurus, Gemini, Cancer and Leo from January to the end of August 2006.

SATURN, magnitude +0.1, continues to be visible as an evening object in the south-western sky.

Summer Time. British Summer Time this year begins during the early morning hours of Sunday 26 March and ends on Sunday 29 October. Clocks are put forward one hour ahead of GMT, as has been the practice for most of the period between 1916 and the present.

The idea of 'daylight saving' seems to have been due originally to Benjamin Franklin, in 1784, but apparently in a rather light-hearted way. The first serious suggestion for Britain was made in 1907 by William Willett, who proposed advancing clocks by 80 minutes in four stages of 20 minutes each, and then returning to GMT in a similar fashion – which would most certainly have led to a great deal of confusion. In 1908, a Bill to advance the clocks by one hour during the spring and summer months was introduced in the House of Commons, but was rejected.

The idea was revived in 1916, during the First World War, as a measure to save energy for war production by taking advantage of the later daylight hours between March and October. Then came the Summer Time Acts of 1922 and 1925, and so from 1916 up to the Second World War the clocks were put forward by one hour during the spring and summer months. It was pointed out that this would continue to save fuel, because the evenings would be lighter, and it would also increase the daylight 'leisure period' for people who came home after a day's work.

Then came the Second World War, when saving fuel assumed even greater importance. Therefore summer time was used throughout the year, and double summer time – 2 hours ahead of GMT – for the period during which normal summer time would have been in operation. (On one occasion in the summer of 1944, the editor of this *Yearbook* remembers coming home to Sussex on a few days' leave from the RAF and playing tennis quite happily at midnight!) Double summer time was abandoned at the end of the war, and there was a return to the old system.

There was one more experiment, from 1968 to 1971, when summer time (called British Standard Time) lasted throughout the year, and there was no changing of the clocks in spring and autumn. England and Wales generally approved, but Scotland did not; it was pointed out that in parts of Scotland the Sun did not rise until about 10 a.m. during the midwinter period, and children had to travel to school in darkness. So, once again, all Britain reverted to the tried and tested system, and GMT was reinstated for the winter period. There are slight variations, but in the United Kingdom summer time begins during the early morning hours of the last Sunday in March (i.e. between 25 and 31 March) and ends on the last Sunday in October (i.e. between 25 and 31 October) each year.

Many countries now use daylight saving time in one form or another, including Russia, most of Europe and most English-speaking countries, and there is much to be said in its favour, though naturally, there are also disadvantages.

The Brightest Stars. Sirius, the brightest star in the night sky, is well placed early on March evenings. According to the latest measurements, the ten apparently brightest stars are as follows:

	Magnitude
1. Sirius	−1.44
2. Canopus	−0.62
3. Alpha Centauri	−0.27 (combined mag. of two components)
4. Arcturus	−0.05
5. Vega	+0.03
6. Capella	+0.08
7. Rigel	+0.18
8. Procyon	+0.40
9. Achernar	+0.45
10. Betelgeux	+0.45 (mean)

Of these Canopus, Alpha Centauri and Achernar are invisible from Britain. Note that the mean magnitude of Betelgeux (also called Betelgeuse) is given here, because it is variable and at maximum it may rise to around +0.1.

If we now turn to absolute magnitude – that is to say the apparent magnitude these ten stars would have if observed from a standard distance of 10 parsecs (32.6 light-years) – then we have a very different story! The order now becomes:

1. Rigel	−6.69
2. Canopus	−5.53
3. Betelgeux	−5.14
4. Achernar	−2.77
5. Arcturus	−0.31
6. Capella	−0.48
7. Vega	+0.58
8. Sirius	+1.45
9. Procyon	+2.68
10. Alpha Centauri	+4.08

Clearly, appearances can be deceptive! These are the Hipparcos Catalogue values; they do not differ wildly from the older estimates, except in the case of Canopus.

Of the fifty apparently brightest stars, the most luminous is Deneb (absolute magnitude −8.73), followed by Wezen or Delta Canis Majoris (−6.87), then Rigel (−6.69) and Alnilam or Epsilon Orionis (−6.38). The least luminous is Alpha Centauri, which is of course our nearest stellar neighbour after the Sun.

March Eclipses. There are two eclipses this month: a penumbral eclipse of the Moon on 14–15 March, and a total eclipse of the Sun on 29 March. Penumbral lunar eclipses occur when the Moon misses the main cone of the Earth's shadow (the umbra), and merely enters the zone of partial shadow (the penumbra) to either side. There is a very slight dimming of the Moon's light, but a penumbral eclipse is not easy to detect with the naked eye. This month's penumbral eclipse lasts from 21h 22m to 02h 13m. It is visible from Asia, western Australia, Africa, Europe and the Americas.

The total solar eclipse on 29 March is visible as a partial eclipse from the extreme east of Brazil, the Atlantic Ocean, most of Africa, Europe, Iceland, north-east Greenland, the Arctic Ocean and most of Asia. From London, the partial phase begins at 09h 45m and ends at 11h 22m. Maximum eclipse is at 10h 33m when about 17 per cent of the solar disk will be obscured by the Moon. The Sun's altitude at mid-eclipse will be 38°. Since the clocks will have gone forward by one hour in the United Kingdom on 26 March, observers will need to add one hour to the times given here to obtain British Summer Time. The path of totality for this eclipse starts in the extreme eastern part of Brazil, crosses the Atlantic Ocean, passes through Ghana, Togo, Benin, Nigeria, Niger, extreme north-west Chad, Libya, extreme north-west Egypt, Turkey, Georgia and southern Russia, before ending in Kazakhstan. Totality begins at 8h 34m and ends at 11h 48m. The maximum duration of totality is 4m 7s.

April

New Moon: 27 April *Full Moon:* 13 April

MERCURY is visible in the mornings to observers in tropical and southern latitudes, but not to those in the latitudes of the United Kingdom. For observers in southern latitudes this will be the most favourable morning apparition of the year. Figure 8 shows, for observers in latitude 35°S, the changes in azimuth (true bearing from the north through east, south and west) and altitude of Mercury on successive evenings when the Sun is 6° below the horizon. This condition is known as the beginning of morning civil twilight and in this latitude and at this time of year occurs about 30 minutes before sunrise. The changes in the brightness of the planet are indicated by the relative sizes of the circles marking Mercury's position at five-day intervals. It will be noticed that Mercury is at its brightest after it reaches greatest western elongation (28°) on 8 April, only one day before aphelion. During the month its magnitude brightens from +0.7 to −0.4.

VENUS, magnitude −4.2, continues to be visible as a brilliant object in the morning sky before dawn. However, it is visible to observers in northern temperate latitudes for only a short while before sunrise, low above the east-south-eastern horizon. Southern Hemisphere observers will continue to enjoy a three-hour period of visibility before dawn. Venus is very close to the waning crescent Moon on the morning of 24 April.

MARS continues to be visible as an evening object in the western sky in the evenings, though it is now setting before midnight, except for observers in northern temperate latitudes who will be able to see it for a little longer. During the month, as its magnitude fades from +1.2 to +1.5, Mars passes from Taurus into Gemini.

JUPITER, magnitude −2.5, is now visible for the greater part of the night since it comes to opposition early next month. It is moving slowly

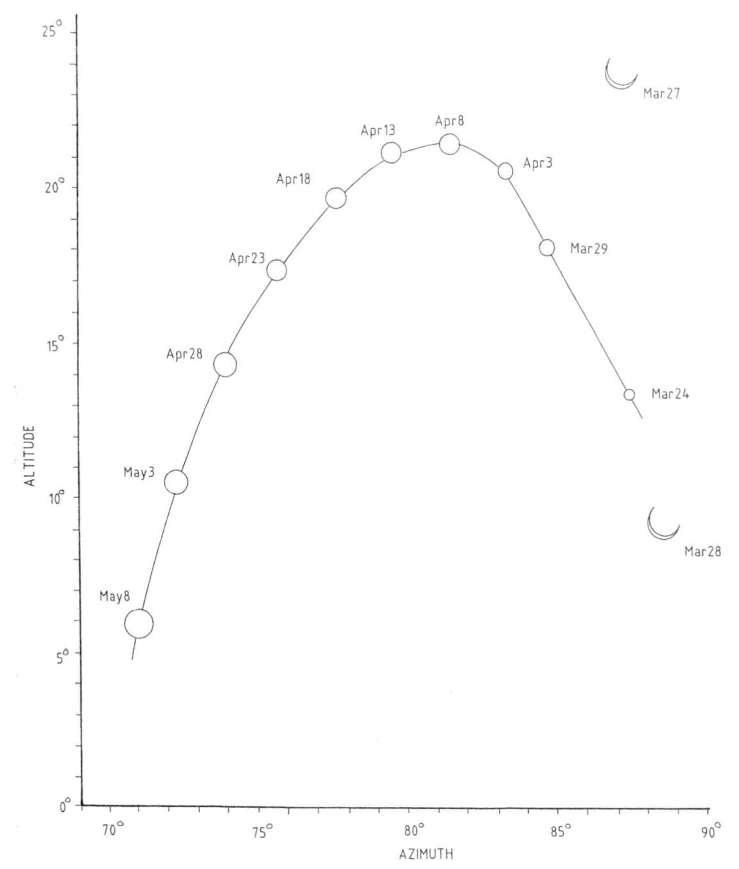

Figure 8. Morning apparition of Mercury, from latitude 35°S. (Angular diameters of Mercury and the crescent Moon not to scale.)

retrograde in the constellation of Libra, passing north of the star Alpha Librae again at the end of the month.

SATURN continues to be visible as an evening object in the constellation of Cancer. Its magnitude is +0.3. It reaches its second stationary point on 5 April, and resumes its direct motion.

Catching the Express to Venus. The planet Venus continues to be a brilliant early-morning object in the dawn twilight sky. In the past, both the Russians and Americans have sent probes to Venus, carrying out in-depth investigations of the planet's dense atmosphere and surface. Indeed, most of our detailed knowledge of the surface has come from NASA's Magellan radar mapper, which operated well for over four years (1990–4). It revealed Venus as a world of volcanic plains – which cover almost two-thirds of the surface – with the rest mainly lowlands and less than 10 per cent highlands. Vulcanism dominates the surface and there are lava flows everywhere.

Although the Cassini spacecraft did make limited observations of Venus during its fly-bys in 1998 and 1999 en route to Saturn, there have been no space missions specifically targeted at Venus during the past decade. Although it is true that the emphasis of space research has shifted to Mars, and Venus has been out of the limelight recently, many intriguing problems remain to be solved, particularly where the Venusian atmosphere is concerned. For example, Venus spins on its axis only once in 243 days, yet in the upper atmosphere hurricane-force winds sweep around the planet in just four days. What drives this rapid circulation? Other questions include: how does the composition of the atmosphere change with depth; how does the atmosphere interact with the surface; and how does the upper atmosphere interact with the solar wind in the absence of any detectable Venusian magnetic field?

All being well, in late-March or April 2006, a new spacecraft called Venus Express will arrive in orbit around Venus to carry out a comprehensive study of the planet's atmosphere and clouds, and make global maps of the surface temperatures. Launched by the European Space Agency, Venus Express was built around the design of the highly successful Mars Express spacecraft, making it quicker and cheaper to develop. After a journey from Earth lasting about six months, Venus Express will arrive at Venus and use its main engine to reduce speed so it is captured by the planet's gravity. The spacecraft will take five days to manoeuvre into its final highly elliptical operating orbit, looping above the poles of the planet, its distance varying from just 250 kilometres at closest to 66,600 kilometres when furthest away.

The operational orbit of Venus Express has been chosen so that global coverage of the planet will be achieved in one 243-day axial rotation period. The nominal length of the mission is two axial rotations, or almost 500 days. During this time, the suite of instruments aboard the spacecraft will study the composition, circulation and evolution of the atmosphere of Venus, and its interaction with the planet's surface and the solar wind. Such studies will undoubtedly greatly enhance our understanding of a world that is often dubbed 'Earth's twin' in terms of size and mass, but which is so different in every other way.

Cancer and its Clusters. This month Saturn lies in Cancer, the Crab, which is one of the most obscure of the Zodiacal constellations, but is redeemed by the presence of two magnificent open clusters. In mythology, Cancer was a sea-crab which Juno, Queen of Olympus, sent to the rescue of the multi-headed hydra which was engaged in a fierce battle with the hero Hercules during the performance of his twelve labours. Hercules, not unnaturally, trod on the crab and squashed it, but as a reward for its efforts, Juno placed it in the sky.

Cancer lies inside the large triangle outlined by the stars Procyon (Alpha Canis Minoris), Regulus (Alpha Leonis) and Pollux (Beta Geminorum). There are only two stars above the fourth magnitude, and in shape Cancer looks not unlike a dim and ghostly Orion (Figure 9). The leading stars are:

Star	Name	Magnitude	Spectral Type
Beta	Altarf	3.52	K4
Delta	Asellus Australis	3.94	K0
Iota	–	4.02	G8
Alpha	Acubens	4.25	A3
Gamma	Asellus Boralis	4.66	A1
Zeta	Tegmine	4.67	F7 + G2
Chi	–	5.12	F5

Zeta is a multiple star, first seen as such by T. Mayer in 1756. In 1781, William Herschel discovered the third component. The closer pair (AB), magnitudes 5.6 and 6.0, form a binary system with a period of 59.7 years; the separation ranges from 0.6 to 1.2 arcseconds, and is currently about 1 arcsecond. The third member (C), magnitude 6.2, revolves round the main pair at a separation of 5.9 arcseconds, in a period of 1,150 years. The fourth component (D), lies at a separation of 288 arcseconds, magnitude 9.7.

The open cluster M44 (Praesepe, also known as the Beehive Cluster) is easily visible with the naked eye, and has been known since ancient

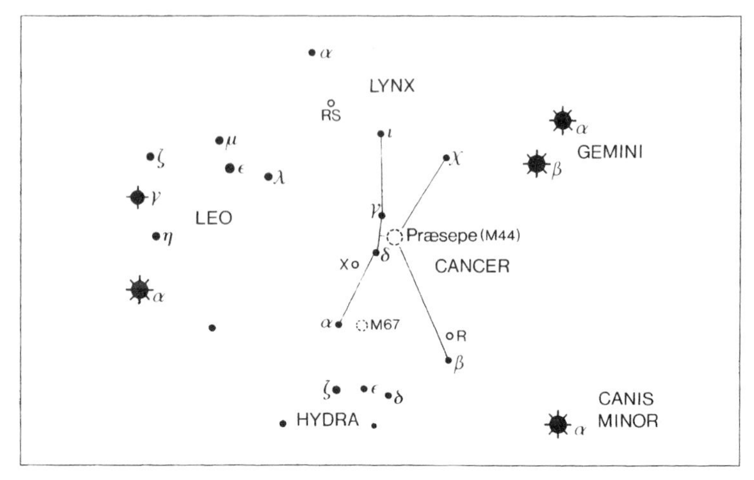

Figure 9. The rather obscure Zodiacal pattern of Cancer, the Crab, lies within the triangle formed by the first magnitude stars Pollux (Beta Geminorum), Regulus (Alpha Leonis) and Procyon (Alpha Canis Minoris). The two open clusters M44 and M67 are also shown.

times. It contains no nebulosity, and its main stars (there are about 50 altogether) are yellow or orange, meaning this is an old cluster. It has been nicknamed the 'Manger', and the two stars flanking it, Delta and Gamma, are Aselli or 'Asses'. The distance from Hipparcos data is 577 light-years. With a diameter of about 1.5°, Praesepe is a fine sight in binoculars. It was given a stellar designation by Bayer, in his famous *Catalogue* – as Epsilon Cancri – but this is never used.

The other cluster, M67, is only just below naked-eye visibility; it was discovered by J. Köhler around 1775, and in 1783 was described by William Herschel as 'a very beautiful and pretty much compressed cluster of stars . . . I have observed 200 stars in the field of view of my great telescope with a power of x157.' It seems to be one of the oldest of all known open clusters, and has escaped disruption because it is well away from the main plane of the Galaxy; its distance is about 2,600 light-years.

Also in Cancer, note the semi-regular variable X Cancri (not to be confused with Chi), which lies near Praesepe. It has a range of magnitudes 5.6 to 7.5, so it is always within binocular range; there is a very rough period of about 195 days. The spectral type is N, and it is one of the very reddest of the brightish stars.

Bart Jan Bok. This month we mark the hundredth anniversary of the birth of Bart J. Bok, a very distinguished Dutch-American astronomer (Figure 10). He was born in Hoorn, the Netherlands, on 28 April 1906, and educated at the universities of Leiden and Groningen, before moving to the United States and becoming an American citizen in 1938. He worked at Harvard University from 1929 to 1957, after which he directed the Mount Stromlo Observatory in Australia (1957–66). He ended his career as director of the Steward Observatory at the University of Arizona in Tucson, USA (1966–74).

Sometimes called Mr Milky Way, Bart Bok carried out very important work in connection with the structure and evolution of our Galaxy, the Milky Way, and he also studied theories of star formation. Small, dark clouds of dust and gas condensing to form one or more stars are now called Bok globules, since it was he who first drew attention to them; he studied them extensively. He also initiated radio astronomy at Harvard. Apart from all this he was an enthusiastic popularizer of astronomy. Bok also served as a vice-president of the International Astronomical Union (1970–6) and was president of the American Astronomical Society (1972–4). He died on 5 August 1983 at the age of 77.

Figure 10. 'Mr Milky Way', the Dutch-American astronomer Bart Jan Bok sitting at his desk. (Image courtesy of American Institute of Physics.)

May

New Moon: 27 May *Full Moon:* 13 May

MERCURY is not visible to observers in the latitudes of the United Kingdom because of the long duration of morning twilight. However, it may be seen by observers further south where it remains visible as a morning object for the first week of the month low above the eastern horizon for a short while around the beginning of morning civil twilight. During the week its magnitude brightens from −0.5 to −1.0. Mercury passes through superior conjunction on 18 May, and ten days later becomes visible as an evening object, but only for those in equatorial latitudes. Its magnitude is then −1, and it may be detected low above the western horizon for a short while at the end of evening civil twilight.

VENUS is still a splendid object in the early mornings before sunrise, at magnitude −4.1. Observers in northern temperate latitudes will find it visible only for a short while before dawn low above the eastern horizon.

MARS, magnitude +1.6, continues to be visible as an evening object in the western sky. Mars is in the constellation of Gemini, moving eastwards south of the Twins, Castor and Pollux, during the second part of the month. The planet enters the constellation of Cancer at the very end of May.

JUPITER is at opposition on 4 May and is therefore visible throughout the hours of darkness. Two days later it is at its closest to the Earth, at a distance of some 660 million kilometres (410 million miles). Its magnitude is −2.5. Figure 11 shows the path of Jupiter among the stars during the year.

SATURN, magnitude +0.4, is still visible in the western sky in the evenings, setting several hours after sunset.

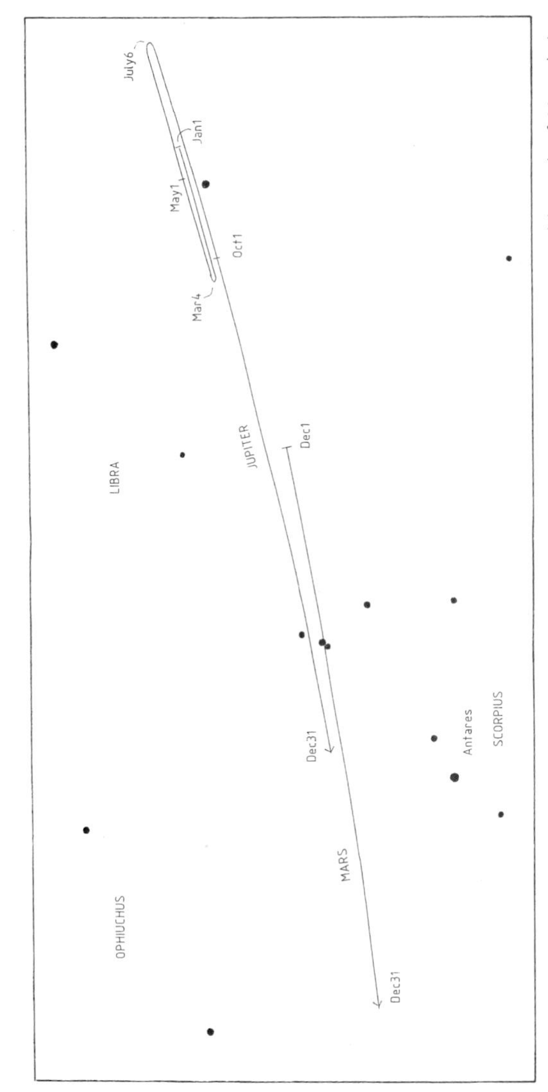

Figure 11. The path of Jupiter against the background stars of Libra and Scorpius during 2006. (The path of Mars during December 2006 is also shown.) Jupiter passes less than a degree north of the star Alpha Librae three times during the year; once in mid-January, again at the end of April and finally in mid-September.

Mu Cephei and the Largest Known Stars. Until quite recently the star with the largest diameter of any normal star known was the red supergiant Mu Cephei, also called Herschel's Garnet Star and identified occasionally by its proper name of Erakis. However, the discovery of three red supergiants having even larger diameters means that Mu Cephei has now been relegated to fourth place.

Cepheus is not a very prominent constellation, but late on May evenings it will be found in the north-eastern sky above the familiar 'W' of Cassiopeia. The brightest stars of Cepheus are Alpha or Alderamin (magnitude 2.44), Gamma or Alrai (3.21), Beta or Alphirk (3.23, slightly variable), Zeta (3.35), Eta (3.43) and Iota (3.52). The prototype Cepheid variable Delta Cephei has a range of from 3.5 to 4.4; period 5.37 days. It forms a little triangle with Epsilon (4.19) and Zeta, which make good comparison stars.

Roughly midway between Alpha and Zeta lies Nu Cephei, and Mu is slightly south of Nu (Figure 12). Although Mu looks faint, it is at least 50,000 times as luminous as the Sun. It is classed as a semi-regular variable varying between 3.4 and 5.1, and its variation period is very long: indeed there appear to be two coherent periods of about 850 and 4,400 days. Mu is a red supergiant, far larger and more remote than Betelgeux (or Betelgeuse) in Orion; the spectrum is of type M2. Although it is undoubtedly one of the reddest stars visible with the

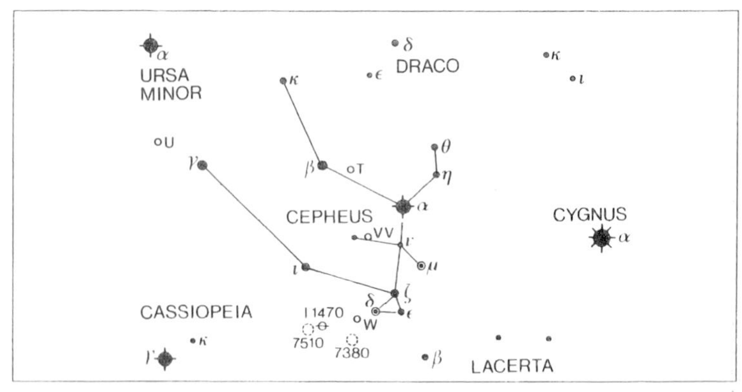

Figure 12. The principal stars of Cepheus. The red supergiant star Mu Cephei, also known as Herschel's Garnet Star, is one of the largest stars known, as is the eclipsing binary VV Cephei. However, recent studies have shown that a star called V354 Cephei has a greater diameter than either of these two; it is the second largest star discovered to date.

naked eye, optical aid is needed to bring the colour out really well. Binoculars show it beautifully. Up to now its only rival for the title of the largest known star lay not far from it in the sky – the eclipsing binary VV Cephei, which consists of a red supergiant and a hot companion orbiting within a common gaseous envelope.

However, it has now been found that three stars – KW Sagittarii (distance 9,800 light-years), V354 Cephei (distance 9,000 light-years) and KY Cygni (distance 5,200 light-years) – are even larger, all with diameters about 3,000 times that of the Sun or about 4,200 million kilometres. If any one of these stars was placed at the centre of our Solar System, its outer layers would extend to midway between the orbits of Jupiter and Saturn. None of these three stars are thought to be binaries, so their properties tell us about the extreme sizes that normal stars can attain. However, these stars are not the most massive known, and neither are they the most luminous; each has a mass about 25 times that of the Sun, with about 300,000 times the solar luminosity. The outer layers of such vast supergiant stars are very rarefied.

At the other end of the scale there is a very low mass star, known only as OGLE-TR–122B, which weighs just one-eleventh of the mass of the Sun, and has a diameter just one-eighth of the solar one. So, although this stellar 'gnome' has 96 times the mass of Jupiter, it is only 16 per cent larger than the giant planet. There is certainly plenty of variety among the stars!

The Celestial Lynx. Constellations vary enormously in size and importance. Some, such as Orion and Ursa Major, can be identified at a glance because of their obvious patterns and their bright stars; others are so dim they hardly seem to merit a separate identity. The far south of the sky abounds with very small, obscure constellations – which is understandable since these regions were unobservable by the ancient observers who formed the constellations we know, and later astronomers were only too anxious to secure lasting recognition by adding new groups to the sky-map!

Even in the northern hemisphere there are some very faint, barren groups, and one of these is Lynx, which was formed by the Gdansk astronomer Hevelius in the seventeenth century. It lies between the 'Pointers' of Ursa Major (Dubhe and Merak) on the one side, and Capella and the Twins on the other, and it will be found high in the western sky on May evenings. Of course, Lynx has no mythological associations, and neither has it any star as bright as the third magnitude. Most of it is circumpolar from Britain. There is no definite pattern, and not even the most vivid imagination can make a lynx or any other animal out of it! From time to time there have been suggestions about revising the entire sky-map, but our present-day constellations have become so firmly established it would be pointless to try to alter them now.

June

New Moon: 25 June *Full Moon:* 11 June

Solstice: 21 June

MERCURY reaches greatest eastern elongation on 20 June. It is an evening object for most of the month, observers in tropical and southern latitudes only losing it for the last couple of days of June, while those in the latitudes of the United Kingdom are likely to detect it only during the first three weeks of the month, though with some difficulty because of the long evening twilight. Mercury may be located above the west-north-west horizon around the time of the end of evening civil twilight. On 1 June its magnitude is −0.8 but this has faded to +1.8 by 28 June.

VENUS continues to be a splendid object in the morning skies, with a magnitude of −4.0, visible above the eastern horizon before dawn. Observers in the latitudes of the United Kingdom will find it becomes visible for a little longer each morning as the month progresses. This effect is the result of its northward movement in declination, which more than offsets the fact that Venus is slowly moving in towards the Sun.

MARS, magnitude +1.8, is still an evening object, low in the western sky as soon as it is dark, but coming towards the end of its apparition. Before the end of the month it will be lost to view in the gathering twilight for observers in the latitudes of the United Kingdom. Observers in tropical and southern latitudes will be able to see it throughout the month and be able to see it as it passes south of the Beehive Cluster (Praesepe) around the middle of the month.

JUPITER continues to be visible in the south-western quadrant of the sky, in the evenings, in the constellation of Libra. Its magnitude is −2.4.

SATURN is still visible low in the western sky in the early evenings, though for observers in the latitudes of the United Kingdom it is no longer an easy object to detect in the lengthening twilight, and will be lost to view before the end of the month. Its magnitude is +0.4. Mars passes 0.5° north of Saturn on 18 June. Saturn passes 1° south of Praesepe again early in June.

PLUTO reaches opposition on 16 June, in the constellation of Serpens, at a distance of 4,506 million kilometres (2,800 million miles) from the Earth. It is only visible with a moderate-sized telescope, since its magnitude is +14.

Pluto and the Kuiper Belt. Pluto is at opposition this month. Since its path is highly inclined with respect to the orbits of the other major planets, Pluto currently lies in Serpens, which is not one of the twelve constellations of the Zodiac. Pluto has remained an enigma ever since Clyde Tombaugh discovered it in 1930. With a diameter of just 2,320 kilometres (1,442 miles) – much smaller than our Moon – Pluto is too small to be a bona-fide planet (although it is still officially classified as one), and has a much higher orbital inclination and eccentricity than any of the other planets. It is probably better understood as the largest known Kuiper Belt object (KBO). The Kuiper Belt is a region of the outer Solar System, populated by small icy bodies, extending from the orbit of Neptune (at 30 AU) out to at least five times that distance. The total mass of the Kuiper Belt is probably no more than about one-fifth the mass of the Earth.

There are three main categories of KBOs. Most have orbits with low inclination and eccentricity, and these so-called 'classical' KBOs are probably icy débris left over from the formation of the Solar System. Other KBOs are in orbital resonance with Neptune, such as those which complete two orbits for every three completed by Neptune (the 3:2 resonance), and as Pluto is one of these, the members of this class are often refered to as 'Plutinos'. Finally, we have the 'scattered' KBOs, of which only a few are known, having large, highly eccentric orbits.

Pluto is accompanied by its only satellite Charon, which, with a diameter of 1,270 kilometres, is just over half Pluto's size. It may have been formed in the same region of the outer Solar System and been captured by Pluto, but according to Dr Robin Canup, of the Southwest

Research Institute in Boulder (Colorado) it may have resulted from a collision between Pluto and another body around 1,500 kilometres in diameter. It will not be easy to decide between these two theories.

Apart from Pluto and Charon, the largest-known members of the Kuiper Belt include an object called 2004 DW, a Plutino about 1,500 kilometres across (more than half the diameter of Pluto), Quaoar, which is a classical KBO roughly 1,200 kilometres across, and Ixion, another Plutino, with a diameter of about 1,065 kilometres. Then there is the extraordinary Sedna, discovered in 2003, which has a diameter of 1,000 to 1,500 kilometres. At discovery, Sedna was about 90 AU from the Sun. Sedna takes 10,500 years to complete one orbit of the Sun, and is due to reach perihelion (its minimum distance from the Sun) in the year 2076, and will then start to draw away once more. When furthest from the Sun, Sedna is almost 990 AU distant. What is unusual is that at perihelion Sedna is still 76 AU from the Sun. This distance seems too great for an object so large to have formed by accretion in the tenuous outer regions of a very extended solar nebula at its current location. Presumably, Sedna must have formed elsewhere, either among the outer planets or the inner Kuiper Belt, and been ejected outwards. Later, its perihelion was lifted beyond the gravitational scattering influence of Neptune.

The last week of July 2005 turned out to be a very exciting time in studies of the outer Solar System, with the existence of three new KBOs being announced, these new objects being brighter than all previously known KBOs (with the exception of Pluto). The first object, 2003 EL61, was announced by a team of astronomers from Spain. The second two objects, 2003 UB313 and 2005 FY9, were announced by astronomers Mike Brown (Caltech), Chad Trujillo (Gemini Observatory), and David Rabinowitz (Yale University), discovered during their ongoing survey with the Palomar Observatory's Samuel Oschin telescope. 2005 FY9 is the 2nd brightest KBO discovered to date, and 2003 EL61 is the 3rd brightest; both are thought to be about three-quarters the diameter of Pluto, that is about 1,700 kilometres in diameter. The third object, 2003 UB313, the 4th brightest KBO known, appears to be the first object bigger than Pluto to be found in the outer Solar System. Although its diameter has still to be accurately determined, 2003 UB313 appears to be almost 3,000 kilometres across. It is far more remote than Pluto, currently lying about 97 AU from the Sun, although its eccentric, highly tilted orbit can bring it as close as

38 AU; the orbital period is around 560 years. Like Pluto, 2003 UB313 appears to have a surface coated with methane ice.

If Pluto ranks as a planet, then presumably so does 2003 UB313, but it is looking increasingly likely that both must be regarded merely as large KBOs.

Sagittarius and the Galactic Centre. To British and North American observers, June evenings provide the best times for seeing the lovely star-clouds of Sagittarius, the Archer. Not only are they beautiful, but they are also significant. When we look at them, we are looking in the direction of the very centre of our Galaxy.

Sagittarius, the Archer, is a fairly prominent constellation, although unlike its neighbour, the Scorpion, it contains no first-magnitude star, but there are seven stars above magnitude 3 (Figure 13). The two leaders are Epsilon or Kaus Australis (magnitude 1.9) and Sigma or Nunki (2.0). Incidentally, the stars lettered Alpha and Beta are relatively

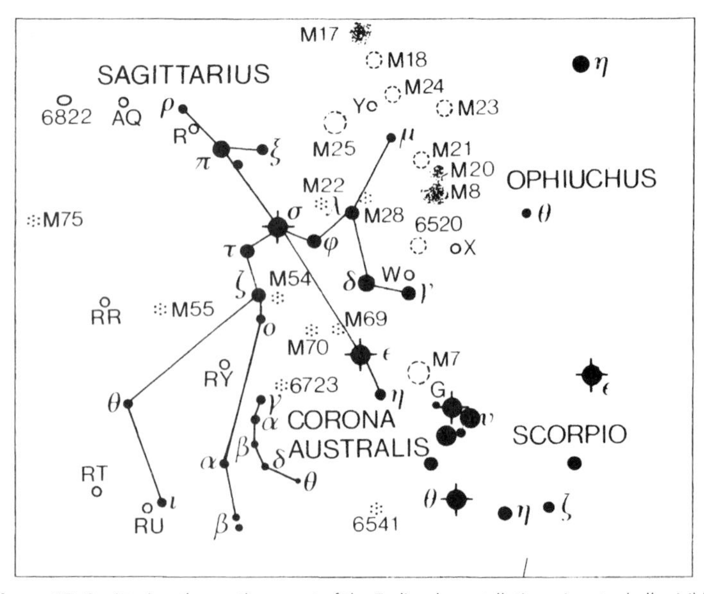

Figure 13. Sagittarius, the southernmost of the Zodiacal constellations, is not wholly visible from the United Kingdom. The centre of the Milky Way lies behind the star-clouds here; the whole area is exceptionally rich, and it contains numerous Messier objects.

faint. The outline of Sagittarius is nothing like that of an archer, and some people have compared it with a teapot. Deneb in Cygnus, Altair in Aquila, and Sagittarius lie in more or less a straight line, with Altair in the middle; this is probably the best way to locate the constellation.

There are plenty of interesting telescopic objects in Sagittarius, including the Omega or Horseshoe Nebula (Messier 17) in the northern part of the constellation, not far from Gamma Scuti; the Lagoon Nebula (Messier 8) near Mu Sagittarii, and the bright globular cluster Messier 22, between Mu and Nunki. Unfortunately, Sagittarius lies well to the south of the celestial equator – it is the southernmost of the Zodiacal constellations – and so it is never seen at its best from latitudes such as those of London or New York. Of course, this is to the advantage of Australians and South Africans, who are able to see both Sagittarius and Scorpius in their true glory.

The star-clouds of Sagittarius are rich indeed, and the observer with a small telescope will find endless enjoyment in sweeping round them. This is, in fact, the richest part of the Milky Way. For centuries now we have known that the Galaxy is a flattened disk, and it has been found that the Sun lies not far from the main plane, at a distance of about 26,000 light-years from the galactic centre. The whole system is rotating, and the Sun takes some 225 million years to complete one orbit.

The real galactic centre is hidden, simply because there is too much dust and gas in the way, and this blocks out light-waves as effectively as a thick fog will blot out a landscape. This makes it rather difficult to see all the way to the galactic centre in visible light. But visible light is just one form of electromagnetic radiation, and we can peer through the dust and gas using other wavelengths of such radiation, including radio waves, infra-red, X-rays and gamma-rays. Each wavelength reveals something different about the heart of our Galaxy. The big question has been, 'What lies at the centre of it all?'

In 1974, a strong radio source, known as 'Sagittarius A-star' (Sgr A*) was discovered by astronomers Bruce Balick and Bob Brown right at the centre of the Galaxy. Since then, the nature of Sgr A* has been a long-standing mystery, but careful observations at many wavelengths have revealed there is something very massive, compact and dark at the centre of our Galaxy – probably a massive black hole. Some of the evidence comes from more than 10 years' worth of observations of a fast-moving star known simply as S2 which orbits close to the hole.

By acquiring detailed images of the central region over a period of years, astronomers watched carefully to see if anything moved. They reasoned that any star in orbit close to the black hole would be moving fast enough for its motion to be detectable if monitored for several years. Most of the stars in this region have orbital periods between hundreds and millions of years, but S2, which is about 15 times as massive as our Sun, is so close that it circles the galactic centre every 15 years. Calculations based on the behaviour of this fast-moving star suggest the black hole at the heart of our Galaxy has a mass almost 3 million times that of the Sun. The star S2 appears to be living dangerously, because at closest, it just skims the black hole's event horizon – the boundary inside which matter cannot escape – travelling at an astonishing 18 million kilometres an hour.

July

New Moon: 25 July *Full Moon:* 11 July

EARTH is at aphelion (farthest from the Sun) on 3 July at a distance of 152 million kilometres (94 million miles).

MERCURY passes rapidly through inferior conjunction on 18 July and although its elongation from the Sun is in excess of 15° at either end of the month its magnitude is so faint that it will not be possible to see it with the naked eye against the twilight background.

VENUS, magnitude −4.0, continues to be visible as a brilliant object in the eastern morning skies before sunrise. From the latitudes of the British Isles the planet is visible low in the east-north-east as early as 03h. Venus passes 4° north of Aldebaran on 2 July.

MARS continues to be visible as an evening object low in the western sky, magnitude +1.8. It will only be visible to observers in tropical and southern latitudes, since the long duration of twilight precludes observation from latitudes as far north as the United Kingdom. During the month, Mars passes from Cancer into Leo, passing 0.7° north of Regulus on 22 July. Observers in the latitudes of the British Isles will not be able to see Mars again until next year.

JUPITER, continues to be visible as a brilliant evening object in the south-western sky, magnitude −2.2. It reaches its second stationary point on 6 July and resumes its direct motion. The four Galilean satellites are readily observable with a small telescope, or even a good pair of binoculars provided they are held rigidly.

SATURN is no longer visible to observers in high temperate latitudes, but further south is visible for the first half of the month low in the western sky as soon as the sky is dark enough in the early evenings. Its magnitude is +0.4.

The Galilean Satellites. Jupiter is still well placed this month, so this is a good time to follow the movements of the four main satellites. They are always known as the Galileans, because they were studied by Galileo in 1610 with his first telescope. They were also seen about the same time by the German astronomer Simon Marius, and it was he who gave them their names: Io, Europa, Ganymede and Callisto. Strangely, these names were not widely used until fairly modern times, and the satellites were referred to as merely I, II, III and IV.

Before the Space Age it was tacitly assumed they would be icy worlds very like each other. But we now know this is very definitely not true. Ganymede and Callisto are icy and crater-scarred; Europa is also icy, but smooth; Io is violently volcanic, with eruptions going on all the time. Each has its own special points of interest. However, they do have one characteristic in common: their atmospheres are so rarefied they correspond to what we would normally call a laboratory vacuum. In the Solar System, Titan is the only satellite to hold down a dense atmosphere.

Io is perhaps the most amazing of the Galileans (Figure 14). The temperatures of the volcanoes reach over 2,000°C, and one of them, now named Loki, is the most powerful volcano known to us. In fact, it emits more heat than all the Earth's volcanoes combined. Io moves within Jupiter's lethal radiation zone, and is connected to the planet by a strong magnetic flux tube. Europa may well have an ocean or layer of slush beneath its icy surface, and the same could be true of Ganymede and Callisto. Ganymede has a magnetic field of its own, and is the largest satellite in the Solar System; it is larger than the planet Mercury, though not so massive. Jupiter's remaining satellites are all small.

The grand total of known Jovian satellites (as of August 2005) is now 63. Of this total, only four are closer in than the orbit of Io; all the rest move outside the orbits of the Galileans. The innermost eight satellites (Metis, Adrastea, Amalthea, Thebe and the four Galileans) are classed as regular satellites, in that they have small circular orbits and low inclinations. These bodies probably formed in an early disk of gas and dust around Jupiter during the planet's formation. The remaining 55 satellites of Jupiter are all classed as irregular. Beyond the Galileans are seven irregular satellites in direct (or prograde) orbits, moving around the planet in the same direction as the regular satellites. The outermost 48 irregular satellites all orbit Jupiter in a direction opposite to that in which the planet spins, and this probably means they are

Figure 14. NASA's Galileo spacecraft acquired this mosaic of images of Jupiter's remarkable volcanic moon Io on 3 July 1999. Most of Io's surface has pastel colours, punctuated by black, brown, green, orange and red units near the active volcanic centres. (Image courtesy of NASA Jet Propulsion Laboratory and Planetary Image Research Laboratory, University of Arizona.)

captured asteroids rather than bona-fide moons of the planet. These retrograde irregular satellites seem to fall into three main groups.

Data for the Galilean moons are as follows:

Name	Mean Distance from Centre of Jupiter (km)	Orbital Period (days)	Diameter (km)
Io	421,800	1.77	3643
Europa	671,100	3.55	3122
Ganymede	1,070,400	7.16	5262
Callisto	1,882,700	16.69	4821

Eta Aquilae. Aquila, the Eagle, is one of the more prominent of the northern constellations, and is well placed on July evenings. Its leader, Altair, is one member of the unofficial 'Summer Triangle' (the others are Vega in Lyra and Deneb in Cygnus), and, like Antares, it is flanked by a fainter star to either side. Aquila is crossed by the Milky Way, and is very rich in star-fields.

Below Altair may be seen a line of three stars – Theta, Eta and Delta Aquilae (Figure 15). The central member, Eta, is of special interest, as it is a Cepheid variable. (The name 'Cepheid' derives from the first of this class of variable star to be discovered – Delta Cephei.) Eta Aquilae ranks with Delta Cephei, Zeta Geminorum and the southern hemisphere's Beta Doradûs as the brightest of its class; had it been studied first, these vitally important variables might well have been called Aquilids!

Cepheid variables are usually classed as F- and G-type yellow supergiant stars, although they are not as massive as true supergiants. Cepheids vary by between one and a couple of magnitudes over periods of from one to 100 days. There is a clear relationship between a Cepheid's pulsation period and its luminosity as defined by its absolute magnitude (the magnitude the star would appear to have if observed from a standard distance of 32.6 light-years). This so-called period-luminosity law allows us to determine the distances of Cepheids. For any particular Cepheid, the pulsation period gives the absolute

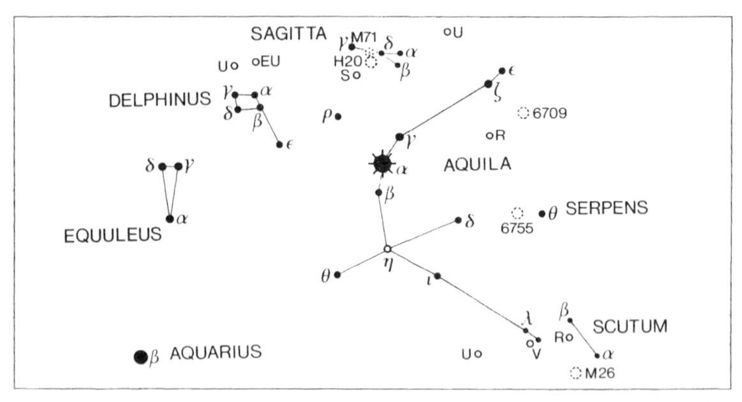

Figure 15. The principal stars of Aquila, the Eagle, showing its brightest star Altair, which is flanked on either side by a fainter star. Beneath Altair is the line of three stars, Theta, Eta and Delta. Eta is one of the brightest Cepheid variable stars.

magnitude, and comparison of this with the apparent magnitude gives the distance. Cepheids are of major importance in measuring the distances to other galaxies.

The magnitude range of Eta Aquilae is from 3.5 to 4.4, and the period is 7.18 days, so the fluctuations may be followed with the naked eye and are quite obvious, from one night to the next. Suitable comparison stars, all in Aquila, are Theta (magnitude 3.2), Delta (3.4), Beta (3.9), Iota (4.4) and Nu (4.6). Delta Cephei, which is very high during summer evenings and is circumpolar from Britain, also has a range of from 3.5 to 4.4 and a period of 5.37 days. According to the period-luminosity law, it follows that since the period of Eta Aquilae is greater than that of Delta Cephei, Eta Aquilae must be more luminous than Delta Cephei; and as the two appear equally bright (or virtually so), Eta must be the more remote of the two.

Not many Cepheids are conspicuous objects with the naked eye. The brightest Cepheid in the sky is the Pole Star, Polaris, although with a range of just one tenth of a magnitude in a period of about four days, its variations are too small to be detected by the naked eye. The other brightest members of the class are given in the following table:

Star	Max.	Min.	Period (days)
Zeta Geminorum	3.6	4.2	10.15
Eta Aquilae	3.5	4.4	7.18
Delta Cephei	3.5	4.4	5.37
Beta Doradûs	3.5	4.1	9.94
Kappa Pavonis	3.9	4.8	9.09

In addition to these Cepheids, there are others (such as Polaris) whose fluctuations are too slight to be detected with the naked eye. Kappa Pavonis and Beta Doradûs are, of course, too far south to be seen from anywhere in Britain.

To be strictly accurate, Kappa Pavonis is a W Virginis star. Short-period variables of this type are less luminous than classical Cepheids, but may be used as 'standard candles' in the same way. Kappa Pavonis is the only naked-eye example.

August

New Moon: **23 August** *Full Moon:* **9 August**

MERCURY becomes a morning object at the beginning of the month, and remains visible until about 19–20 August for observers in northern and equatorial latitudes, and until about 12 August for those in temperate southern latitudes. The planet will be seen low above the east-north-eastern horizon around the time of beginning of morning civil twilight. It will be noticed that Mercury is at its brightest after it reaches greatest western elongation (19°) on 7 August. The actual magnitudes are +1.2 on 1 August and −1.3 on 20 August.

VENUS, magnitude −3.9, continues to be visible as a splendid morning object. It is clearly seen above the east-north-east horizon before sunrise.

MARS, magnitude +1.8, is still visible to observers in tropical and southern latitudes, low in the western sky as soon as it is dark. Mars is moving eastwards in Leo, crossing into Virgo at the end of the month as it disappears from view in the gathering twilight.

JUPITER, magnitude −2.0, is still a bright evening object in the south-western skies.

SATURN passes through conjunction on 7 August and is not well placed for observation. However, it is just possible that, under good conditions, observers in the latitudes of the United Kingdom could detect the planet as a morning object, on the last few days of the month, low above the east-north-eastern horizon before the sky gets too bright prior to sunrise. Saturn's magnitude is +0.3. The planet passes from Cancer into Leo at the very end of the month. There is a conjunction of Venus and Saturn on 27 August at 0^h when Venus passes only 4 arc-minutes north of Saturn. Although at this time the planets are below the horizon for observers anywhere near the Greenwich meridian, Venus could still be used as a guide to pick up Saturn in the early morning before dawn, if the observer uses the fact that Venus is moving eastwards relative to Saturn, at the rate of 1° in 24 hours. Work it out for yourselves and see if you can pick them up using binoculars!

NEPTUNE is in the constellation of Capricornus and comes to opposition on 11 August. It is not visible to the naked eye since its magnitude is +7.8. The accompanying diagram (Figure 16) shows the path of Neptune against the stars during the year. The two brightest stars in the diagram are Theta Capricorni (magnitude +4.1, RA 21h 06.3m, Dec. −17.21°), and Iota Capricorni (magnitude +4.3, RA 21h 22.6m, Dec. −16.81°). These two stars are shown on Northern Star Chart 8S, Theta being the star just to the left of '310', with Iota to the left of Theta. The same stars are also shown on Southern Star Chart 8N, Iota being just above the '3' of '320', with Theta to the left. At opposition Neptune is 4,344 million kilometres (2,699 million miles) from the Earth.

The Discoverers of Neptune. The story of the discovery of Neptune, which comes to opposition this month, has been told time and time again – but who were the actual discoverers? It seems there is often an element of injustice here.

Some facts are indisputable. Based upon studies of the perturbations of Uranus, two mathematicians – John Couch Adams in England and Urbain Le Verrier in France – independently, and unknown to each other, worked out a position for the unknown planet (Neptune). Adams actually finished first, but the Astronomer Royal, Airy, did not promptly organize a search, and Adams published nothing. Le Verrier sent his results to the Paris Observatory, but nothing was done quickly, and Le Verrier sent his calculated position to Johann Galle, at the Berlin Observatory. Galle was enthusiastic, so he went to Johann Encke, Director of the Observatory, and asked for permission to use the Observatory's 23-cm Fraunhofer refractor to make a search.

Initially Encke was lukewarm, but felt bound to acquiesce: 'Let us oblige the gentleman from Paris!' During the discussion they were joined by a young staff member, Heinrich D'Arrest, who was anxious to take part. Encke agreed. It was 23 September 1846. As soon as darkness fell, Galle and D'Arrest went into the dome. Luckily they had a good star map of the relevant part of the sky to hand: Hora XXI of the

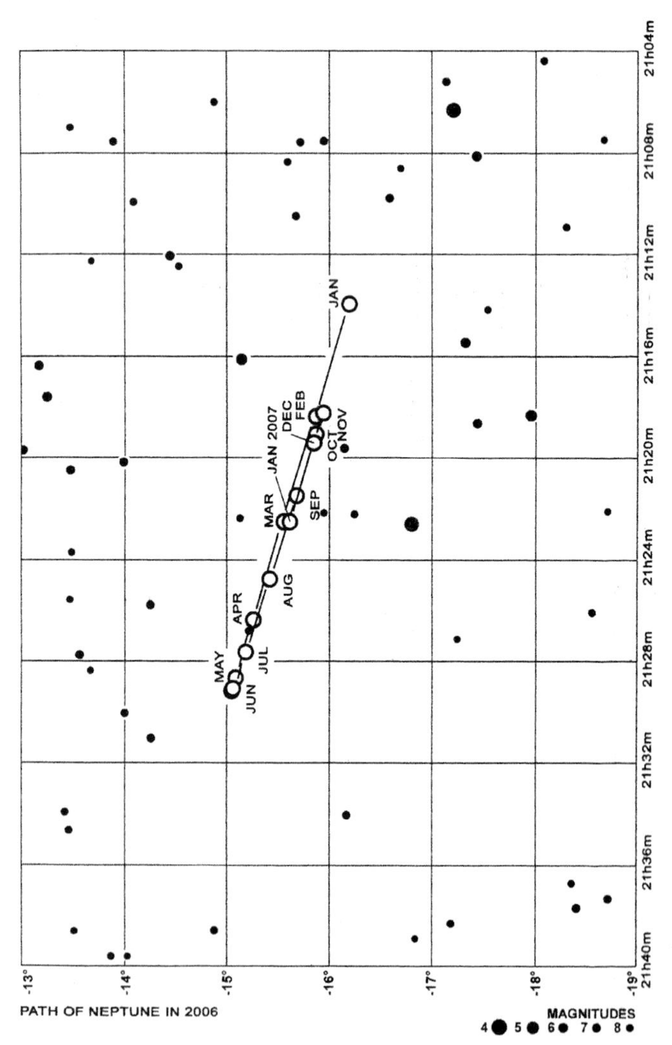

Figure 16. The path of Neptune against the stars of Capricornus during 2006. The two brightest stars on the chart are Theta Capricorni (lower right) and Iota Capricorni (below centre). A general map of Capricornus is shown in Figure 21.

Berlin Academy's Star Atlas, drawn up by Bremiker, which had already been printed but had not yet been widely distributed to other observatories. Galle used the telescope, calling out the positions and appearances of the stars which came into view, while D'Arrest checked them against the chart. Eventually, Galle called out a position: D'Arrest responded, 'That star is not on the map!' Neptune had been found.

Encke joined them in the dome, and they followed the object until it set. The next night they obtained confirmation, and Encke sent a message to Le Verrier; 'The planet whose position you have predicted actually exists.'

Note that the Germans were using Le Verrier's position; they knew nothing about Adams. A search had been started at Cambridge by James Challis, using Adams' position, but though Challis had actually seen Neptune he had not compared his observations, and did not recognize it as being anything but a star.

Many books list Adams and Le Verrier as co-discoverers of Neptune, but this is frankly illogical; Adams' work was not used in the vital observations. In any case, neither Adams nor Le Verrier could lay claim to be active observers. There is thus no alternative to saying that the actual discoverers of Neptune, in 1846, were Johann Galle and Heinrich D'Arrest.

Chi Cygni. During August evenings, Cygnus, the Swan, is at its best, though part of it is always circumpolar from Britain. It is a large and imposing constellation, containing one star of the first magnitude (Deneb) and several more of the second and third; it is crossed by the Milky Way, and there are many rich star-fields.

Cygnus is also rich in variable stars. Of these, one of the most interesting is Chi Cygni, which should be visible with the naked eye this month. Its variability was discovered by the German astronomer Gottfried Kirch – one of the earliest systematic observers of variable stars – as long ago as 1686. Chi Cygni is a rather rare spectral class S (S6) star, which means that visually it is deep red in colour. Lying about 300 light-years distant, it is a red giant star that has expanded to about 300 times the diameter of our Sun, so if it were placed in the centre of the Solar System it would extend out to the orbit of Mars. Such bloated stars pulsate slowly, causing variations in brightness, and there is a steady loss of mass from the star's extended atmosphere.

Chi Cygni belongs to the Mira class of long-period variables; the

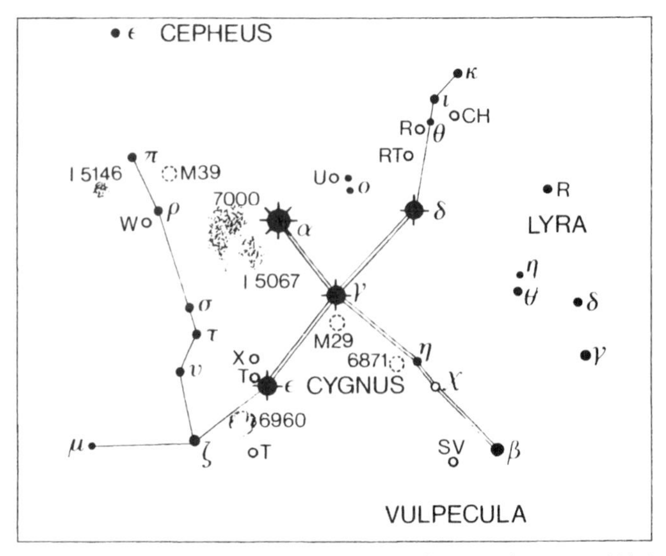

Figure 17. Deneb is the brightest star in the pattern of Cygnus, the Swan, which is also known as the Northern Cross. The remarkable long-period variable star Chi Cygni lies in the longer arm of the 'Cross' (which forms the neck of the Swan), between Eta Cygni and the beautiful double star Beta or Albireo.

current period is around 408 days, though of course this is subject to significant fluctuations from one cycle to the next. It also seems likely that the star's average period has increased by about four days since its discovery more than three centuries ago. What makes Chi Cygni notable is its tremendous magnitude range – one of the greatest known. Occasionally, it can brighten to magnitude 4, but at minimum it can sink to below 14, disappearing altogether when viewed through small telescopes.

Chi Cygni is easy to locate, because it forms part of the pattern of the Cross of Cygnus lying between the centre star (Gamma) and the lovely coloured double Beta or Albireo (Figure 17). Not far from Chi, and also in the neck of the Swan, are the stars Eta Cygni (magnitude 4.0, roughly midway between Gamma and Beta) and Phi Cygni (magnitude 4.8, between Chi and Beta), which make excellent comparisons when the variable is bright.

It is useful to note the maximum magnitude. On rare occasions the star has reached magnitude 3, but certainly most maxima are much below this, and there are some years in which the star remains a rather faint magnitude 5 object at maximum, just discernible with the naked eye. Observed through a telescope or with binoculars, when the star is near maximum, the deep red colour is very obvious indeed.

By the autumn Chi Cygni will have dropped below naked-eye visibility, and by the beginning of March next year it will be approaching minimum, so it cannot then be identified except with a powerful telescope and an adequate set of detailed charts.

September

New Moon: **22 September** *Full Moon:* **7 September**

Equinox: 23 September

MERCURY passes through superior conjunction on 1 September and becomes an evening object by the middle of the month, though not to observers as far north as the latitudes of the United Kingdom. For observers further south, reference should be made to the diagram (Figure 20) given with the notes for October. The magnitude of Mercury fades slightly during its period of visibility in September from −0.6 to −0.2.

VENUS, magnitude −3.9, remains a brilliant object low above the eastern horizon before dawn. However, it is getting noticeably closer to the Sun and observers in southern latitudes are not likely to be able to see it after the first two weeks of the month. By the end of September, observers in the latitudes of the United Kingdom are unlikely to be able to see it for more than about ten minutes or so before it is lost in the glare of the rising Sun. Only for observers in the tropics will Venus remain visible until almost the end of September.

MARS is unsuitably placed for observation.

JUPITER, magnitude −1.8, is still visible in the south-western sky in the early evenings, though for observers in the latitudes of the United Kingdom it will be difficult to detect, low in the south-western sky shortly after sunset. It can still be seen more easily by those in Mediterranean latitudes and further south. Jupiter passes near Alpha Librae again on about 10 September.

SATURN continues to be visible as a morning object in the south-eastern quadrant of the sky. Its magnitude is +0.5. Saturn is in the constellation of Leo.

URANUS, magnitude +5.7, is barely visible to the naked eye, though it is readily located with only small optical aid. Figure 18 shows the path of Uranus among the stars during the year. The two brightest stars in the diagram are Sigma Aquarii (magnitude +4.8, RA 22h 31.0m, Dec. −10.64°), and Lambda Aquarii (magnitude +3.7, RA 22h 53.0, Dec. −7.54°). These two stars are shown on the Northern Star Chart 9S, Lambda being shown close to the ecliptic at a longitude of 342°, with Sigma being below and to the right at a longitude of about 335°. The same stars are shown on Southern Star Chart 9N. At opposition on 5 September, Uranus is 2,854 million kilometres (1,773 million miles) from the Earth.

This Month's Eclipses. There are two eclipses this month, neither of which will be exciting for observers in the United Kingdom. The first, on 7 September, is a partial lunar eclipse. From Europe, the Moon will rise in eclipse and, weather permitting, should be seen easily, but less than 20 per cent of the Moon will be covered by the umbral portion of the Earth's shadow at maximum. However, astrophotographers will no doubt wish to take advantage of it. The Moon enters the umbra at 18h 05m, mid-eclipse is at 18h 51m and the Moon exits the umbra at 19h 38m. (Note that observers in the UK will need to add one hour to these times to obtain British Summer Time.) The second of this month's eclipses – the annular eclipse of the Sun on 22 September – will not be seen at all from Britain. From the north-eastern part of South America, observers will see the annular phase at or shortly after sunrise. The track then passes out over the Atlantic Ocean and never crosses land again.

Storms on Uranus. When it flew by the planet in January 1986, Voyager 2 revealed little detail on Uranus, and the planet was regarded as rather bland. Now, however, observations using the Hubble Space Telescope and our largest ground-based telescopes have revealed seasonal changes on the planet, including some of the brightest clouds in the outer Solar System and violent storms (Figure 19). Seasonal changes on Earth are caused by our planet's spin axis being tilted at 23.5° from the vertical. As Earth orbits the Sun, the northern and southern hemispheres are alternately tipped towards or away from the Sun. Uranus, which takes 84 years to make one orbit of the Sun, is tilted over on its side, giving rise to extreme 21-year-long seasons and

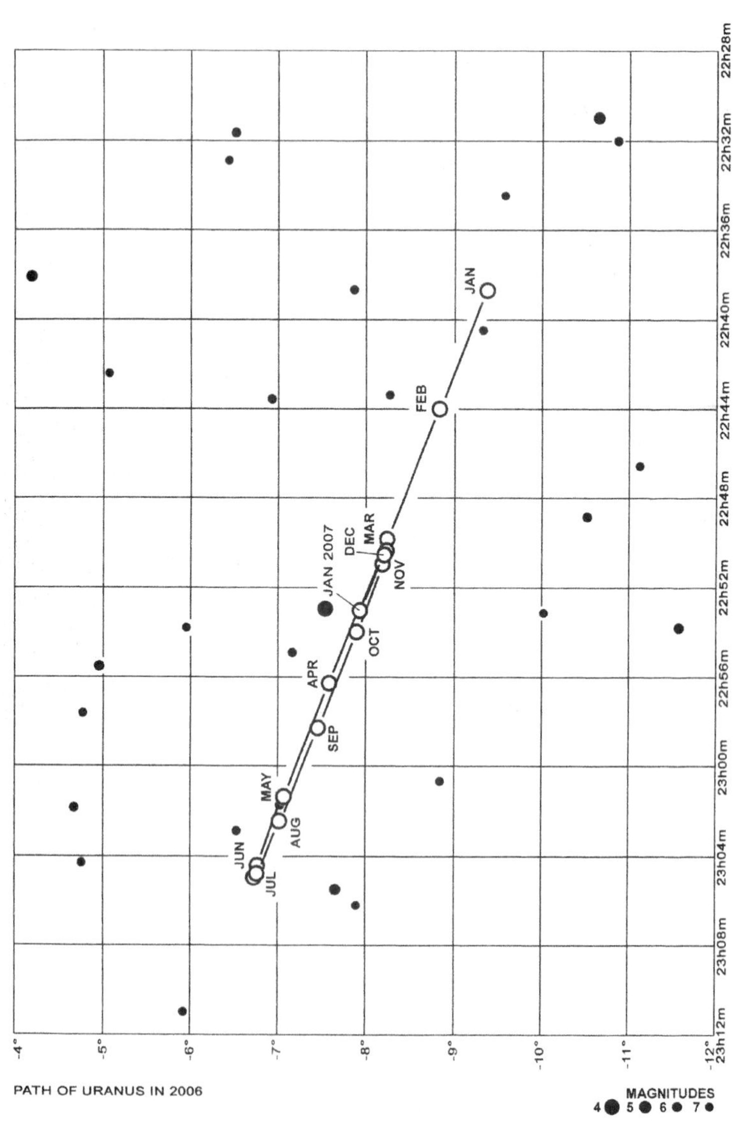

Figure 18. The path of Uranus against the stars of Aquarius during 2006. The two brightest stars on the chart are Sigma Aquarii (extreme lower right) and Lambda Aquarii (slightly above centre).

Figure 19. Hubble Space Telescope view of Uranus with some of its major rings and ten of its known satellites. This image was generated by Erich Karkoschka using data taken on 8 August 1998 with Hubble's Near Infrared Camera and Multi-Object Spectrometer. About 20 bright clouds are visible – nearly as many as the previous total in the history of modern observations. (Image courtesy of Kenneth Seidelmann, U.S. Naval Observatory and NASA Space Telescope Science Institute.).

highly unusual weather patterns. For nearly a quarter of the Uranian year, the Sun shines directly on to each pole, leaving the other half of the planet in darkness and in the grip of a long, frigid winter. The northern hemisphere of Uranus is now emerging from winter, and as sunlight reaches these latitudes, it warms the atmosphere, causing it to stir back into life. Since the Voyager 2 encounter, Uranus has moved far enough along its orbit for the Sun to shine at successively lower latitudes in the Northern Hemisphere. By the year 2007, the Sun will be shining directly over Uranus' equator.

The main difference between the two ice giants, Uranus and Neptune, is that Neptune has an internal heat source, whereas Uranus has little internal heat – perhaps no heat source at all. Consequently, the cloud-top temperatures of the two planets are much the same, despite the fact that Neptune is so much further from the Sun.

C.A.F. Peters. The German astronomer Christian August Friedrich Peters was born two hundred years ago this month, on 7 September 1806, in Hamburg. He demonstrated a flair for mathematics and astronomy at an early age, and in 1826 became assistant to Heinrich Christian Schumacher at Altona Observatory. In 1834, Dr Peters became an assistant at Hamburg Observatory, and in 1839, at the request of W. Struve, he joined the staff of the Pulkovo Observatory near St Petersburg. While at Pulkovo, he published two valuable memoirs, *Numerus Constans Nutationis* and *Recherches sur la Parallaxe des Etoiles Fixes*, for which he was jointly awarded the Gold Medal of the Royal Astronomical Society in 1852.

In 1849, he became professor of Astronomy at Königsberg, and soon after succeeded Friedrich Wilhelm Bessel as director of the observatory there. In 1854, Peters left Königsberg to become director of Altona Observatory and to carry on with the publication of *Astronomische Nachrichten*, which had been for many years the principal organ for astronomical science in Germany. In 1872, the Observatory relocated to Kiel, and Peters moved there, continuing in his post as director and filling also the office of professor of Astronomy at the university. He was an expert on stellar parallaxes, and in 1851 demonstrated the existence of an unseen companion to Sirius and calculated its orbit. He died in Kiel on 8 May 1880. C.A.F. Peters was the father of astronomer Carl Friedrich Wilhelm Peters, who succeeded him as editor of *Astronomische Nachrichten.*

October

New Moon: 22 October *Full Moon:* 7 October

Summer Time in the United Kingdom ends on 29 October.

MERCURY remains unobservable to those in the latitudes of the United Kingdom, though further south it continues to be visible as an evening object throughout the month. For observers in southern latitudes this will be the most favourable evening apparition of the year. Figure 20 shows, for observers in latitude 35°S, the changes in azimuth (true bearing from the north through east, south and west) and altitude of Mercury on successive evenings when the Sun is 6° below the horizon. This condition is known as the end of evening civil twilight and in this latitude and at this time of year occurs about 30 minutes after sunset. The changes in the brightness of the planet are indicated by the relative sizes of the circles marking Mercury's position at five-day intervals. It will be noticed that Mercury is at its brightest before it reaches greatest eastern elongation (25°) on 17 October. Mercury's magnitude fades from −0.1 to +1.2 during October.

VENUS is still a splendid morning object, magnitude −3.9, but very low above the eastern horizon shortly before dawn. After the first week of the month it becomes too close to the Sun to be seen by those in northern temperate latitudes. Observers further south are unlikely to be able to glimpse the planet at all during October. Venus passes through superior conjunction on 27 October.

MARS remains too close to the Sun for observation as it passes through conjunction on 23 October.

JUPITER, magnitude −1.8, is coming to the end of its evening apparition for observers in the latitudes of the United Kingdom who may be able to see it low in the south-western sky shortly after sunset, but only for about the first week of the month. Further south it may be seen for

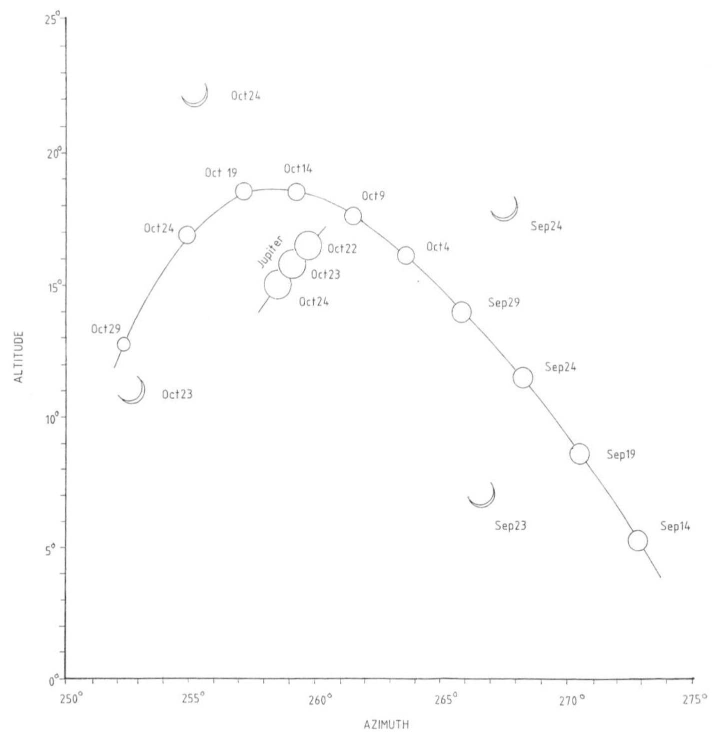

Figure 20. Evening apparition of Mercury, from latitude 35°S. (Angular diameters of Mercury, Jupiter and the crescent Moon not to scale.)

longer, and in southern latitudes it should be possible to see Jupiter until the end of the month.

SATURN, continues to be visible in the eastern sky in the early mornings. The planet has a magnitude of +0.5.

Diphda. Two bright stars are visible in the southern evening sky this month, well below the Square of Pegasus, in an otherwise fairly barren part of the sky. One is the first-magnitude star Fomalhaut in Piscis Austrinus (the Southern Fish); the other is Diphda, or Beta Ceti, the brightest star in the vast, sprawling constellation of Cetus, the Whale (sometimes identified with the fearsome sea-monster of the Perseus and Andromeda legend). Diphda is sometimes also known as Deneb

Kaitos, a name which relates to its location in the tail of the whale.

Diphda may be found by following down the line from Alpheratz (Alpha Andromedae), in the Square, through Algenib (Gamma Pegasi). Diphda is of the second magnitude (2.04) and has a K-type spectrum (almost type G), so it is somewhat orange in hue. It has a luminosity 145 times that of the Sun, and its distance from us is 96 light-years.

Diphda is interesting because it has been suspected of variability. There have been reports that for brief periods it increases in brightness, reaching the first magnitude. These reports are very probably wrong; all the same, Diphda is worth watching, though comparisons are not easy, because there are no comparable stars anywhere near it. There should be no chance of confusing Diphda with Fomalhaut. Of the two, Fomalhaut is lower down, white in colour, and very much the more brilliant of the two, even though it is never seen to advantage from anywhere in the British Isles, and from northern Scotland it barely rises above the horizon.

Capricornus. The constellation of Capricornus, the Sea-Goat, is not a very conspicuous pattern, and its outline bears no resemblance to a goat, marine or otherwise (Figure 21). It lies within the band of the Zodiac between Sagittarius and Aquarius, and from northern temperate latitudes is visible fairly low in the south on October evenings. There seem to be no firm mythological legends attached to it, though the image of a goat may well date back to Babylonian times, being

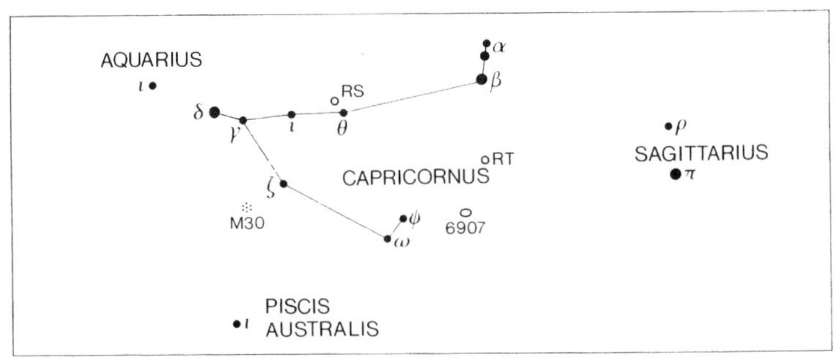

Figure 21. The principal stars of the somewhat obscure Zodiacal pattern of Capricornus, the Sea-Goat. The planet Neptune is moving against the background stars of Capricornus this year; use the star Iota Capricorni (to the left of Theta here) as a guide, referring also to the detailed chart in Figure 16.

linked with the powerful god Ea. The Greeks associated the pattern rather loosely with a legendary goat said to have nursed the infant Zeus, or with the demigod Pan, who was the son of Hermes and a forest nymph.

Today, the Sun passes through Capricornus from late January to mid-February. In ancient times the Sun reached its furthest point south of the equator in this constellation at the northern hemisphere winter solstice. The latitude line around the Earth at which the Sun appeared overhead at noon on the winter solstice (23.5°S.) consequently became known as the Tropic of Capricorn. Due to precession of the Earth's axis of rotation, the position of the winter solstice has now shifted westwards into the neighbouring constellation of Sagittarius, but the Tropic of Capricorn has kept its name.

The brightest stars of Capricornus are:

Star	Name	Magnitude	Spectral Type
Delta	Deneb al Geidi	2.87	A5
Beta	Dabih	3.08	F8
Alpha^2	Al Giedi	3.57	G9
Gamma	Nashira	3.68	F0p
Zeta	Yen	3.74	G4

Alpha is a naked-eye double, magnitudes 3.6 and 4.2, separation 378 arcseconds, position angle 291°. However, the two components are not genuinely associated. The brighter (Alpha^2) is 117 light-years away; the fainter (Alpha^1) is in the background, at over 1,500 light-years, and is a very powerful G-type giant, about 4,000 times as luminous as the Sun. Each component is itself closely double, and the fainter component of Alpha^2 is also a close double.

Beta is another wide double: magnitudes 3.1 and 6.0, separation 205 arcseconds. The fainter component is again double.

There are not very many objects of immediate interest in Capricornus, but the globular cluster M30 is easily found with binoculars or a small telescope; RA 21h 37.5m, Dec. −23° 25′, not far from Zeta and close to the star 41 Capricorni (magnitude 5½). Its integrated magnitude is 7.5, distance 41,000 light-years. There is a bright nucleus.

November

New Moon: 20 November *Full Moon:* 5 November

MERCURY passes through inferior conjunction on 8 November, when it transits the Sun (see page 149) and reappears as a morning object by the middle of the month. It is then visible to observers low above the east-south-eastern horizon around the beginning of morning civil twilight. During its period of visibility its magnitude brightens from +1.0 to −0.6. For observers in northern temperate latitudes this will be the most favourable morning apparition of the year. Figure 22 shows, for observers in latitude 52°N, the changes in azimuth (true bearing from the north through east, south and west) and altitude of Mercury on successive mornings when the Sun is 6° below the horizon. This condition is known as the beginning of morning civil twilight, and in this latitude and at this time of year occurs about 35 minutes before sunrise. The changes in the brightness of the planet are indicated by the relative sizes of the circles marking Mercury's position at five-day intervals. It will be noticed that Mercury is at its brightest after it reaches greatest western elongation (20°) on 25 November.

VENUS remains too close to the Sun for observation throughout the month, except for observers in the tropics. They should be able to see the planet for a short while, low above the south-western horizon immediately after sunset, during the last ten days of the month. Its magnitude is −3.9.

MARS remains unsuitably placed for observation.

JUPITER's magnitude is −1.7. For observers in equatorial and southern latitudes, it may still be seen low above the south-western horizon shortly after sunset, though only for about the first week of the month before it is lost in the gathering evening twilight. It is no longer visible from northern temperate latitudes. Jupiter passes through conjunction on 21 November.

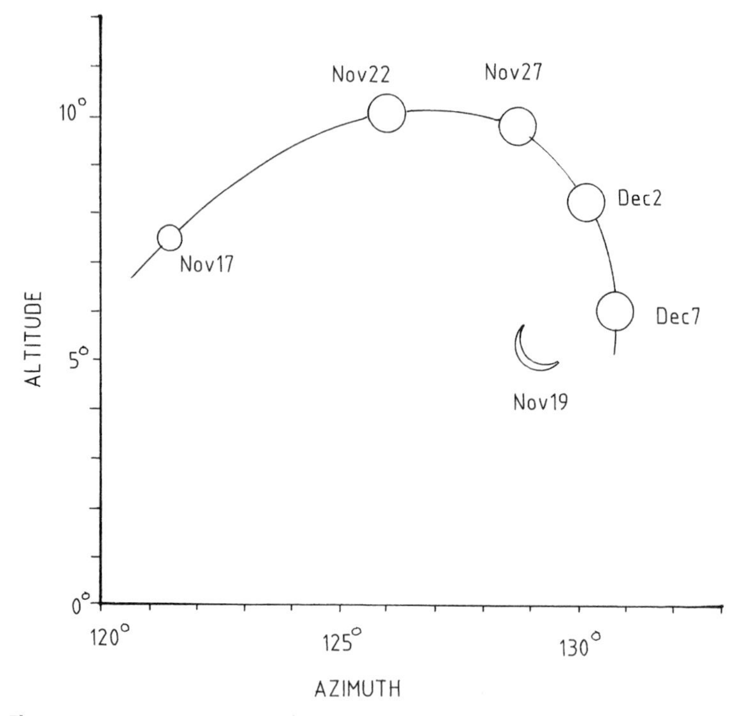

Figure 22. Morning apparition of Mercury, from latitude 52°N. (Angular diameters of Mercury and the crescent Moon not to scale.)

SATURN is still visible in the eastern and southern skies, rising a little north of east well before midnight by the end of the month for observers in the latitudes of the United Kingdom. It is moving very slowly direct in the constellation of Leo. Its magnitude is +0.4.

Mercury Crossing. It is unfortunate that this month's transit of Mercury will not be visible from Britain. It has to be admitted that transits are not (now) important to astronomers, but they are interesting to watch. On average, there are 13 transits of Mercury each century. At the present time, all transits of Mercury occur within a few days either side of 8 May and 10 November. The next Mercury transits, following that of 8 November 2006, will be as follows (those marked * will be visible in full or in part from Britain):

9 May 2016*
11 November 2019*
13 November 2032*
7 November 2039*
7 May 2049*
9 November 2052
10 May 2062*
11 November 2065
14 November 2078*
7 November 2085*
8 May 2095*
10 November 2098*

Venus can also pass in transit – as it last did on 8 June 2004; the next transit will be on 6 June 2012, but from Britain the transit will already be in progress at sunrise and only the very end of the event will be visible. We must then wait until the next pair of Venus transits on 11 December 2117 and 8 December 2125. During such a transit, Venus may be seen with the naked eye, provided that the greatest care is taken; a dark filter suitable for direct solar viewing is essential – and ordinary sunglasses, or smoked glass, will not suffice.

Mercury is much smaller, and to see the planet in transit a telescope has to be used. As with all observations of this kind, one must take the very greatest care. A moment's carelessness can result in serious damage to your eyesight. The safest method is to use the telescope as a projector, and show the solar image on a screen held or fixed behind the telescope eyepiece.

One interesting aside refers to the phenomenon known as the Black Drop effect. Transits of Venus were once regarded as very important, because they could be used to determine the Earth–Sun distance or astronomical unit. The method depended upon making accurate timings of the passage of Venus on and off the brilliant face of the Sun during a transit, and recording the track of Venus across the solar disk. Armed with this information from different locations on the Earth, it was possible to use simple trigonometry to calculate the distance to Venus, and hence derive a value for the astronomical unit. The method was originally proposed by Edmond Halley, but is now obsolete, and in any case his method proved impractical, since contact timings of the required accuracy proved extremely difficult to make. As the dark silhouette of Venus moves on to the face of the Sun at ingress, it seems to draw a strip of darkness after it – and when this strip disappears, the transit has already begun. A similar effect occurs at egress. This so-called Black Drop effect ruined the precision. In fact, Halley had originally worked out his method for transits of Mercury, but realized that the disk of the planet would be too small to make accurate timings possible. But does Mercury also show a Black Drop?

It was once thought that with Venus, the phenomenon was caused by the planet's dense atmosphere, in which case nothing of the kind would be expected with Mercury, whose atmosphere is far too thin to have any effects. However, it now seems that Venus' atmosphere is not responsible and, at the last Mercury transit (that of 7 May 2003), the effect was clearly seen by many observers. No doubt further observations of it will be made this month.

When seen in transit, Mercury is far blacker than any sunspots which happen to be on the solar disk. The dark side of Mercury really is jet black, whereas a sunspot looks black only by contrast against the surrounding bright surface or photosphere.

Faint Alphas. Below the Square of Pegasus lies Pisces, the Fishes – officially the last constellation of the Zodiac, though since it now contains the vernal equinox it really ought to be the first. Pisces, which is well placed during November evenings, is entirely unremarkable, and is one of the more obscure of the Zodiacal groups. It is, however, ancient, and there is even a mythological legend attached to it. It is said that Venus and her son, Cupid, once escaped from the fire-breathing, hissing monster Typhon (who could live in flames and fire but not in water) by throwing themselves into the River Euphrates and changing themselves temporarily into fishes. Apparently, they tied themselves together with a cord so as not to lose each other in the dark waters of the river. Subsequently, two fishes tied together by their tails were placed in the sky in memory of this rather curious episode!

There are few notable objects in Pisces, though Alpha, sometimes known by its old proper name of Al Rischa, is a fairly easy double, with two components of magnitudes 4.2 and 5.1, separation 1.8 arcseconds, position angle 268°. Actually, it is not the brightest star in the constellation; this distinction goes to Eta, or Alpherg, which is slightly more conspicuous even though it is still well below the third magnitude.

The system of allotting Greek letters to stars was introduced by

Johann Bayer in 1603. The principle is to letter the brightest star in a constellation Alpha, the second Beta, and so on down to Omega, the last letter in the Greek alphabet. There are, however, various exceptions to the rule – Pisces being one. The most glaring examples are Corvus and Sagittarius. In Corvus there are four stars of magnitude 3 or above, making up a conspicuous little quadrilateral; these are Gamma, Beta, Delta and Epsilon, while Alpha Corvi is a full magnitude fainter. The other faint Alpha is in Sagittarius, where the two brightest stars are Epsilon (magnitude 1.9) and Sigma (2.0), while Alpha is a modest 4.0.

Of course, in many cases where Alpha is not the leader of a constellation the difference is so slight that naked-eye estimates might lead to an error; thus in Ursa Major Epsilon (Alioth) is 1.77 and Alpha (Dubhe) fractionally fainter at 1.79 – although in this case it seems that Bayer lettered the principal stars in order of right ascension rather than brilliancy. There are also cases of revisions of constellation boundaries. In Puppis the brightest star is Zeta; but Puppis is part of the dismembered constellation of Argo Navis, and Alpha, Beta, Gamma, Delta and Epsilon of Argo are now in different parts. (Alpha is, of course, Canopus.)

The following are cases of faint Alphas, where the star lettered Alpha is at least 0.4 magnitude fainter than the brightest star in the constellation.

Constellation	Brightest Star	Magnitude of Alpha
Cancer	Beta, 3.5	4.3
Capricornus	Delta, 2.9	3.5 (a double star)
Cetus	Beta, 2.0	2.5
Corvus	Gamma, 2.6	4.0
Draco	Gamma, 2.2	3.6
Gemini	Beta (Pollux), 1.2	1.6 (Castor)
Sagitta	Gamma, 3.5	4.4
Sagittarius	Epsilon, 1.8	4.0

The Alphas of Andromeda, Aquarius, Camelopardalis, Delphinus, Hydrus, Libra, Microscopium, Monoceros, Pegasus, Pisces and Ursa Major are slightly fainter than the leader of each constellation. We also have two variable Alphas, in Hercules and Orion; Alpha Herculis (Rasalgethi) is a semi-regular red giant ranging between magnitudes 3 and 4, whereas the two leaders, Beta and Zeta, are both ranked as 2.8;

and, of course, Betelgeux (or Betelgeuse) in Orion is not quite equal to Rigel, though when it is at maximum the two are strictly comparable. (Herschel, on one occasion, even made Betelgeux the brighter, though this was a naked-eye estimate and cannot be regarded as precise.) Finally, there are suspicions that Castor and Pollux are less equal than they used to be in ancient times, though the evidence is very uncertain.

December

New Moon: **20 December** *Full Moon:* **5 December**

Solstice: 22 December

MERCURY continues its morning apparition, with a magnitude of −0.6. It may be seen above the south-eastern horizon around the beginning of morning civil twilight. Although observers in the latitudes of the United Kingdom are unlikely to see it after the first week of the month, those in equatorial latitudes can hope to see it during the first half of the month. The longer twilight in southern temperate latitudes precludes observation.

VENUS, magnitude −3.9, is an evening object, though observers in the latitudes of the British Isles will have to wait until the last ten days of the month before they are able to detect the planet, because it is so far south of the celestial equator. Venus will be seen low above the south-western horizon for a short while immediately after sunset. Both Mercury and Venus are at aphelion on 27 December at 21h.

MARS is not observable at first, but for the last week of the month it may be detected low above the east-south-eastern horizon about an hour before dawn, though only by observers in tropical and southern latitudes. Its magnitude is +1.5. During December, Mars moves eastwards from Libra, through Scorpius and into Ophiuchus, some degrees above Antares, which has a magnitude of +1.0. However, both Mars and Antares will be completely outshone by the proximity of Jupiter. Figure 23 shows the paths of Mars and Jupiter during the month.

JUPITER, becomes a brilliant morning object as it emerges from the dawn twilight after the first 10 or 12 days of the month, when it may be seen low in the south-eastern sky for a short while before dawn. Its magnitude is −1.7. At the beginning of the month Jupiter moves eastwards from Libra into Scorpius.

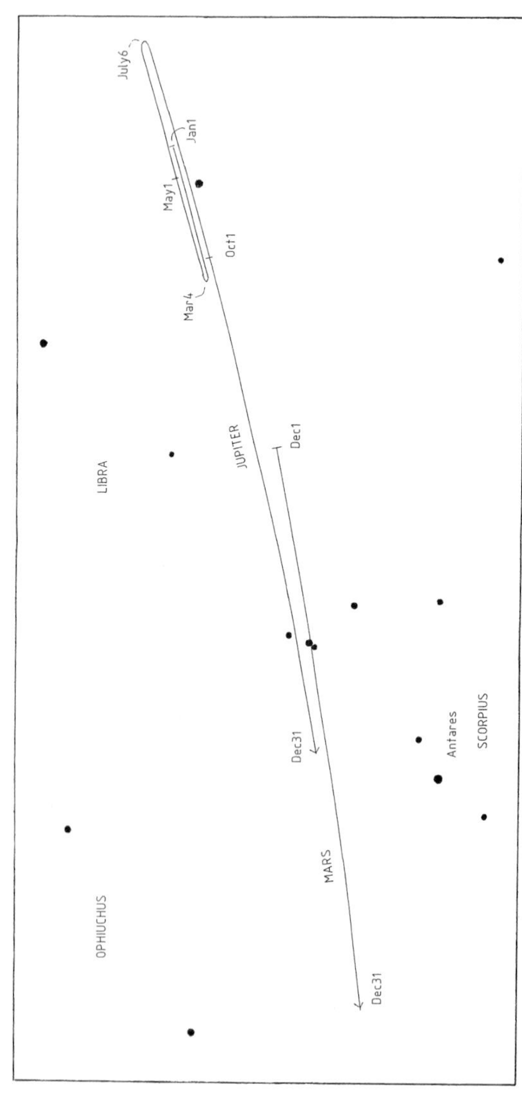

Figure 23. The path of Mars against the background stars of Libra, Scorpius and Ophiuchus during December 2006. (The path of Jupiter during the year is also shown.)

SATURN, magnitude +0.3, is now visible in the south-eastern quadrant of the sky from the late evening onwards, crossing the meridian well before dawn. Saturn reaches its first stationary point on 6 December and then moves slowly retrograde. The planet is in the constellation of Leo.

How Large Are the Lunar 'Seas'? It is now a long time since anyone believed that the lunar maria are, or ever have been, water-filled. They are lava plains, and by terrestrial standards are ancient; the dinosaurs could have seen them just as we do today (though it seems rather unlikely that they ever thought much about it!). It is interesting to check on their sizes:

Mare		Area, sq. km
Oceanus Procellarum	Ocean of Storms	2,290,000
Mare Imbrium	Sea of Showers	863,000
Mare Frigoris	Sea of Cold	441,000
Mare Tranquillitatis	Sea of Tranquillity	440,000
Mare Foecunditatis	Sea of Fertility	344,000
Mare Serenitatis	Sea of Serenity	314,000
Mare Nubium	Sea of Clouds	265,000
Mare Crisium	Sea of Crises	200,000
Mare Australe	Southern Sea	149,000
Mare Humorum	Sea of Humours	118,000

By way of a rough comparison, Saudi Arabia has a surface area of 2,200,000 sq. km, approximately the same as that of the Oceanus Procellarum. Sweden has an area of 450,000 sq. km, Italy 301,000 sq. km, United Kingdom 242,000 sq. km, and Greece 132,000 sq. km. The Mare Imbrium is the largest regular mare region.

Suspected Variable Stars. The familiar 'W' of Cassiopeia is high up on December evenings. Alpha Cassiopeiae or Shedir, in the 'W', is an orange star of spectral type K; it was long regarded as slightly variable over a small range, possibly 2.1 to 2.4, though opinions differ, and in recent catalogues it is listed as constant at magnitude 2.23. Shedir is about 120 light-years away, and is almost 200 times as luminous as the Sun.

Other naked-eye stars have in the past been suspected of variability. In 1890, G.F. Chambers gave a list of them in the fourth edition of his famous astronomical textbook. Here are some of his examples:

Star	Max.	Min.	Authority for Variation
Gamma Pegasi	$2\frac{1}{2}$	3	Schwabe
61 Ceti	6	7	William Herschel
Nu Fornacis	5	6	Gould
Gamma Eridani	$2\frac{1}{2}$	$3\frac{1}{2}$	Secchi
R Eridani	$5\frac{1}{2}$	6	Gould
31 Orionis	$4\frac{3}{4}$	6	Gould
Sigma Canis Majoris	$4\frac{1}{2}$	5	Gould
Beta Volantis	4	5	Gould
Eta Crateris	$4\frac{1}{2}$	$6\frac{1}{2}$	Houzeau
Epsilon Corvi	3	4	Gould
Delta Ursae Majoris	$2\frac{1}{2}$	4	Pigott
Gamma Corvi	$2\frac{1}{2}$	3	Gould
Eta Virginis	3	4	Gould
Delta Corvi	$2\frac{3}{4}$	$3\frac{1}{2}$	Gould
Eta Ursae Majoris	2	$2\frac{1}{2}$	Espin et al.
Upsilon Bootis	4	$4\frac{1}{2}$	Schmidt
Beta Ursae Minoris	$2\frac{1}{4}$	$2\frac{3}{4}$	John Herschel, Espin
Mu Draconis	4	5	J. Johnson
Gamma Sagittarii	3	$3\frac{1}{2}$	Gould
Beta Cygni	3	4	Klein
Mu Aquilae	4	5	Gould
Epsilon Draconis	$3\frac{3}{4}$	$4\frac{3}{4}$	Gould
Rho Pavonis	$4\frac{1}{2}$	$5\frac{1}{4}$	Gould
Beta Cephei	3	$3\frac{1}{2}$	various
Epsilon Pegasi	2	$2\frac{1}{2}$	Schwabe
Eta Pegasi	3	$3\frac{1}{4}$	Christie
Iota Andromedae	$4\frac{1}{2}$	5	Gore

The list is of historical interest, though it is not likely that many of these stars, if any, are real variables. Beta Cephei is, of course, a giant pulsating star with a very small amplitude (magnitude 3.16 to 3.27); its variations are too small to be noticed with the naked eye. However, the amateur astronomer who is learning their way around the night sky may care to identify the stars in Chambers' list; and when they have gained experience it might be worth making a few brightness estimates – just in case any of the stars do prove to be variable after all!

Eclipses in 2006

During 2006 there will be four eclipses, two of the Sun and two of the Moon.

1. *A total eclipse of the Sun on 29 March* is visible as a partial eclipse from the extreme east of Brazil, the Atlantic Ocean, Africa (except the south-west), Europe, Iceland, north-east Greenland, the Arctic Ocean, Asia (except the east, and southern India). The partial phase begins at 7h 37m and ends at 12h 46m. The track of the central line starts in the extreme eastern part of Brazil, crosses the Atlantic Ocean, passes through Ghana, Togo, Benin, Nigeria, Niger, extreme north-west Chad, Libya, extreme north-west Egypt, Turkey, Georgia and southern Russia, before ending in Kazakhstan. Totality begins at 8h 34m and ends at 11h 48m. The maximum duration of totality is 4m 7s.

2. *A penumbral eclipse of the Moon on 14–15 March* lasts from 21h 22m to 02h 14m. It is visible from Asia, western Australia, Africa, Europe and the Americas.

3. *An annular eclipse of the Sun on 22 September* is visible as a partial eclipse from Central and South America, the Atlantic Ocean, west and south Africa, southern Madagascar and Antarctica. The partial phase begins at 08h 40m and ends at 14h 40m. The path of annularity starts in Guyana, crosses Surinam and French Guiana, and ends in the south Atlantic Ocean. Annularity begins at 09h 48m and ends at 13h 31m. The maximum duration is 7m 09s.

4. *A partial eclipse of the Moon on 7 September* is visible from the western Pacific Ocean, Australasia, Asia, Africa, Europe, Antarctica, Iceland and eastern Brazil. The eclipse begins at 18h 05m and ends at 19h 38m. At maximum, 19 per cent of the Moon's disc is obscured.

Transit of Mercury in 2006

A transit of Mercury across the face of the Sun occurs on 8–9 November. The beginning is visible from the Americas, Hawaii and New Zealand. The end is visible from Hawaii, Australasia and extreme eastern Asia. Geocentric times and position angles are as follows:

				PA					PA
Ingress	d	h	m	°	**Egress**	d	h	m	°
External contact	8	19	12	141	Internal contact	9	00	08	269
Internal contact	8	19	14	141	External contact	9	00	10	269

For any place on the surface of the Earth, the times will not differ from those above by more than about 1 minute.

Occultations in 2006

In the course of its journey round the sky each month, the Moon passes in front of all the stars in its path, and the timing of these occultations is useful in fixing the position and motion of the Moon. The Moon's orbit is tilted at more than 5° to the ecliptic, but it is not fixed in space. It twists steadily westwards at a rate of about 20° a year, a complete revolution taking 18.6 years, during which time all the stars that lie within about 6.5° of the ecliptic will be occulted. The occultations of any one star continue month after month until the Moon's path has twisted away from the star, but only a few of these occultations will be visible from any one place during the hours of darkness.

There are five occultations of bright planets in 2006, two of Venus, two of Mars and one of Saturn.

Only four first-magnitude stars are near enough to the ecliptic to be occulted by the Moon: these are Aldebaran, Regulus, Spica and Antares. Both Spica and Antares undergo occultation in 2006.

Predictions of these occultations are made on a worldwide basis for all stars down to magnitude 7.5, and sometimes even fainter. The British Astronomical Association has produced a complete lunar occultation prediction package for personal-computer users. Occultations of stars by planets (including minor planets) and satellites have aroused considerable attention.

The exact timing of such events gives valuable information about positions, sizes, orbits, atmospheres and sometimes of the presence of satellites. The discovery of the rings of Uranus in 1977 was the unexpected result of the observations made of a predicted occultation of a faint star by Uranus. The duration of an occultation by a satellite or minor planet is quite small (usually of the order of a minute or less). If observations are made from a number of stations it is possible to deduce the size of the planet.

The observations need to be made either photoelectrically or visually. The high accuracy of the method can readily be appreciated when one realizes that even a stopwatch timing accurate to a tenth of a second is, on average, equivalent to an accuracy of about 1 kilometre in the chord measured across the minor planet.

Comets in 2006

The appearance of a bright comet is a rare event which can never be predicted in advance, because this class of object travels round the Sun in enormous orbits with periods which may well be many thousands of years. There are therefore no records of the previous appearances of these bodies, and we are unable to follow their wanderings through space.

Comets of short period, on the other hand, return at regular intervals, and attract a good deal of attention from astronomers. Unfortunately they are all faint objects, and are recovered and followed by photographic methods using large telescopes. Most of these short-period comets travel in orbits of small inclination which reach out to the orbit of Jupiter, and it is this planet that is mainly responsible for the severe perturbations that many of these comets undergo. Unlike the planets, comets may be seen in any part of the sky, but since their distances from the Earth are similar to those of the planets their apparent movements in the sky are also somewhat similar, and some of them may he followed for long periods of time.

The following comets are expected to return to perihelion in 2006, and to be brighter than magnitude +15.

Comet	Year of Discovery	Period (years)	Predicted Date of Perihelion 2006
P/1999 RO28 LONEOS	1999	6.6	May 13
71P Clark	1973	5.5	Jun 7
73P-C Schwassmann–Wachmann	1930	5.4	Jun 7
73P-B Schwassmann–Wachmann	1930	5.4	Jun 8
73P-E Schwassmann–Wachmann	1930	5.4	Jun 9
41P Tuttle–Giacobini–Kresák	1858	5.4	Jun11
45P Honda–Mrkos–Pajdusakova	1948	5.3	Jun 29
4P Faye	1843	7.5	Nov 15
1991 V1 (P/Shoemaker–Levy)	1991	7.5	Nov 17

An ephemeris for Comet 41P Tuttle–Giacobini–Kresák follows:

Date 2006	2000.0 RA		Dec.		Distance from Earth	Distance from Sun	Elong-ation from Sun	Mag.
0h	h	m	°	′	AU	AU	°	
Mar 26	5	51.278	+21	26.05	1.184	1.450	82.8	+9.8
Apr 5	6	9.137	+22	44.99	1.185	1.370	77.1	+9.4
15	6	31.165	+23	54.02	1.177	1.294	72.3	+9.0
25	6	57.286	+24	48.13	1.159	1.224	68.4	+8.6
May 5	7	27.469	+25	21.04	1.132	1.162	65.4	+8.2
15	8	1.593	+25	25.34	1.098	1.111	63.4	+7.9
25	8	39.424	+24	52.69	1.060	1.074	62.4	+7.6
Jun 4	9	20.620	+23	34.08	1.020	1.052	62.3	+7.4
14	10	4.531	+21	22.12	0.984	1.048	63.2	+7.3
24	10	50.345	+18	12.75	0.956	1.062	65.1	+7.3
Jul 4	11	37.084	+14	8.85	0.943	1.092	67.6	+7.4
14	12	23.665	+ 9	22.92	0.948	1.137	70.6	+7.7
24	13	9.086	+ 4	15.93	0.977	1.194	73.6	+8.1
Aug 3	13	52.608	− 0	48.06	1.030	1.261	76.2	+8.6
13	14	33.715	− 5	27.74	1.107	1.334	77.9	+9.1
23	15	12.210	− 9	30.27	1.206	1.413	78.7	+9.7

Minor Planets in 2006

Although many thousands of minor planets (asteroids) are known to exist, only a few thousand of them have well-determined orbits and are listed in the catalogues. Most of these orbits lie entirely between the orbits of Mars and Jupiter. All these bodies are quite small, and even the largest, Ceres, is only 913 kilometres (567 miles) in diameter. Thus, they are necessarily faint objects, and although a number of them are within the reach of a small telescope few of them ever attain any considerable brightness. The first four that were discovered are named Ceres, Pallas, Juno and Vesta. Actually the largest four minor planets are Ceres, Pallas, Vesta and Hygeia. Vesta can occasionally be seen with the naked eye, and this is most likely to happen when an opposition occurs near June, since Vesta would then be at perihelion. Below are ephemerides for Ceres, Juno and Vesta in 2006.

1 Ceres

		2000.0 RA		Dec.		Geo-centric Distance	Helio-centric Distance	Elong-ation	Visual Magni-tude
		h	m	°	′			°	
May	9	21	47.57	−21	06.0	2.839	2.949	86	+9.0
	19	21	56.10	−21	04.1	2.707	2.954	94	+8.9
	29	22	03.02	−21	13.0	2.577	2.958	102	+8.8
Jun	8	22	08.11	−21	34.2	2.451	2.961	110	+8.6
	18	22	11.17	−22	08.4	2.333	2.965	119	+8.5
	28	22	11.99	−22	55.7	2.226	2.968	129	+8.3
Jul	8	22	10.42	−23	54.7	2.135	2.971	138	+8.1
	18	22	06.49	−25	02.2	2.062	2.974	148	+8.0
	28	22	00.39	−26	13.3	2.012	2.976	158	+7.8
Aug	7	21	52.62	−27	21.3	1.987	2.978	165	+7.6
	17	21	43.93	−28	19.8	1.990	2.980	165	+7.6
	27	21	35.25	−29	03.3	2.020	2.982	158	+7.8
Sep	6	21	27.54	−29	28.7	2.075	2.983	149	+8.0
	16	21	21.58	−29	35.6	2.154	2.985	139	+8.2

1 Ceres – *cont.*

		2000.0 RA		Dec.		Geo-centric Distance	Helio-centric Distance	Elong-ation	Visual Magni-tude
		h	m	°	′			°	
	26	21	17.87	−29	25.5	2.252	2.986	129	+8.3
Oct	6	21	16.66	−29	00.6	2.366	2.986	119	+8.5
	16	21	17.91	−28	23.6	2.491	2.987	110	+8.7
	26	21	21.46	−27	36.5	2.624	2.987	102	+8.8
Nov	5	21	27.08	−26	41.1	2.761	2.987	93	+8.9
	15	21	34.45	−25	38.7	2.900	2.986	85	+9.0

3 Juno

		2000.0 RA		Dec.		Geo-centric Distance	Helio-centric Distance	Elong-ation	Visual Magni-tude
		h	m	°	′			°	
Jan	5	4	55.82	− 0	18.3	1.169	2.033	142	+7.9
	15	4	53.61	+ 1	08.5	1.243	2.048	133	+8.2
	25	4	54.64	+ 2	48.9	1.332	2.064	125	+8.4
Feb	4	4	58.83	+ 4	35.5	1.434	2.082	117	+8.6
	14	5	05.93	+ 6	21.8	1.546	2.101	110	+8.9

4 Vesta

		2000.0 RA		Dec.		Geo-centric Distance	Helio-centric Distance	Elong-ation	Visual Magni-tude
		h	m	°	′			°	
Jan	5	7	08.00	+22	46.5	1.553	2.536	179	+6.2
	15	6	56.89	+23	31.4	1.560	2.531	168	+6.4
	25	6	46.86	+24	10.6	1.595	2.525	156	+6.7
Feb	4	6	39.08	+24	42.5	1.655	2.519	144	+6.9
	14	6	34.33	+25	07.4	1.737	2.513	133	+7.1
	24	6	32.89	+25	26.0	1.834	2.506	122	+7.2
Mar	6	6	34.72	+25	39.1	1.944	2.499	113	+7.4
	16	6	39.55	+25	47.1	2.061	2.492	104	+7.6
	26	6	47.01	+25	49.8	2.183	2.485	95	+7.7
Apr	5	6	56.72	+25	46.8	2.305	2.477	88	+7.8
	15	7	08.32	+25	37.6	2.426	2.469	81	+7.9
	25	7	21.47	+25	21.6	2.543	2.460	74	+8.0
May	5	7	35.89	+24	58.1	2.656	2.452	67	+8.1

4 Vesta – *cont.*

		2000.0				Geo-centric	Helio-centric	Elong-	Visual Magni-
		RA		Dec.		Distance	Distance	ation	tude
		h	m	°	′			°	
	15	7	51.33	+24	26.9	2.762	2.443	61	+8.1
	25	8	07.56	+23	47.5	2.861	2.434	55	+8.2
Jun	4	8	24.42	+22	59.9	2.952	2.425	50	+8.2
	14	8	41.73	+22	04.2	3.034	2.416	44	+8.2
	24	8	59.40	+21	00.5	3.107	2.406	39	+8.2
Jul	4	9	17.31	+19	49.0	3.171	2.397	34	+8.2
Nov	11	13	15.56	– 2	21.5	3.066	2.269	30	+8.0
	21	13	34.10	– 4	03.5	2.990	2.259	36	+7.9
Dec	1	13	52.64	– 5	40.3	2.905	2.250	41	+7.9
	11	14	11.12	– 7	10.8	2.812	2.242	46	+7.9
	21	14	29.50	– 8	34.2	2.712	2.233	51	+7.9
	31	14	47.66	– 9	49.4	2.606	2.225	57	+7.8

Meteors in 2006

Meteors ('shooting stars') may be seen on any clear moonless night, but on certain nights of the year their number increases noticeably. This occurs when the Earth chances to intersect a concentration of meteoric dust moving in an orbit around the Sun. If the dust is well spread out in space, the resulting shower of meteors may last for several days. The word 'shower' must not be misinterpreted – only on very rare occasions have the meteors been so numerous as to resemble snowflakes falling.

If the meteor tracks are marked on a star map and traced backwards, a number of them will be found to intersect in a point (or a small area of the sky) which marks the radiant of the shower. This gives the direction from which the meteors have come.

The following table gives some of the more easily observed showers with their radiants; interference by moonlight is shown by the letter M.

Limiting Dates	**Shower**	**Maximum**	**RA**		**Dec.**	
			h	m	°	
Jan 1–6	Quadrantids	Jan 3	15	28	+50	
April 19–25	Lyrids	Apr 22	18	08	+32	
May 1–8	Aquarids	May 4	22	20	−01	
June 17–26	Ophiuchids	June 19	17	20	−20	
July 29–Aug 6	Delta Aquarids	July 29	22	36	−17	
July 15–Aug 20	Piscis Australids	July 31	22	40	−30	
July 15–Aug 20	Capricornids	Aug 2	20	36	−10	
July 23–Aug 20	Perseids	Aug 12	3	04	+58	
Oct 16–27	Orionids	Oct 20	6	24	+15	
Oct 20–Nov 30	Taurids	Nov 3	3	44	+14	
Nov 15–20	Leonids	Nov 17	10	08	+22	M
Nov 27–Jan	Puppids-Velids	Dec 9–26	9	00	−48	M
Dec 7–16	Geminids	Dec 14	7	32	+33	M
Dec 17–25	Ursids	Dec 22	14	28	+78	

Some Events in 2007

ECLIPSES

There will be four eclipses, two of the Sun and two of the Moon.

3 March:	Total eclipse of the Moon – Australia, Asia, Africa, Europe, North and South America
19 March:	Partial eclipse of the Sun – central and eastern Asia, Alaska
28 August:	Total eclipse of the Moon – the Americas, Pacific Ocean, Australasia, eastern Asia
11 September:	Partial eclipse of the Sun – South America (except the northern part), Falkland Islands

THE PLANETS

Mercury may be seen more easily from northern latitudes in the evenings about the time of greatest eastern elongation (7 February) and in the mornings about the time of greatest western elongation (8 November). In the southern hemisphere the corresponding most favourable dates are around 22 March (mornings) and 29 September (evenings).

Venus is visible in the evenings from the beginning of the year until early August. From mid August until the end of the year it is visible in the mornings.

Mars is at opposition on 24 December in Gemini.

Jupiter is at opposition on 5 June in Ophiuchus.

Saturn is at opposition on 10 February in Leo.

Uranus is at opposition on 9 September in Aquarius.

Neptune is at opposition on 13 August in Capricornus.

Pluto is at opposition on 19 June in Sagittarius.

Part II

Article Section

Huygens Makes History: Successful Landing on Titan

GARRY E. HUNT

Dominated by nitrogen, methane and a variety of other carbon-based molecules, conditions on Titan are believed to resemble those on Earth 4.6 billion years ago, although Titan is far colder. This planet-sized satellite of Saturn has always been a major object in planetary missions as we seek to understand our Solar System.

A SUCCESSFUL LANDING ON TITAN'S SURFACE

History was made on the 14 January 2005, when the ESA Huygens spacecraft landed successfully on the surface of Titan. This historic landmark was achieved following the epic seven-year journey through the Solar System and final tantalizing journey of three weeks after leaving the mothercraft Cassini in Saturn's orbit on 25 December 2004. Having been launched as part of the NASA, ESA, Italian Space Agency Cassini–Huygens mission on 15 October 1997, the probe Huygens now rests frozen at a temperature of −180°C on Titan's landscape, a symbolic finale to the engineering and flight phase of this historic mission.

Huygens entered the upper atmosphere 1,270 kilometres (789 miles) above Titan at 1013 GMT on 14 January and at a speed of about 22,000 km/h (13,700 mph). A series of three parachutes slowed the craft to just 24 km/h (15 mph). In the lower atmosphere it drifted sideways at about 1.5 metres per second. The probe rocked more than expected in the upper atmosphere. During its descent through high-altitude haze, it tilted at least 10 to 20 degrees. Below the haze layer, the probe was more stable, tilting less than 3 degrees.

Finally, when the probe landed, it was not with a thud, or a splash, but a 'splat'. It landed in Titanian 'mud'. After many theories about the expected properties of Titan, the landing was a lot friendlier than anticipated. But that was not the end. The descent module was designed so that a 20-watt landing lamp should turn on 700 metres above the surface and illuminate the landing site for as long as 15 minutes after touchdown. It worked perfectly; indeed, it was still shining more than an hour later, when Cassini moved beyond Titan's horizon for its continuing exploratory tour not only of Titan but of the entire Saturnian system.

This certainly was an historic landing, and the first results are providing many fascinating results on Titan's atmosphere, surface and local environment.

DESCENT ACTIVITIES

The descent through Titan's atmosphere was planned meticulously with a large number of commands, checks and double checks, to perform operations to slow down the craft, provide engineering information and start the scientific measurements during the descent. All these vital engineering and scientific data were then sent back to the Cassini spacecraft in orbit around Saturn and subsequently relayed to Earth, for analysis by the teams anxiously waiting there.

At an altitude of 1,270 kilometres above the surface of Titan, the pilot parachute was deployed. This was the probe's smallest parachute, only 2.6 metres in diameter, and its sole purpose was to pull off the probe's rear cover, which protected Huygens from the frictional heat of atmospheric entry. A further 2.5 seconds after the pilot parachute was deployed, the rear cover was released, the pilot parachute pulled away and then the main parachute, which is 8.3 metres in diameter, unfurled.

It was at this stage that Huygens began its transmissions to Cassini. At an altitude of 160 kilometres the front shield was released and the probe began to get ready for the scientific measurements as the inlet ports were opened up for the Gas Chromatograph Mass Spectrometer and Aerosol Collecting instruments, and booms extended to expose the Huygens Atmospheric Structure instruments. The Descent Imager/Spectral Radiometer then obtained the first images of the surface while further measurements of the atmosphere were made. These images included the historic panorama picture which will, I feel sure, become part of every future astronomy textbook for many years to come.

A 3-metre drogue parachute was deployed at about 125 kilometres altitude, since the large main parachute would have slowed Huygens down so much that the batteries would not have lasted to the surface. The drogue allowed the craft to descend at the correct speed to collect the maximum amount of data. At 60 kilometres altitude, the surface proximity sensors – a pair of radar altimeters – were activated. The last instrument to be activated fully was the Gas Chromatograph Mass Spectrometer, which began sampling the atmosphere. Finally, the Descent Imager/Spectral Radiometer lamp turned on. The light was particularly important for the 'Spectral Radiometer' part of the instrument to enable it to determine the composition of Titan's surface accurately.

Sadly, not everything worked as planned. The loss of one of the Huygens' communications channels and a configuration problem with one of Cassini's receivers meant that the Doppler analysis to measure the winds in Titan's atmosphere could not be made as originally planned. Fortunately, spacecraft engineers and scientists are imaginative and resourceful so they used a global network of radio telescopes to measure the speed of the winds faced by Huygens during its descent through the atmosphere of Titan. It was a great global achievement.

The safe descent of Huygens to the surface of Titan is not the end, but the beginning of this part of the mission. Now we have decades of detailed scientific analyses to be made of these unique measurements to help us improve our understanding of the distant world of Titan.

SURFACE AROUND THE LANDING SITE

The landing site area has been described by mission scientists as 'muddy'. A probe on the bottom of the lander found the soil to be uniformly soft – like wet sand – under a thin crust on top. The lander itself settled about 10 or 15 centimetres (4 or 6 inches) into this material, and the probe's warmth apparently evaporated liquid permeating the soil. The other indication was a puff of methane gas, released from the soil when the hot spacecraft landed. It showed that methane must be present in large quantities near the surface. Confirming this, a mass spectrometer aboard Huygens also found that the amount of methane in the atmosphere jumped by 30 per cent near the surface.

The first images of the surface of Titan brought to an end the years of speculation about this distant object. They showed lots of evidence for many familiar Earth-like processes of precipitation and erosion and abrasion – but they had been sculptured in a weird and cold world, with exotic materials.

These first impressions suggest the Titan surface is a smoggy world; an arid, icy desert, where periodic storms of methane rain create transient rivers that wash sooty soil from icy highlands out to short-lived pools and lakes. The pools dry up, perhaps sinking into a sandy soil of glass-like water ice, and then the Titanian desert waits for another methane storm. Some scientists have suggested this picture is strangely similar to the climate in Arizona, and it may be typical of arid regions on the Earth. So far there is no evidence of any liquid in any of these features, but there are suggestions of streams, rivers and even rainfall.

The materials involved are familiar ones – water, natural gas and smog particles – but under Titan's temperature conditions they behave in quite unfamiliar ways. The Huygens landing site appears to

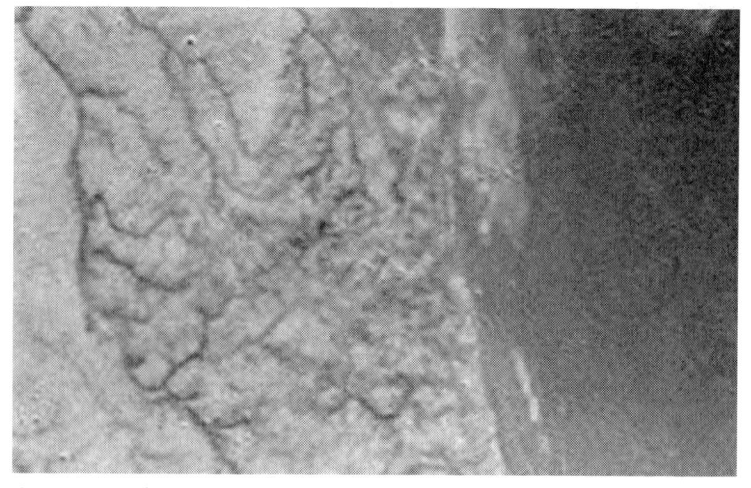

Figure 1. One of the first raw images returned by the Descent Imager/ Spectral Radiometer (DISR) instrument on the Huygens probe during its successful descent, taken from an altitude of 16.2 kilometres with a resolution of approximately 40 metres per pixel. It apparently shows short, stubby drainage channels leading from a high-ridge area to a shoreline. (Image courtesy of European Space Agency, NASA Jet Propulsion Laboratory and University of Arizona.)

have steep hills, arroyos or dry gullies choked with sediment, and dry flat valleys with liquid pools. But these features are made of very different materials on Titan. Where Arizona's hills are made of silicate rocks, Huygens's hills are made of 'frozen hard water ice'. The hills are fairly steep, with heights varying some 100 metres over a span of a kilometre, and they exert topographic control over the pattern of the drainage visible in the Huygens images.

Titan's surface is at a frigid temperature, and at the landing site it was 93K, −180°C. Whereas the Earth has an oxidizing atmosphere and very little fuel for our oxygen to burn, Titan has a reducing atmosphere that is abundant with methane, familiar to us as natural gas – but no oxygen.

The similarity stems from the fact that the temperature is so cold that methane cycles between gas and liquid in the same way water does on Earth. The Titan atmosphere has a troposphere with weather systems where the precipitation is liquefied natural gas, which runs off the land in rivers to flow out on to vast, smooth floodplains, where it soaks into the ground and evaporates back to the atmosphere.

As soon as Huygens descended below Titan's high-altitude smog deck, its images changed from blank views of murk to jaw-dropping snapshots of rugged terrain with branched channels running to an apparent shoreline, which even shows signs of beaches, on the edge of what looked like a wide, dark sea. Huygens landed a few kilometres 'offshore'; the 'sea' proved to be bare ground, though still damp with liquid methane just below the surface. The ground right around the lander looked for all the world like a pebbly tide flat on Earth.

The landing site is close to a border between the bright and dark regions seen from space. Stereo images of the bright headland reveal a ridgeline as much as 100 metres high in a frame 1 kilometre wide, for an average slope of 10 per cent (which would be considered a dangerous slope for a road on Earth). But the grade is far from smooth. The uplands are cut almost everywhere by channels with dark-stained bottoms. It is likely that rainfall washes dark material off the Titanian 'bedrock', which consists of permanently frozen water ice, not rock, and deposits it on the channel bottoms and the plain.

Titan's surface would look orange as the dim sunlight filters through high-altitude orange smog. The lumps are probably water ice, Titan's equivalent of rock. The ones in the foreground are roughly fist-size. Note their rounded shapes.

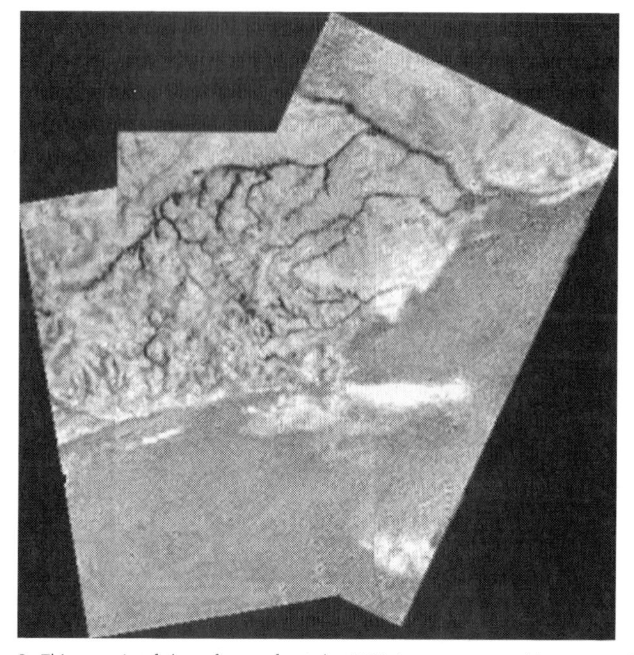

Figure 2. This mosaic of three frames from the DISR instrument provides unprecedented detail of the high-ridge area including the flow down into a major drainage channel from different sources. (Image courtesy of European Space Agency, NASA Jet Propulsion Laboratory and University of Arizona.)

The 'dirt' is apparently a mix of ice bits eroded from the land and tarry hydrocarbons that have fallen out of the photochemical smog blanketing the upper atmosphere. The smog is formed by sunlight breaking methane molecules apart. Some scientists are puzzled why the methane remains. Perhaps it is to compensate for the methane loss in the upper atmosphere and then new methane must still be welling up from Titan's interior. As Toby Owen of the University of Hawaii commented, 'It might have rained yesterday.'

The rounded 'pebbles' on the ground at the lander site are probably dirty water ice, shaped by flowing liquid just like pebbles of rock that are rolled in rivers and waves on Earth. On a larger scale, low elevations on the plain appear to have been sculpted by flowing liquid. The dark, oval features seen in the surface images may be pools of dried-up liquid.

These initial results suggest a location which is like that of a terrestrial desert, such as Arizona, familiar to so many of the project scientists. The 'river beds' appear to be dry some of the time and so the rain sinks below the surface. However, on Titan, the 'groundwater' under Huygens is just a few centimetres, rather than many metres, down as we find on Earth.

Figure 3. Image of the Huygens landing site taken on 14 January 2005. The rounded lumps are probably water ice, Titan's equivalent of rock. The ones in the foreground are roughly fist-size. Titan's surface would look orange as the dim sunlight filters through high-altitude orange smog. (Image courtesy of European Space Agency, NASA Jet Propulsion Laboratory and University of Arizona.)

SURFACE OF TITAN AWAY FROM THE LANDING SITE

The Huygens landing site is just one point on the surface of Titan, so it is correct to question whether these observations are representative of the satellite as a whole. Although we cannot gain measurements from other surface sites directly from Huygens, the Cassini spacecraft is in orbit around Saturn and has periodic close encounters with Titan to provide other views and measurements to add to the jigsaw puzzle of information. The radar observations from Cassini are particularly instructive as they are able to observe the surface features with a resolution ranging from about 0.3–1.7 kilometres, without being affected by the ubiquitous haze. The images are created using synthetic aperture radar (SAR) when a radar signal at a wavelength of 2.3 centimetres is scattered by Titan. The brightness in SAR images can result from the slope of the surface, the roughness of the surface and the intrinsic radio-scattering properties of the surface material. SAR images can be difficult to interpret without any easily recognizable topographic features.

A huge basin called 'Circus Maximus', about 444 kilometres in diameter, which is nearly 10 per cent of the diameter of Titan, has been seen in the north-east of the bright region on Titan known as Xanadu. This is a multi-ringed impact basin which some scientists consider could have been created by a massive impact, such as by a comet. The pattern of brightness suggests that there is topography associated with this feature; for example, in the centre of the image there appear to be mounds each about 25 kilometres across. Since they are dark on their lower edges that face away from the radar and bright on the opposite face, they must be elevated above the surrounding terrain.

Bright dendritic channels can also be seen on the surface, and this intrinsic brightness suggest the channels may contain pebbles or cobbles a few centimetres in diameter. This would be similar to the features at the landing site.

The crater has similarities to multi-ringed structures on the Moon and other Solar System bodies. Such craters are also important to planetary geologists in order to estimate the age of planetary surfaces and the history of geologic events. The smaller crater appears relatively fresh and well preserved, and it is thought to be a younger feature than others seen on the surface. The geologists concerned estimate the age of

Figure 4. A huge circular feature, approximately 440 kilometres (273 miles) across, appears in this image taken with Cassini's radar mapper during the spacecraft's third close flyby of Titan on 15 February 2005. Named Circus Maximus, it resembles a large crater or part of a ringed basin. Seams between radar segments are visible as horizontal, sawtooth-shaped lines. (Image courtesy of NASA Jet Propulsion Laboratory and University of Arizona.)

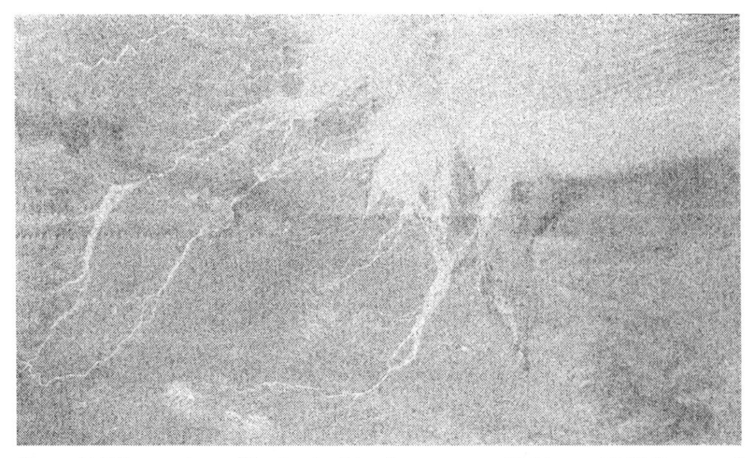

Figure 5. This area, imaged by the Cassini radar system on 15 February 2005, lies east of Circus Maximus. The white streaks could be channels in which fluid flowed from the slopes of Circus Maximus towards the bright area at upper right. The longest channel here is about 200 kilometres (124 miles) long. The fluid was most likely liquid methane. (Image courtesy of NASA Jet Propulsion Laboratory and University of Arizona.)

the surface may be less than a billion years, that the surface has been modified, and that the objects seen relate to events in the most recent quarter of the age of the Solar System.

Scientists are also fascinated by a dark lake-like feature measuring 234 × 73 kilometres. There is no agreement on the identification; possible explanations are a liquid hydrocarbon lake, or a dried-up lake with dark deposits, or even a lava lake. It is certainly a puzzling feature.

HUYGENS' MEASUREMENTS AND TITAN'S ATMOSPHERE

We knew from ground-based and the Voyager observations that Titan's atmosphere is made up almost entirely of nitrogen, with less than 1 per cent of methane in the upper layers. With a surface pressure of 1.5 times that of the Earth and with a surface temperature of a mere 93K, Titan is quite different from our planet. But Titan and Earth have some similarities, as they are both bodies with nitrogen-rich atmospheres, so there is the possibility of learning more about the evolution and development of the early Earth, as well as planetary atmospheres in general, from this encounter with Titan. It is also apparent from the SAR images and the pictures from the surface that the atmosphere of Titan has an important rôle in protecting the surface from bombardment by interplanetary objects.

On Titan it is thought that about 95 per cent of the disassociated methane is irreversibly converted into acetylene and ethane. The constant removal of methane from the upper atmosphere by chemical reactions will require a constant replenishment from the surface. The structure of the atmosphere will regulate these processes and the supply of materials from the lower to the upper levels in the atmosphere. The probe measurements of methane are very similar to those made from the Earth. In the upper atmosphere, nitrogen is the dominant gas but in the lower atmosphere the chemistry changes and methane becomes much more abundant. This is similar to the Earth and the behaviour of water vapour between the stratosphere and the troposphere.

There are several other hydrocarbon species that are present in Titan's atmosphere, including ethane and acetylene, and small differences in pressure and temperature conditions could have made some of these other substances more important on Titan's surface.

There have been some surprises too from the continuing Cassini observations. During its closest flyby of Saturn's moon Titan on 16 April 2005, the Cassini spacecraft came within 1,027 kilometers (638 miles) of the moon's surface and found that the outer layer of the thick, hazy atmosphere is brimming with complex hydrocarbons. Hydrocarbons containing as many as seven carbon atoms were observed, as well as nitrogen-containing hydrocarbons (nitriles). Titan's atmosphere is composed primarily of nitrogen, followed by methane, the simplest hydrocarbon. The nitrogen and methane are expected to form complex hydrocarbons in a process induced by sunlight or energetic particles from Saturn's magnetosphere. However, it is surprising to find the plethora of complex hydrocarbon molecules in the upper reaches of the atmosphere. Titan is very cold, and complex hydrocarbons would be expected to condense and rain down to the surface.

We now need to understand the source of the organic material in the Solar System. Interstellar clouds produce abundant quantities of organic material, which may be viewed as the dust and grains incorporated in comets. This material may have been the source of early organic compounds on Earth from which life formed. Atmospheres of planets and their satellites in the outer Solar System, while containing methane and molecular nitrogen, are largely devoid of oxygen. In this non-oxidizing environment, under the action of ultraviolet light from the Sun or energetic particle radiation from Saturn's magnetosphere in this case, these atmospheres can also produce large quantities of organic material. Titan is the prime example in our Solar System. This same process is a possible pathway for the formation of complex hydrocarbons on early Earth. Fortunately another thirty-nine flybys of Titan are planned during the Cassini mission which may provide the necessary observations to answer this question.

Another uncertainty relates to argon, as currently only A^{40} has been detected. Additional isotopes of argon, along with other noble gases like krypton and xenon, should have been present in Titan's primordial atmosphere when it was first formed, but they appear to be absent. These noble gases occur in our atmosphere, on Venus and on Jupiter, but so far they have not been found on Titan. An explanation of this situation has important implications for the origin of Titan.

Knowledge of the weather systems is crucial for understanding the mixing and distribution of the atmospheric constituents. Winds on

Titan are found to be blowing in the direction of Titan's rotation (from west to east) at nearly all altitudes. The maximum speed of roughly 120 metres per second (430 km/h) was measured about ten minutes after the start of the descent, at an altitude of about 120 kilometres. The winds are weak near the surface and increase slowly with altitude up to about 60 kilometres. This pattern does not continue at altitudes above 60 kilometres, where large variations in the Doppler measurements are observed. Scientists believe that these variations may arise from significant vertical wind shear. That the probe had a rough ride in this region was already known from the science and engineering data recorded on board Huygens. These simple statements hid the incredible effort by scientists and radio astronomers to gain this information. After a problem with the configuration of a Cassini receiver, a global network of radio telescopes in Australia, China, Japan and the United States enabled scientists to measure the speed of the winds faced by Huygens during its descent through the atmosphere of Titan.

Observations from the Cassini orbiter have shown an unusual bright spot approximately the size and shape of West Virginia just

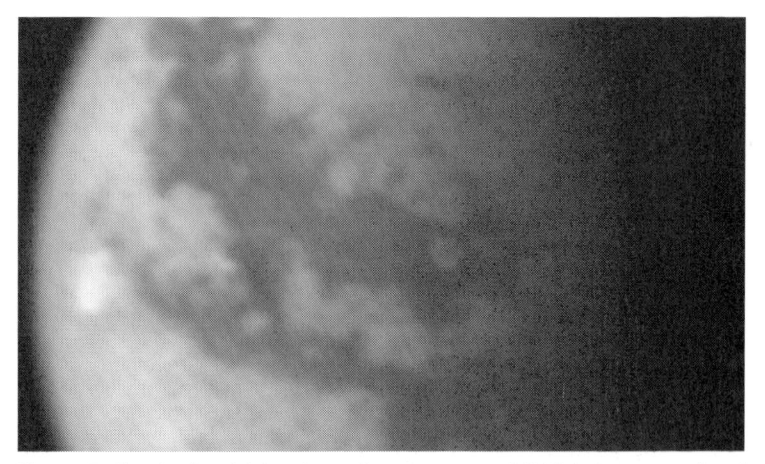

Figure 6. The visual and infrared mapping spectrometer (VIMS) instrument on board Cassini has found an unusual infrared-bright spot on Titan, as shown in this image acquired on 16 April 2005. In the centre are the dark lanes of the 'H'-shaped feature discovered from Earth and first seen by Cassini in July 2004. The bright area is about 500 kilometres (300 miles) across, and lies at the south-western edge of the 'H' feature, near Titan's limb. (Image courtesy of NASA Jet Propulsion Laboratory and University of Arizona.)

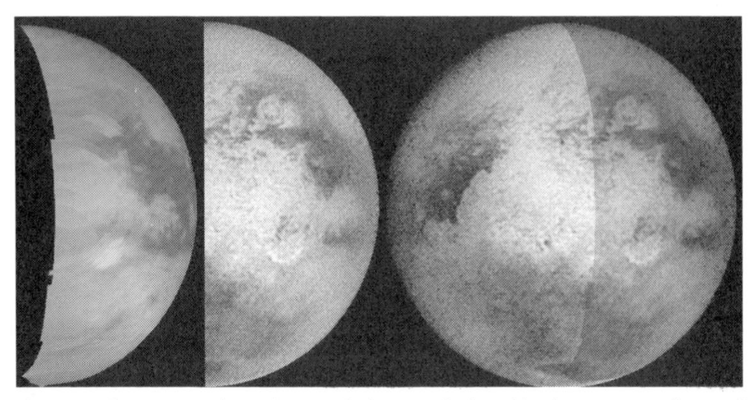

Figure 7. This montage shows the recently discovered infrared-bright spot as seen by VIMS (left), by the imaging science subsystem (centre) and a combination of both data sets (right). The strange, bright curving feature in the centre image was flagged as unusual and informally dubbed 'The Smile' by imaging team members in December 2004. Together (right) the images show that The Smile bounds the infrared-bright spot towards the south-east. (Images courtesy of NASA Jet Propulsion Laboratory and University of Arizona.)

south-east of the bright region now called Xanadu. At wavelengths shorter than 5 microns, the spot is not unusually bright. The strange spectral character of this enigmatic feature suggests it could be a surface colouration, a mountain range, a cloud or even a hot spot. This latter hypothesis will be tested with further observations during a subsequent flyby when the visual and infrared spectrometer will take night-time images of this area. If it is hot, it will glow at night.

There is still much to observe and understand with Titan.

Imaging Comets: A Beginner's Guide

MARTIN MOBBERLEY

Back in the 1980s, when this author started his comet-imaging career, taking a good photograph of a comet was a tricky business. Apart from sketching the appearance of a comet through the eyepiece, the only method of recording these nebulous visitors was by using photographic film and spending a night or two in the darkroom, immersed in all manner of noxious chemicals. Nowadays, with CCD equipment, things are much easier, but it is still just as difficult to take a better image than your rivals! Equipment may have improved but every other keen imager has the same equipment too. So how do you make sure your pictures of the next bright comet are up to the required standard?

Before we get too detailed, let us start at the beginning as, for some readers of the *Yearbook*, this may be their first foray into the world of astronomy.

When is the next good comet coming our way?

These days the vast majority of new comet discoveries are made by two prolific robotic telescope systems called LINEAR (Lincoln Laboratories Near Earth Asteroid Research) and NEAT (Near Earth Asteroid Tracking). The two LINEAR telescopes are based in New Mexico and NEAT's telescopes are based at Mt Palomar and Hawaii. More than 1,200 comets are known, with the vast majority (more than 1,000) having periods of hundreds or thousands of years; these long-period comets tend to produce the spectacular Hale–Bopps and Hyakutakes. A few shorter-period comets like Halley (orbital period 76 years) can be spectacular, but, in the main, spectacular comets are just seen once.

LINEAR and NEAT are such powerful patrols that they usually alert us to incoming bright comets a year or two before they peak in brightness; however, some comets sneak through and a few are still

Figure 1. The author with his main instrument: a Celestron 14 on a Paramount ME mounting. (All photographs courtesy of the author.)

discovered by amateurs. In recent years the amateur astronomers Machholz, Tucker, Juels, Holvorcem, Yeung, Bradfield, Tabur, Hoenig, Utsunomiya, Ikeya, Zhang, Kudo, Fujikawa, Jones, Snyder, Petriew and Murakami all snatched discoveries from LINEAR and NEAT, and the comets they bagged peaked in brightness a few weeks later. How did LINEAR and NEAT miss these comets?

Well, the majority were missed because they approached the Inner Solar System from the southern part of the sky and were close to the Sun's glare as they moved further north. LINEAR and NEAT cannot patrol below declinations of 35°S and they generally avoid regions within 90° of the Sun. Another way a comet can sneak through is if it is intrinsically small, or just plain inactive, until it flares up at perihelion. In this case it may be too faint for LINEAR or NEAT to detect but, when it gets really close to the Sun, the brightness will rocket, placing it within amateur discovery range. So, as we can see, there are two types of good comets to prepare for: those we have plenty of warning for and those that are discovered when they are almost at their brightest. Either way, we need to be prepared.

Websites – a mine of information

There are a variety of good comet websites, and a search engine like Google will pick the best ones out with no difficulty. At the time of writing my favourite ones are the following:

The British Astronomical Association's Comet Section
http://www.ast.cam.ac.uk/jds
This is a comprehensive mine of information, primarily for the visual observer, but it lists the current brightness of all the best comets and ephemerides for finding them in the sky.

The *Astronomer Magazine*'s website
http://www.theastronomer.org
If you want to see the most recent amateur CCD images of good comets, essential for planning your own imaging sessions, the chances are there will be a good selection on the TA site.

The Minor Planets Center and Central Bureau for Astronomical Telegrams
http://cfa-www.harvard.edu/iau/Ephemerides/Comets/index.html
This is the definitive site for obtaining the ephemerides and orbital elements of all observable comets. There are also pages containing upgrades for popular software planetarium programs.

The *International Comet Quarterly* magazine home page can be found at http://cfa-www.harvard.edu/icq/icq.html
This is the only professional magazine devoted to comet observing.

Charles Morris runs a website at JPL which features quality images of the best comets around at http://encke.jpl.nasa.gov

Finally, the master of historical comet information and author of the awesome *Cometography* book volumes, Gary Cronk, runs a comet information page at http://cometography.com

Circulars

Websites alone will not alert you to a new bright comet discovery unless you meticulously check the websites every day. You need to know about new comet discoveries as soon as they occur. The definitive sources of astronomical information are the International Astronomical Union Circulars. These are issued from the Central Bureau for Astronomical Telegrams (CBAT) in Boston, Massachussets, and cost $72 per year for the online service. Amateur organizations such as the *Astronomer* magazine, the *British Astronomical Association* and *Sky & Telescope* magazines also offer email alert systems. For most bright comets a subscription to a monthly astronomy magazine will keep you informed but this will not always alert you in time for the bright amateur comet discoveries.

A systematic approach

Like everything else in life, practice makes perfect in comet imaging and dedication is essential to achieve the best results. You also need a certain amount of hunger to take a good image on a freezing cold night when you are tired and a warm bed is so tempting. If you are not at least partially obsessed by this hobby you will not get the best results. In astronomical imaging there are many subtle factors that can prevent success. Listed below are a few hurdles that have conspired to prevent me from taking a cracking comet picture from time to time. I have also listed some possible solutions.

1. Total cloud

It might be thought that this is an insurmountable hurdle. However, every cloud has a silver lining! Most cloudy nights are not totally cloudy. Indeed, cloud is often indicative of an active weather front sweeping through. Cloud gaps in this situation are often crystal clear and far preferable to the clear but horribly hazy skies seen when the UK is under a clear high-pressure system. When there are cloud gaps about and a bright comet is in the sky my telescope is waiting and ready for that gap near where the comet is. Remember, 60 seconds is all that is needed to clinch a fine shot with a cooled CCD camera. In windy conditions I have rolled my run-off sheds half over the telescope to shield it and still bagged a good picture!

2. Obstructions

Comets, by their very nature, tend to be at their best when physically nearest the Sun. This usually means that they are very close to the Sun in the sky. Thus, the best time to bag a comet is often an hour or two after sunset (in the western sky) or an hour or two before sunrise (in the eastern sky). In such circumstances the comet is nearly always very low down in the sky. Below an altitude of around 15° the comet will be rather blurred by the Earth's atmosphere. However, above 20° altitude a cracking picture can be obtained, provided there are no trees or buildings in the way. If you site your telescope near to a building, trees or a fence you can find yourself stuffed time and time again for all the bright comets! Also, if your observatory walls are too high a similar problem can arise. If you really are hemmed in by obstructions, a portable set-up or mounting the telescope on a balcony/flat roof must be seriously considered. If the obstructing objects are trees or bushes a chainsaw can do a wonderful job (assuming the foliage is yours and not the neighbour's). Comets rarely peak in brightness in the north or south, so choosing a site with good east and west horizons is a key consideration. In practice, most observers tend (for social reasons) to concentrate on evening comets so a good north-west to south-west view is highly desirable.

3. Unfriendly equipment and observatories

After more than twenty-five years of serious astrophotography and CCD imaging I can honestly say that I would rate equipment hassles as the number-one reason why many amateurs quickly lose the will to live when it comes to this hobby. Any equipment used for imaging comets should be tried and tested and used on a regular basis before that great comet arrives. There are an infinity of reasons why a picture of a comet might not be perfect but, in many cases, unfriendly equipment is to blame. There is no substitute for a well-used telescope that has, over the years, been tweaked to behave reliably and whose faults have all been ironed out.

As far as observatories are concerned, I vastly prefer the run-off shed or run-off roof building to the more traditional dome. In addition, I prefer a system that can be opened up to the night sky with the bare minimum of physical effort. If opening up the observatory is a daunting physical challenge you will simply lose interest. I have a variety of observatories in my back garden and all are geared to quick and easy

Figure 2. On 18 August 1990 the third magnitude Comet Levy passed within a quarter of a degree of the globular cluster M15. The comet was moving very fast, but it was virtually tailless, so the author decided on an 8-minute exposure ignoring the comet's motion. This nicely preserved the appearance of the globular cluster and made a very pleasing shot.

operation. Firstly, there are two lightweight run-off sheds housing 30- and 35-centimetre Schmidt–Cassegrains; one shed is wooden and one plastic. They both take only a minute to roll back.

In addition, there is what I call my 'kennel observatory', in which my 250-millimetre planetary-observing Newtonian is stored. In this observatory, the telescope itself glides out. All these systems are geared for easy use: the finders are properly aligned, the Schmidt–Cassegrains are precisely polar aligned, motorized focusers and dew heaters are fitted and routine maintenance is regularly carried out. As they are all used regularly I know all their faults and idiosyncrasies. The novice might be fooled into thinking that the glossy telescopes and CCD cameras in the magazine ads do everything for you. They do not! Almost all

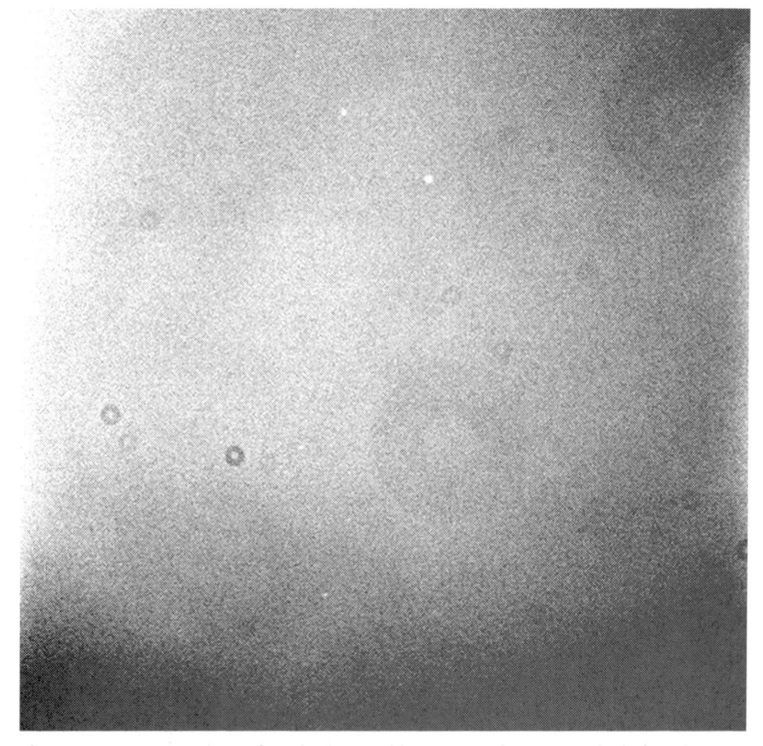

Figure 3. By imaging the uniform background brightness of a twilight sky before the stars come out, a record of the telescope and camera's vignetting and dust-speck characteristics is secured: a flat field. By dividing the comet image with this flat-field the image is transformed and looks, well, much flatter. A typical flat field may look horrible but it magically removes the shadows and dust-doughnuts from your next images.

telescopes and cameras have a learning curve associated with them: after a year or so of use you will know how to get the best out of them. For imaging comets, experience and familiarity with the equipment is absolutely essential.

4. Light pollution

If you live in a light-polluted area then comet imaging may not be your best option. The visibility of the subtle details in a comet's tail are greatly enhanced by a dark sky and almost wiped out by city street lights. Having said that, if you live on the edge of an urban area you may have certain directions where skyglow is not prohibitive. Another point to bear in mind here is that some brilliant sungrazing comets only peak in twilight. With such a brilliant comet, light pollution will be irrelevant. On crystal-clear nights, after a cold front or heavy rain, light pollution is less intrusive as the haze and dust responsible for reflecting the street-light glow is not present. Under such circumstances comet imaging can be carried out even from urban areas. CCDs are far more tolerant of light pollution than photographic film, especially at large-image scales (but not with wide-angle lenses). The advantage is created by the ease with which images can be stacked and contrast stretched. However, a dark sky is infinitely preferable to a polluted one.

5. Software hassles

Computer software hassles are one of the most stressful features of modern life. Almost every amateur astronomer uses software, but few are experts in those infuriating bugs that cause programs to crash or even corrupt the Windows Registry. Although PC operating systems are advertised as being ultra-friendly life-enhancing toys for everyone, there are times when we are all expected to have a degree in computer science to debug the faults. Fortunately, there is a good solution to this form of misery: the user support group. Most of the major CCD and software providers have free user groups. On the bigger groups on Yahoo, like the SBIG CCD User Group, there are literally hundreds of fellow amateurs, many of them experts, just waiting to answer or debate other users' software problems. Internet user groups are an absolute godsend for software hassles and I would strongly recommend anyone interested in CCD imaging to join one relevant to their equipment.

ADVANCED PLANNING WITH PLANETARIUM SOFTWARE

As soon as a new comet is discovered the imager will want to study its trajectory in the sky with particular regard to the obstructions on his or her horizon. In most cases, the observer will be looking to bag the comet when the Sun is at least 12° below the horizon, and the comet at least 15° above it. Really bright comets can be imaged with the Sun only

10° below the horizon but, ideally, the Sun should be 15° or 16° down to create a nice dark sky. In theory, 18° is the point at which twilight absolutely disappears, but I have found that 16° is as close as makes no difference. An excellent piece of freeware, available on the Internet, is CMTWIN32.EXE by W. Schwitteck. At the time of writing it could be downloaded from the BAA Comet Section site at

http://www.ast.cam.ac.uk/jds.

CMTWIN32 tells you the Right Ascension, Declination, Altitude and Azimuth of any comet at local midnight or when the Sun is six, twelve or eighteen degrees below your dusk or dawn horizon. It will even give you a plot of altitude versus azimuth for the months ahead . . . and it's free! Of the major commercial software planetarium packages my preference is for *Planet Pluto's Guide 8.0* and *Software Bisque's The Sky*.

Although *The Sky* has an impressive array of features I prefer *Guide 8.0* for user-friendliness, ease of installation and low cost. I particularly like *Guide*'s 'Add a Trail' feature, which, at a stroke, will plot a comet's path through the sky over the coming months. It is simplicity itself to add new comet elements to both *The Sky* and *Guide 8.0* from the Minor Planets Center website. Once a comet's path is on the screen you can hunt for 'photo opportunities', i.e., when the comet is going to pass near a bright galaxy or a nebula. Such cometary 'appulses' can lead to images that you will treasure for a lifetime. *The Sky* has a very slick feature whereby you can input your own horizon obstructions into the database as a set of lines, thus showing when trees and buildings will hide the comet!

COMETS CAN MOVE RAPIDLY!

One feature of comets (and asteroids) that complicates any kind of astrophotography, is the fact that they move. The complications are twofold. Firstly, unlike nebulae and galaxies, comets need to be relocated every night and always sit on top of a different star background. Secondly, allowance needs to be made for the comet moving during the imaging exposure. Personally, I vastly prefer a comet image in which the comet is frozen in space, with the stars as points. However, with a rapidly moving comet, i.e., one that is close to the Earth, you may wish to consider stacking multiple images, all centred on the comet's bright inner coma. Various astronomical image-processing packages allow you to do this and the end result is a comet against a background of streaked stars: the comet is flying through space. So how do you find out how fast the comet is moving, and for how long can you expose without the comet appearing blurred? With *Guide 8.0*, simply right-clicking on the comet and selecting 'More Info' will produce the cometary motion in arcminutes per hour of time at a specific position angle in the sky (one degree = 60 arc-minutes = 3,600 arcseconds)]. *The Sky* Object Information box provides similar information. My main instrument for imaging comets is a Celestron 14, which I use at an *f* ratio of 7.7. This gives me a focal length of 2.7 metres and an image scale of 1.5 arc-seconds per pixel with my SBIG ST9 CCD (20 micron pixels). At such a long image scale, a comet's motion is an important factor. I usually tolerate a maximum cometary drift of about 3 pixels as a 'rule of thumb', which translates into 4.5 arcseconds. For a 60-second exposure this equates to an hourly drift rate of 270 arcseconds per hour. For faster comets I usually stack the images using Richard Berry and James Burnell's excellent AIP4WIN software. Those with shorter focal-length systems can tolerate larger drifts without allowing for the comet's motion.

DIFFERENT COMETS: DIFFERENT EQUIPMENT

Comets can be very frustrating objects: they come in a variety of shapes and sizes. I have imaged comets with 49- and 35-centimetre telescopes that are as faint as 18th magnitude and are no more than dots in a crowded star field. I have also photographed zero-magnitude comets with camera lenses where 20° of tail were captured (and in the case of Comet Hyakutake, 40 more degrees were off the frame!). It is impossible to predict exactly how big a comet will be until it actually arrives; however, its proximity to both Earth and Sun will give a good idea of its size and brightness. Here are some specific examples of four recent good comets and a comparison of their magnitudes with their physical size.

Comet Hyakutake: magnitude zero; passed within 15 million kilometres from the Earth. Had a photographable tail more than 40° long for a week in late March 1996.

Figure 4. An image of the long-period comet Ikeya-Zhang, taken at its return in 2002. The author used a modest, 160mm aperture, f/3.3 Takahashi reflector (focal length 530mm) and a Starlight Xpress MX916 CCD. This 90-second exposure was taken on 6 April 2002 when the comet was a third magnitude object. The field is just under one degree high.

Comet Hale–Bopp: magnitude zero; did not pass close to Earth but it was a monster and had a photographable tail more than 15° long even when 200 million kilometres away in March 1997!

Comet 2001 Q4 (NEAT): passed within 50 million kilometres of the Earth in May 2004 at magnitude three. Even from hazy UK skies it had a photographic tail 3° long.

Comet Ikeya–Zhang: during March and April 2002 this comet produced an easily recordable tail three degrees long even when the comet was third and fourth magnitude and between 70 and 100 million kilometres from the Earth.

Figure 5. Comet Hyakutake on the night of 22–23 March 1996. The author took this 4-minute exposure from Tenerife with an 85mm f/1.2 aspheric Canon lens, stopped to f/1.8. The hypered 2415 film and Vixen mounting were provided by Dr Glyn Marsh. The tail of the comet stretches 15° in this photograph and the comet was magnitude zero at the time.

Figure 6. The small, but famous comet Encke made a rather close approach to the Earth, within 40 million kilometres, on 16 November 2003. At the time it was travelling across the sky at 450 arcseconds per hour, or 5 pixels per minute with the author's C14 at f/7.7. For this shot he decided to take brief 20-second exposures and stack eleven of them, centred on the comet's nucleus. Thus the comet appears to be flying through space and the stars are trailed.

It should be stressed that comets like these will produce a cracking picture, with a bit of care, even if only a fraction of the tail is recorded. In the case of Ikeya–Zhang I used a 530mm focal length reflector which only captured one degree of Ikeya–Zhang's long tail. Nevertheless, the results were very pleasing. However, some consideration of how a comet will fit on to your CCD is essential. The arc-tangent of the CCD chip size/focal length will give your system's field coverage so, for example, a 10mm chip and 1,000mm focal length gives arc-tan (0.01) or 0.57°. As a general rule you may want to use 100 to 200mm camera lenses for the brightest zero- to second-magnitude comets, 200 to 500mm for third- and fourth-magnitude comets and telescopes or long lenses for the rest. However, see my notes on image mosaicing for an alternative approach.

DIGITAL SLRs FOR COMET WORK

The telescope choices are further complicated by the increasingly affordable range of excellent digital SLRs (DSLR) with removable lenses. Featuring large CCD and CMOS sensors with dimensions 0.66 the size of 36 × 24mm film, but without the reciprocity failure of that less sensitive medium, these are a serious alternative to CCD cameras. On the plus side, DSLRs are a self-contained package (no computer and cabling needed) and through-the-lens/telescope focusing is a huge benefit. On the minus side, the colour sensors in DSLRs are not as sensitive as dedicated astronomical CCDs and are not cooled either, so images are noisier. In addition, file sizes are typically in excess of a megabyte, and multi-megabytes in some cases. Nevertheless, for large comets, with tails spanning 10 degrees or more, a picture with a multi-megapixel DSLR will yield a photographic quality to an image, especially if a good dark frame is subtracted and/or if many images are stacked to reduce noise. A DSLR makes a good portable package too for those trips to dark sites, or foreign countries: there is no need to cart a laptop and cables around!

MOSAICING IMAGES

One technique I especially favour, even for big comets, is creating a mosaic of images along the comet's tail with a large telescope, rather than simply using a smaller telescope. There are a number of reasons why I like this approach. Firstly, a large aperture, long focal-length system, like that of my 35-cm Celestron 14, has superb resolution and light grasp and will detect very fine details that a smaller instrument would not. Secondly, I like to use the same instrument night after night, as then I have knowledge of all the instrument's idiosyncracies and a good set of dark frames and flat fields. I draw the line if the comet's head is bigger than a single CCD frame, but otherwise I prefer

Figure 7. A mosaic of six 80-second images down the tail of comet 2001 Q4 (NEAT) taken on 21 May 2004 when the comet was magnitude 3. Each frame is just over 10 arcminutes wide and so the total field width is one degree. Celestron 14 at f/7.7 and ST9XE CCD. Paramount ME mounting.

Figure 8. A mosaic of four 80-second images down the tail of comet 2002 V1 (NEAT) taken on 25 January 2003 when the comet was magnitude 5. Each frame covers just over 15 arcminutes and so the total field width is one degree. 30 cm LX200 at f/6.8 and ST9XE CCD.

this technique. The tricky aspects of the mosaic technique, which can be used for large galaxies as well as comets, are repositioning each frame along the tail and making the join between images as invisible as possible!

The first problem is solved by having an intimate knowledge of how accurately your telescope can be repositioned between exposures and remembering that, at high declinations, a movement in Right Ascension will be smaller than at zero Declination (because the lines of RA converge towards the pole). With bright comets it will be fairly obvious, when the first image downloads, which way the tail is pointing and, with a cool head and a bit of experience, moving the telescope in RA and Dec. (with plenty of overlap between frames) will become second nature.

Making the join between images invisible (almost) is best achieved by butting the images against each other and tweaking the brightness and contrast until the background sky looks the same shade of grey.

Figure 9. Perhaps the most famous comet of the twentieth century, the author bagged this photograph of Hale-Bopp on 30 March 1997 using ISO 400 Kodak colour film with a 160mm f/3.3 Takahashi Astrographic reflector. Using a separate guide telescope the author guided the exposure on the nucleus of the comet for fifteen minutes! Two types of tail, a bright dusty swath and a fainter, intricate, ion tail are shown, although much of the blue ion tail detail is lost in this black and white reproduction.

Figure 10. The inner coma of Hale-Bopp was so extraordinarily bright and active that even short exposures revealed a wealth of detail. The author obtained this CCD image by stacking four 2-second exposures taken with a 36 cm f/5 Newtonian.

This can be a problem if the image was taken in changing twilight conditions but, in a dark sky, it is relatively easy. I paste the mosaic together using a standard image-processing package such as *Paint Shop Pro* or *Adobe Photoshop*. In the former package I start with the image of the comet's head, enlarge the canvas size to accommodate all the images and then copy the images into the canvas by using the 'clone brush' feature, registering the position against stars that appear in the overlap zone between images. It is tricky and frustrating the first time you try it, but practice makes perfect! After the mosaic is completed I resize the whole composite to about 1,000 pixels wide. The resulting image has the wide field of a short-focus instrument and the penetration of a larger one: it also has a far greater tolerance to cometary movement than the full-size single images with the large telescope.

Well, that is pretty much everything I know about imaging comets, except to say that, in any area where excellence is the aim, there is no gain without pain. Anyone who succeeds in any form of astro-imaging will have plenty of disasters along the way and plenty of appallingly bad images you will never show anyone! But the nights when everything works well will reward you with images you will treasure for a lifetime. Good luck!

The Biology of Space

STEPHEN J. WAINWRIGHT

The stars in the night sky are said to be as numerous as the grains of sand on a beach. Moreover, the distances between the stars are enormous. Yet they are clustered together into galaxies; the galaxies form clusters which in turn form superclusters. These structures group together to form walls, between which are huge voids. The Universe is very, very big.

Using a variety of techniques, astronomers have discovered more than 150 mainly Jupiter- and Saturn-sized extrasolar planets (or exoplanets) orbiting main-sequence stars in our Galaxy. (For the latest information, visit the Extrasolar Planets Encyclopaedia at http://www.obspm.fr/encycl/encycl.html.) At present, it is extremely difficult to image extrasolar planets directly, and a variety of other innovative methods have been employed to infer their existence. However, it is still not possible to detect Earth-sized, rocky planets orbiting other stars. But telescope technology is advancing so fast that before long it will be possible to see extrasolar planets directly. All the evidence at the moment suggests that planetary systems may be commonplace in the Universe. Even though there is no direct evidence for the existence of rocky planets, such as the Earth, anywhere but in our Solar System, it seems likely that, if planetary systems were to form around other stars, they would consist of both types of planets that we have in the Solar System: gas giants and rocky planets.

If planetary systems are indeed common, it may seem likely that life might also be widespread in the Universe. We shall consider here whether that is likely to be true. We know, of course, that life *can* originate because we are here to contemplate these questions. Moreover, we also know that complex and intelligent life is possible for the same reason. It does not follow, however, that because not only life but also wonderfully variable and complex life has evolved on the Earth, that life, even simple life, exists anywhere else in the Universe at all. Natural selection and evolution have given rise to the vast array of life on the Earth, but all of this required life to originate in the first place; clearly, it did.

We need to consider a number of questions:

- Given that life did originate, how likely was it to have happened? Is biogenesis, the origin of life, *de novo*, from inanimate chemistry an extremely unlikely event, or is it something that is almost inevitable if the conditions are right?
- We also need to consider that if simple life forms such as bacteria originate on a planet, whether the subsequent evolution of complex life forms from the primitive forms is also inevitable, or whether special, much rarer, conditions are required for life to evolve into complex and maybe intelligent life forms.
- We need to ask whether conditions have always been suitable for the existence of life, or whether there are specific periods in the history of the Universe when the origin of life is possible, and whether there are other periods in the history of the Universe when life is impossible or much less likely.
- We need to think about where in the Universe life is possible; whether there are habitable zones in the Universe and also uninhabitable zones. Moreover, we need to consider whether habitable zones for complex life may be much more restricted than habitable zones for life itself. We also have to consider the scales at which these habitable zones exist.
- Of course, we also have to consider exactly what we mean by 'life' and how life might have originated by natural processes from non-living matter.

THE HYPOTHESIS OF PANSPERMIA

There is an idea that would drastically alter the probabilities of there being life elsewhere in the Universe. This idea basically puts off the problem of biogenisis (the origin of life) to some other time and some other place, but it does not solve the problem of biogenesis. This is the hypothesis of Panspermia, notable proponents of which have been Svante Arrhenius, Fred Hoyle and Chandra Wickramasinghe. In this hypothesis, the suggestion is that life originated elsewhere and that primitive life forms such as bacteria literally infest interstellar and interplanetary space.

These propagules of life are propelled through space by stellar winds and the pressure of light and may eventually reach planets suitable for their nurture and future development. Some of the evidence for this idea comes from spectroscopic studies of interstellar dust grains.

Similarities with the spectra of bacteria have been taken by some to be evidence supporting Panspermia. If this hypothesis were true, the probabilities of there being life elsewhere in the Galaxy would be increased, because life need only have originated once and would then slowly spread like a galactic plague throughout space. Another consequence of this hypothesis would be that life in different parts of the Galaxy might actually be related in the sense of having a common ancestor somewhere in the dim and distant past. In view of the velocities involved, it seems unlikely that any significant transfer of life between galaxies could have occurred in this way, but between stellar systems within a galaxy might not be out of the question.

Space is bathed with deadly radiation, and in the regions close to stars where the planets reside it is likely that any bacteria floating freely there might be killed. However, if they were shielded within dust particles, or covered by sooty deposits, then they might have enough protection to survive the harsh radiation environment.

The transfer of primitive life between planets within a planetary system seems more likely to be successful. We know that the impacts of asteroids on bodies such as the Moon and Mars have caused lunar and Martian rocks to be blasted away from their surfaces with sufficient energy for them to reach escape velocity and to be ejected from the parent body into interplanetary space. We also know that large numbers of lunar- and Martian-derived meteorites produced in this way have landed on the Earth throughout its history. It is also highly likely that some of the larger impacts that have occurred on the Earth have resulted in terrestrial meteorites, some of which could have landed on Mars. Many of these meteorites will have been sterilized by shock compression and drastic heating, and by the passage of enormous lengths of time before they finally make landfall; there are others that will not have suffered the same degree of heating and will have spent relatively short periods of time in space before landing on another planet. It thus seems that the seeding of planets with life within a planetary system is at least possible via this meteoritic exchange of rocky material. To appreciate the scale of the process and thus the likelihood that primitive life could have been transferred from one planet to another in the Solar System, we have to be aware of the fact that over the lifetime of the planet, the Earth could have received large amounts of Martian rock in this way. If primitive, microbial life was thus transferred across the Solar System, it is not impossible that our remote ancestors could have originated on Mars or that any traces of past or present Martian life that may be found by space probes could have had a terrestrial origin.

We shall, however, in the absence of evidence to the contrary, take the view here that terrestrial life originated on the Earth and that, if it exists elsewhere, it may have originated independently there.

WHEN DID IT BECOME POSSIBLE FOR LIFE TO ORIGINATE IN THE UNIVERSE?

The Universe is almost 14 thousand million (14 billion) years old, according to the latest estimates. However, the Sun and the Earth are only one-third of this age. A question that naturally arises is, was it possible for life to have originated elsewhere long before the Sun and its family of planets were formed? Indeed, is it possible that planets could have formed around stars like the Sun say 10 thousand million years ago, and now be extinguished because those stars have gone the way of our own Sun, which will, in about 5 thousand million years' time, swell to become a red giant and extinguish all life on Earth?

From a single cataclysmic event, nearly 14 billion years ago, everything in the Universe came into being. From an infinitesimal speck, and an unimaginably hot and superdense state, matter, space and time emerged – an event that has been dubbed the 'Big Bang', although it was no explosion of the type we understand, and there was no one to hear the 'Bang'. For a time, the Universe was opaque and seethed at unimaginable temperatures. From a 'soup' of subatomic particles, the building blocks of matter – protons and neutrons – were fashioned. One second after the Big Bang, at a temperature of a billion degrees, atomic nuclei began to form from these protons and neutrons. By the end of the third minute after the Big Bang, the first elements had been created – hydrogen, deuterium (heavy hydrogen), helium, with minute traces of lithium and other 'light' elements. As the Universe cooled, electrons were captured into closed orbits around the atomic nuclei. These were the simplest atoms, and hydrogen was present in the greatest quantities. Of the elements created in that early period, about 77 per cent was hydrogen and 23 per cent was helium. A hydrogen atom consists of a single, positive proton in its nucleus, surrounded by a negative electron space containing a single electron. Matter does not come simpler than this. Helium is not much more complex. It is basically formed from the fusion of four hydrogen atoms.

When gravity caused matter to clump together and form the very first stars to exist in the Universe, these stars contained virtually nothing but hydrogen and helium. There was no dust to coalesce to form planets around these stars, for there were none of the elements in existence from which interstellar dust is made. There could have been no life associated with the first stars to form in the young Universe, because life requires more complex elements than were present in those days. The stars are the factories in which these complex elements are manufactured and they only become available when the star 'dies'.

For most of its life a star shines by fusing hydrogen to helium in its core. How long a star lives depends upon its mass: the more massive the star, the shorter its life. The most massive stars die violently in catastrophic explosions called supernovae. Lower-mass stars such as our Sun or up to eight times as massive, die in less spectacular fashion. When a Sun-like star has exhausted the available hydrogen in its core, having fused it to helium, it fuses the hydrogen in an expanding shell around the core. As the star's central temperature climbs, eventually helium fusion is ignited in the core, producing 'ashes' of carbon and oxygen. The star bloats to a red giant, and when helium eventually fuses in a shell around the carbon–oxygen core, a series of convulsions throw off the star's outer layers, producing a planetary nebula. Eventually the remnant core will emerge through the expanding shells of gas as a white dwarf, which slowly fades away 'like a dying ember in a fire'. The veils of ejected material in the planetary nebula eventually disperse into the interstellar medium, enriching it with carbon, oxygen and some nitrogen, which were produced in the stellar interior.

In addition to the fusion of hydrogen and helium, a more massive star (more than eight times the mass of the Sun) undergoes a series of thermonuclear reactions in its core, resulting successively in the fusion of carbon, neon, oxygen and silicon. The star eventually develops a core of iron – and the game is up. Such massive stars end their days as supernovae, gigantic stellar explosions that eject most of the star's material into space at very high speeds, and in which even heavier elements are created.

All of these stellar 'deaths' share something in common: they end up returning elements that they have manufactured during their lives, or at the end of their lives, back into interstellar space. As billions of years pass, the clouds of interstellar dust and gas – now enriched with the heavy elements produced in the nuclear furnaces of long-dead stars – will collapse under gravity and new stars will be born. Our Sun, for example, born just 5 billion years ago, is about 70 per cent by mass of hydrogen, 28 per cent helium and about 2 per cent heavier elements. Such stars are born in an environment rich in interstellar dust that could coalesce to form planets. These planets will contain the elements that are necessary for life. This is a prerequisite of life.

WHERE IS IT POSSIBLE FOR LIFE TO ORIGINATE IN THE UNIVERSE?

We have already seen that planets and life require a particular type of parent star, enriched with heavy elements. They also require a star that will have a lifetime that is long enough for life to originate. Very massive stars live their lives at a hectic pace, and will likely die before life has had a chance to establish itself on any suitable planets that might orbit them. For example, a star with one solar mass will have a lifetime of about 10 billion years. Thus the Sun is about halfway through its life. Although life has been present on the Earth for almost 4 billion years, complex life has only been present for about the last 700 million years or so. If, on the other hand, a star were more massive than the Sun, but not greatly so, for example about 1.5 solar masses, it would have a lifetime of only 3 billion years. This means that although life might originate on a planet orbiting the star, there would most likely only be primitive life present by the time the star came to the end of its life. Conversely, a star with only half of the solar mass would have a lifetime about six times as long as the Sun, but it would only be 8 per cent as luminous as the Sun. Consequently, the habitable zone of such a star would be much closer to the star and there would be the inherent danger of close orbital tidal locking, where tidal effects bring about synchronous rotation of the orbiting planet. This causes one side of the planet always to face the star and the other side always to face away. The side facing the star would be baked dry and the side facing away from the star would be in perpetual frigid night. It is this kind of tidal locking that causes the Moon to have the same side facing Earth all of the time.

The location of a planet in relation to the star it orbits is also very important so far as possible life is concerned. There is a zone surrounding a star that can be thought of as the 'habitable zone'. The zone is defined basically as a region where water can exist in its liquid form, and is neither frozen nor at its boiling point. The inner limit of the habitable zone defines the position where conditions would be too hot and the outer limit where conditions would be too cold. In the Solar System, Venus is on the sunward side of the habitable zone where it is too hot, and Mars is at the outer boundary of the habitable zone where it is too cold. If a planet were too close to its parent star, its water would boil away and be lost for ever by photolysis (splitting by light) in the planet's upper atmosphere. If it were too far from the star, its water and carbon dioxide would freeze out at the poles. Neither of these scenarios are compatible with biogenesis. However, about the time that life originated on the Earth, the Sun was roughly 30 per cent fainter than it is now, and as the Sun gradually brightened the habitable zone moved outwards. The greenhouse gas components of the Earth's early atmosphere would have kept temperatures high enough to prevent the planet from freezing over.

Whether a planet is in the habitable zone or not depends on the type of organisms we are considering, because different life forms have different temperature tolerances. Complex organisms such as animal life and multicellular plants cannot tolerate temperatures above about 50°C. This would place the inner boundary of the habitable zone for these complex organisms further away from the Sun than it would be for, say, eukaryotic micro-organisms (e.g. protozoa, algae and fungi), which are able to tolerate temperatures as high as 60°C. Cyanobacteria (oxygen-producing photosynthetic blue-green bacteria) tolerate temperatures as high as 70°C, with some heterotrophic bacteria (which use an organic carbon source, i.e. they must eat others) existing at temperatures as high as 90°C. The heat-loving thermophiles and hyperthermophiles can withstand temperatures as high as 115°C. At the other boundary of the habitable zone, where conditions are freezing, we again find extremophile microbes that are able to live under these conditions. As we shall see later, it seems unlikely that life originated under the frigid conditions that are found at the outer edge of the habitable zone where Mars orbits. Any life that might hang on there is likely to have evolved to tolerate colder and colder conditions, as have some terrestrial life forms that make their living in icebergs or within the rocks of Antarctica. It seems likely that life originated in very hot aquatic environments on the Earth, in the vicinity of hydrothermal vents under very high temperatures and pressures.

There are three great domains of terrestrial organisms: the bacteria, the archaea and the eukaryota. We, animals, plants, fungi and protists are all eukaryota. The archaea superficially resemble bacteria, but their DNA reveals that they are vastly different from the bacteria. The archaea include inhabitants of some of the most extreme habitats on Earth. Some live near deep-ocean hydrothermal vents at temperatures well over 100°C. Others live around hot springs (such as at Yellowstone Park, Wyoming), or in extremely alkaline or acid waters. Some even thrive in petroleum deposits deep underground. There is a community of microbes in the Columbia River basalts that have been dubbed SLiME (subsurface lithoautotrophic microbial ecosystem). They live about 5 kilometres beneath the surface and survive by consuming the hydrogen given off by a reaction between basalt and groundwater. The environment around deep-sea hydrothermal vents (so-called black smokers) is pretty hostile, but here one finds heat-loving (thermophilic) bacteria that live with no sunlight, no oxygen and no food, just the chemicals in the hot water. Such chemoautotrophic organisms are the providers in the food chain, oxidizing sulphides to produce energy for synthesizing organic compounds. Species of tube worms and other life forms are the consumers. The existence of bacteria in these very hot, high-pressure and dark habitats has fuelled speculation that hydrothermal vents might be where life first appeared on Earth.

The picture we get is that habitable zones for primitive life are much broader than for complex, multicellular life. This means that there are potentially far more habitats available for primitive life forms than there are for complex life forms. The Earth is ideal for all life and as a result is replete with a prolific diversity of living organisms, ranging from primitive organisms that have evolved little if any since their origins, to great complex plants, and animals such as ourselves which have evolved even more remarkable properties that give rise to intelligence and the ability to contemplate life itself.

We have thought about the habitable zones around stars, but what about galaxies themselves? Are there types of galaxies, or regions within galaxies, that are more or less hospitable to life? The answer to this question is 'yes'. Elliptical galaxies are depleted in dust and little or no star formation is taking place in them. They contain some of the oldest stars in the Universe. These stars are of low metallicity and would be unlikely to provide the material of which planetary systems with life are made. Spiral galaxies, on the other hand, have regions of plentiful star formation, where supernovae continually seed the surrounding interstellar medium with heavy elements.

The Sun lies at a distance of almost 30,000 light-years from the centre of the Galaxy, towards the inner edge of a minor spiral arm (the Local Arm) where star density is quite low. This happens to be a region of high metallicity. Moreover, in regions of low star density it is much less likely that a nearby star will go supernova and sterilize any planets in the vicinity with the enormous blast of radiation that results. Above and below this region, in the disc of the Milky Way, are older stars with less-heavy elements. As we move out further still from the disc of the Galaxy, we come to the galactic halo, the realm of the globular clusters. The globular clusters contain stars as old as the Galaxy itself. They are 'metal-poor' and are packed at high densities.

WHAT WAS IT LIKE WHEN THE SUN AND PLANETS FORMED?

As mentioned previously, astronomers call the protoplanetary nebula from which the Sun and planets formed a 'metal-rich' nebula. To an astronomer, a metal is simply an element that is heavier than hydrogen or helium. To a chemist, metals are electropositive substances that are generally good conductors of electricity and heat, which form salts with non-metals, basic oxides with oxygen and alloys with other metals. So we can see that an astronomer's concept of a metal is somewhat simpler than that of a chemist.

In July 2003, Debra Fischer from the University of California at Berkeley presented the results of her team's research work at the International Astronomical Union's General Assembly in Sydney, Australia. They had studied 750 stars and came to the conclusion that 20 per cent of 'metal-rich' stars like our Sun have planets. As planets are made of heavy elements (the astronomers' metals), it is not surprising that they would form around stars that are also rich in metals – after all, they formed together from the same collapsing, metal-rich nebula.

As we have seen, such heavy elements are formed in the interiors of stars and are blown out into interstellar space on stellar winds, or as Sun-like stars end their lives as red giants, puffing off their outer layers into space. Super-massive stars end their lives as supernovae, huge stellar explosions in which the heaviest elements are formed and are blasted out into space. Every time such events take place, interstellar space becomes increasingly enriched with heavy elements.

The Sun and its family of planets formed when a nebula, a cloud of metal-rich gas and dust, collapsed under its own gravity to form a rotating disc. At the centre of this disc, material was collapsing under gravity and becoming more and more compressed. As it became more condensed it grew hotter inside, until finally the temperature at the core became hot enough to ignite the nuclear fusion reactions that generated huge amounts of energy, and a new star burst into life in the heavens. Our Sun was born. Surrounding the newly-born Sun was a flattened disc of dust and gas from which the planets gradually accreted and grew, sweeping up the disc material with their gravitational fields. The planets were born. The inner planets are small, rocky worlds, the outer planets are gas giants, with a ring of icy débris beyond (which includes Pluto). It is thought that stars and planetary systems form in a way approximating to this account. It seems likely, on theoretical grounds alone, that planetary systems have formed round other Sun-like stars, as Debra Fischer and her team concluded.

The comets formed in the outer regions of the Solar System in the region known as the Kuiper Belt, and many of them were gravitationally ejected out into the Oort Cloud,* while others were propelled towards the inner regions of the Solar System. The Earth formed through the accretion of planetesimals, comets, meteorites and dust. Basically, accretion involved the collision of these bodies with the growing Earth. Each large collision released enormous quantities of energy and the Earth would have been molten during the early stages. It is believed that one such collision involved the glancing impact of a planet about the size of Mars with the young, accreting Earth. A huge amount of débris was ejected during this impact and the material of the Earth and the impactor would have combined and melted, the iron content sinking to the centre of the Earth forming its iron core. The ejected

* The Oort Cloud is a roughly spherical region, stretching perhaps halfway to the Sun's neighbouring star, that is a vast repository for comets. This region was named for Jan Oort, but was independently proposed by Ernst Öpik.

material, comprising mainly lighter, mantle material, condensed to form our Moon. Although it took an enormous impact to produce the Moon, other, lesser collisions were taking place all of the time. During this era of intense bombardment, the Earth would have been totally inimical to life. It probably took less than 100 million years for the Earth to form by accretion. After the loss of the hydrogen, helium and other hydrogen-containing gases to space from the primitive Earth, it was virtually devoid of an atmosphere. It would take almost a billion years for the formation of the Earth to be more or less completed. Comets rained down on to the surface of the Earth, bringing with them water and other gases that along with volcanic gases escaping from the planet's interior, would form Earth's first atmosphere and oceans. Asteroids also bombarded the Earth, and it is possible that chondritic meteorites contributed as much or more water than did comets, as the Earth's oceans are not as rich in deuterium-containing water as were the three comets Halley, Hyakutake and Hale–Bopp. (Deuterium is a form of hydrogen that is twice as massive as normal hydrogen, because its nucleus contains a neutron as well as a proton.)

The surface of the early Earth was hot, the atmospheric pressure was high, and there were deep oceans. Comets also brought with them organic compounds that could have been prerequisites for biogenesis, the origin of life on this world. Giotto, the spacecraft that flew by Comet Halley in 1986, detected high proportions of organic materials in the dust grains streaming away from the nucleus to form the huge coma of the comet. On 28 September 1969 fragments of a carbonaceous chondrite meteorite fell near the Australian town of Murchison, Victoria. Characteristic of this type of meteorite, the Murchison meteorite was found to contain a considerable variety of organic materials, including many of biological relevance, such as amino acids with left-handed helicity, the only sort used by life on Earth. If comets and meteorites gave the Earth water and organic materials, one could say, they gave it life. It is not even necessary to invoke terrestrial chemistry as the producer of J.B.S. Haldane's 'primordial soup', or to invoke Stanley Miller and Harold Urey's experiment as evidence of the possibility of the natural synthesis of such a 'soup' that would contain many of the building blocks of life. The ingredients fall to the Earth, courtesy of celestial chemistry. Miller and Urey simulated what they thought was the primordial atmosphere of the Earth, comprising gases such as methane, hydrogen and ammonia in the presence of water.

They caused electrical sparks to pass through the mixture, and eventually the aqueous component became brown in colour and, upon analysis, yielded a number of organic materials including amino acids. It is now believed that their 'atmosphere' was not like the Earth's primordial atmosphere. However, this doesn't matter too much. What they showed was that, given certain conditions, inorganic chemicals in the presence of a suitable source of energy might have given rise to organic substances that might have provided the materials from which life arose. It turns out that chemistry of the sediments in the vicinity of hydrothermal vents on the deep-ocean floor provide the chemically reducing environment that Urey and Miller had assumed of the Earth's early atmosphere. They got it almost right; what they got wrong was the location and the source of energy.

WHAT IS LIFE?

There are probably as many definitions of life as there are branches on the tree of life. I shall use a simple one here. Life is that state of matter which takes energy from its environment and reproduces itself according to a self-contained blueprint. Even the simplest organisms are incredibly complex, and the problem of biogenesis (the origin of life from non-life) is not understood and possibly never will be. Informed speculation is the best that can be done at the moment.

The earliest organisms to be found preserved as fossils in the rocks come from the Apex Chert of Western Australia. Approximately 3.5 billion years ago, these rocks were sediments on the floor of an ancient sea or lake. The fossilized cells contained in these rocks contain examples that seem to be cyanobacteria, some closely resembling living organisms of today. It has become common practice to name the fossil cyanobacteria after their modern counterparts. The cyanobacteria can be thought of as living fossils. For example, the fossil *Paleonostoc* is named after its modern counterpart *Nostoc* (see Figure 1). The cyanobacteria, via photosynthesis, gave the Earth an atmosphere containing oxygen, paving the way for the complex life that was to ebb and flow in the aeons that were to follow. They survived the environmental catastrophes of impacts and astronomical cycles that time and time again saw the extinction of many of the species inhabiting the Earth, and remain almost unchanged to the present day. However, even these

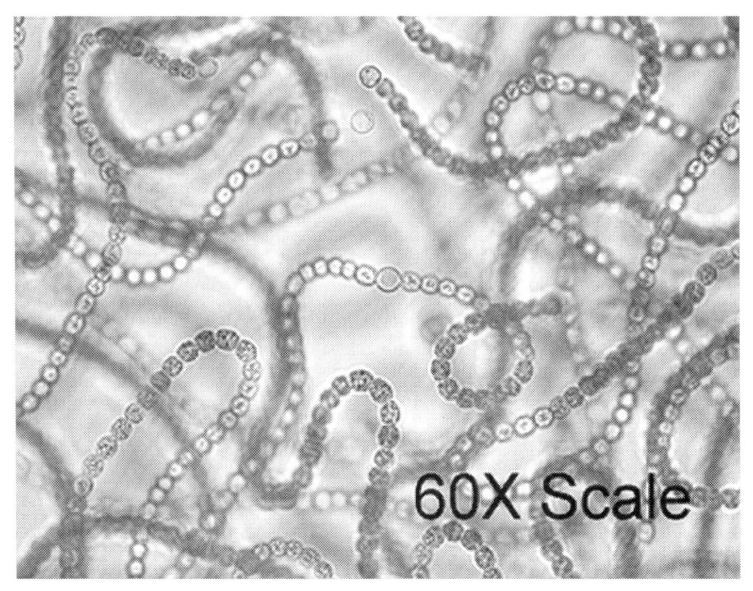

Figure 1. It has become common practice to name the fossil cyanobacteria after their modern counterparts. For example, the fossil *Paleonostoc* is named after its modern counterpart the cyanobacterium *Nostoc* shown here. (Image courtesy of Dr Morgan L. Vis, Ohio University, Athens, Ohio, USA.)

living fossils from the beginning of Earth's biology are very complex organisms.

The genetic blueprint that determines the structure and functioning of most living organisms is DNA (deoxyribonucleic acid). The DNA is in the form of a double helix, which codes for the synthesis of proteins. Many of these proteins are the enzymes that catalyse the reactions of life, allowing them to occur at normal temperatures and pressures. Moreover, enzymes are needed to catalyse the formation of new DNA chains, so we have a chicken-and-egg paradox. The functioning of the genetic blueprint is itself a complex process involving DNA, enzymes and RNA (ribonucleic acid) to mediate the synthesis of proteins from their component amino acids. If only one could get rid of the chicken-and-egg problem, that DNA codes for enzymes and enzymes are needed for the synthesis of DNA, one might be on the way towards the understanding of how such fundamental yet complex blueprint systems might have arisen.

In the 1980s, it was discovered that RNA molecules as well as proteins are capable of the catalysis of RNA splicing. Such catalytic RNAs have been named ribozymes. Moreover, it is known that certain viruses such as HIV, the human immunodeficiency virus, uses RNA and not DNA as its genetic material. It has been suggested that RNA came before DNA and maybe even before proteins, and could possibly have been the basis of a prebiotic RNA world in which replicating systems evolved and eventually gave rise to what we would recognize as life. Viruses of today are not living organisms in their own right. They can only function in the context of the infection of much more complex living cell structures. They are genetic material wrapped in protein that literally usurps the metabolic capabilities of living cells in order to replicate. How genetic material and enzymes became encapsulated within the membranes that delimit living organisms is a matter for speculation. However, it seems certain that biogenesis occurred in a world devoid of oxygen and quite unlike almost anywhere on the Earth. Moreover, there are such sites on Earth at the hot deep-ocean hydrothermal vents, and possibly on other worlds such as within the postulated subsurface deep ocean on Jupiter's ice-covered moon, Europa, where conditions might favour the emergence of life from non-life. There are examples of lakes existing under ice sheets on Earth: Lake Vostok in Antarctica is such a freshwater lake 4 kilometres beneath the Antarctica ice cap which contains twice as much water as Lake Ontario. On Europa, the constant tidal flexing caused by the gravity of Jupiter and neighbouring moons could sustain liquid water beneath the icy surface and possibly hot hydrothermal vents, just as it sustains the volcanic activity on Io, another satellite of Jupiter.

It has still to be determined whether biogenesis is an unbelievably improbable event, or whether it is almost inevitable, given the right conditions.

THE APPEARANCE OF LIFE ON EARTH

Somewhere between 500 and 700 million years after the Earth was formed (between 4.1 and 3.9 billion years ago), life appeared on this planet. So, in geological time, life appeared very quickly after conditions would allow it to exist. It is entirely possible that life originated more than once and that it was wiped out by massive impacts that were taking place in that period. At about the time that the first evidence of life on Earth can be found, huge impacts were also taking place on the Moon. The great lunar maria, the dark features of the 'man in the Moon', were created at this time by huge impacts that left the dark, lava-filled basins that have been only lightly cratered since then. If the Moon had not been there to sweep up the asteroids and comets with its gravitational field, it is likely that some of these major impactors would have left their mark on the Earth, and maybe set life back again many times before it could take its fragile hold. The greatest of the impacts would have released so much energy that they would have boiled Earth's oceans and literally heat-sterilized the planet. If life was extinguished on a number of occasions in those early days, it could point to biogenesis being an inevitable process given sufficient time and the right conditions. If life was not extinguished by giant impacts, then it would point to the resilience and tenacity of life once formed.

Although the Moon is far less massive than the Earth, it may well have protected our planet from potential impactors that otherwise would have hit the Earth if they had remained in Earth-crossing orbits. Each crater on the Moon can be regarded as a possible impact on the Earth if the Moon had not been there. The period of extreme bombardment of the Earth could have been extended for a long time if the Moon had not been there to sweep up potential Earth-sterilizing impactor comets, asteroids and planetesimals.

Impacts undoubtedly still occur on both the Moon and the Earth, as evidenced by what happened in Russia at the beginning of the twentieth century. An object estimated to have a mass of 100,000 tonnes exploded at an altitude of about 6 kilometres over the remote Tunguska River region of Siberia on 30 June 1908. It exploded with an energy equivalent to about 20 million tonnes of TNT, or 1,000 times the explosive power of the Hiroshima A-bomb, laying waste 2,150 square kilometres of forest, and sending shock waves twice around the world. The very remoteness of this impact site from major centres of civilization saved the human population of this planet from untold carnage, but if it had occurred just four hours later it might have flattened St Petersburg. On the scale of cosmic impacts, this was comparatively small, but was quite recent. Indeed, were it not for the gravitational protection of other celestial bodies, impacts on the Earth would be far more frequent than they are, even today.

Comet Shoemaker–Levy 9 showed the world, for the first time, the effects that a series of major impacts can have on a planet when around 20 fragments of it crashed into Jupiter in July 1994. If that comet had hit the Earth, this account would not be written, and nobody would be writing anything from the surface of this planet for maybe millions of years to come, if ever again. Gene Shoemaker knew that impacts on the Earth had shaped the biology of this planet. Comet Shoemaker–Levy 9 made people sit up and take notice. Throughout the history of the Solar System, Jupiter will have done a similar job in capturing comets and other bodies that might otherwise have ended up in Earth-crossing orbits and which, given time, may have hit our planet. It seems that Jupiter-sized planets are common in extrasolar planetary systems. They have been detected indirectly by the programmes searching for planets orbiting other stars. Their huge masses produce detectable wobbles in their parent star's motion, thus revealing their presence. If these planetary systems also contain smaller, rocky planets, as does our Solar System, then these Jupiter-sized giants might also 'shield' their rocky planets from some of their potential impactors, provided, of course, they are in suitable orbits.

If our Moon was indeed produced following an oblique impact of a Mars-sized body with the newly forming Earth that ejected material from the impact into a disc around the Earth and which eventually coalesced into the Moon, then this may be viewed as a chance event. If so, then rocky planets possessing a comparatively large moon may be very rare indeed. An alternative hypothesis that the Earth and Moon formed separately and that the Earth somehow gravitationally captured the Moon would still be an extremely improbable and therefore rare event. It seems unlikely that the Earth and Moon were formed together as a binary planet coalescing together *de novo*. The 'Big Impact' theory for the origin of the Moon seems the most likely scenario.

The Moon is further away from the Earth now than it was at the time it was formed. It is believed that when the Moon first formed it was 20 times closer to Earth than it is today. With the Moon this close, its tidal influence would have been 8,000 times greater than it is today. However, the effects would have quickly diminished as the gravitational pull between the Moon and the tidal bulges on the Earth generated a torque that both caused the rate of Earth's spin to decrease and the distance of the Moon from the Earth to increase (according to the law of the conservation of angular momentum). Using modern distance-measuring technology (lunar laser ranging) the inexorable movement of the Moon away from the Earth can be measured year on year, and we know that the Moon is currently moving away from the Earth at a rate of about 4 centimetres per year.

Another important effect of the Moon is that it stabilizes Earth's obliquity (the angle of tilt of the spin axis relative to the plane of its orbit). This obliquity is the cause of the seasons, and the effect of the Moon has been to cause the Earth's obliquity not to vary by more than a degree or so either side of its present value of 23.5°. If the Earth did not have a relatively large Moon, its obliquity would vary chaotically between zero and almost 90° on timescales of millions of years, due to the influence of planetary perturbations. This would cause correspondingly chaotic and significant shifts in Earth's climate, with attendant dramatic effects on the evolution of life. Eventually, as the Moon gradually recedes from the Earth, it will lose its stabilizing effect on Earth's obliquity. Such an influence may have had little effect on biogenesis, but could have been a profound influence on the evolution of complex life forms from their simple ancestors. Complex life is very fragile (look at the rate of extinction of species on the Earth today caused by anthropogenic habitat loss). Long-period stability of Earth's obliquity would have favoured the survival and subsequent evolution of complex terrestrial life.

CONCLUSIONS

Can we conclude anything at all from our deliberations?

If a monkey were to sit at a typewriter and type for days on end, there is a finite, but infinitesimally small, probability that the result would be a best selling novel. This novel would have originated from purely random keystrokes. It could happen, but no one believes that it would. Similarly, there is a vanishingly small probability that the complex systems that we understand as life could have arisen from a purely chance set of reactions that happened somewhere where conditions made them possible, but not probable. If this is what happened, then life may be very rare indeed in the Universe, and if it occurs in more than one place, it could have been transported there by events such as those described earlier. The Earth *could* be the only planet in the Universe that harbours life. On the other hand, if life originates in an orderly way by a series of poorly understood small steps that simply require enough time in which they might occur, then it might be the case that if conditions are right, biogenesis, if not inevitable, is at least probable.

A question frequently asked is whether there are other intelligent species out there in the Universe with their resulting civilizations. The famous Drake equation attempts to compute the number of civilizations that might be present. However, the values of its parameters can only be guessed at and, depending on the values chosen, predict that the Universe is either teeming with civilizations or that they are virtually absent. This is a fruitless avenue of activity. Before civilizations can occur, there has to be intelligent life. Even the existence of intelligent life does not guarantee civilization, as can be seen with the very intelligent cetaceans in our own oceans. Civilization is not an inevitable consequence of intelligence. If civilizations do exist, only technological civilizations will be detectable, and then only if they use radio. The Earth has had human beings living on it for about two million years and there has been civilization for several thousand years, but radio has only been used for a minute fraction of this time. The SETI programmes have yielded no results to date. Only a positive result will prove the existence of another civilization; negative results prove nothing.

It seems that life may be common in the Universe if it is not an incredibly improbable event. However, any extant life is more likely to be at the bacterial level of complexity. Complex life seems to be less frequent for the reasons outlined above. However, being less frequent in a place as big as the Universe could still mean that there are many instances of complex life out there. The same argument can be applied to intelligent and even technological life.

At the moment, there is only one safe answer to the question of whether there is any life in the Universe other than that on the planet Earth: 'We just don't know.'

ACKNOWLEDGEMENTS

I should like to thank Dr Jo McSweeney for reading and criticizing this article. I should also like to remember with thanks the late Professor John Gallon who talked with me about the cyanobacteria with which he was so familiar.

FURTHER READING

Cohen, J. and I. Stewart (2001), *What Does a Martian Look Like? The Science of Extraterrestrial Life*, Hoboken, New Jersey: John Wiley & Sons.

Davies, P. (1999), *The Origin of Life*, Harmondsworth: Penguin.

Dick, S.J. (1996), *The Biological Universe*, Cambridge: Cambridge University Press.

Hiscox, J.A. (ed.) (1999), *The Search for Life on Mars*, Proceedings of the First UK Conference, The British Interplanetary Society.

Hoyle, F. and C. Wickramasinghe (1996), *Life on Mars? The Case for a Cosmic Heritage*, Redland, Bristol: Clinical Press Ltd.

Schopf, J.W. (1999), *Cradle of Life: the Discovery of Earth's Earliest Fossils*, Princeton: Princeton University Press.

Ward, P.D. and D. Brownlee (2000), *Rare Earth: Why Complex Life is Uncommon in the Universe*, New York: Copernicus, an imprint of Springer.

Webb, S. (2002), *If the Universe is teeming with aliens . . . Where is everybody? Fifty solutions to the Fermi Paradox and the Problem of Extraterrestrial Life*, Pulborough: Praxis.

Scientific American (1995), A Special Issue, 'Life in the Universe', Basingstoke: W.H. Freeman.

More Astronomers Behaving Badly

FRED WATSON

The last time I sallied forth in pursuit of astronomers behaving badly in this fine publication (*2003 Yearbook of Astronomy*), I was taken to task by my colleagues. Not, as you might suppose, for spilling the beans on the human failings of astronomers – which are exactly the same as everyone else's – but for omitting one of the best-known examples of bad behaviour in the whole of British astronomy.

It concerns the eleventh Astronomer Royal, Sir Richard Woolley (1906–86), and a comment he made on his arrival in Britain to take up his post early in 1956. Some poor, unsuspecting journalist asked him what he thought of the prospects for space research. Half a century later, his acerbic put-down still echoes famously through the folklore of British astronomy – 'Utter bilge!'

At almost any earlier time in history, that would have been an appropriate (if undignified) response, but what called Woolley's judgement into question was the launch only 21 months later of the world's first artificial satellite. Of course, that was hardly his fault. The Soviet space programme had been conducted in the utmost secrecy, and Sputnik's debut astonished the entire globe. But he must have been aware of the competing US Vanguard programme, and no doubt shared the embarrassed confusion of its scientists and engineers in the wake of the Russian triumph.

CLASSIC ONE-LINERS

Does one ill-judged remark qualify for an astronomer behaving badly? I don't think so. In the *2003 Yearbook* article, we discovered sword fights, slave labour, violent disagreements between scientists and history rewritten for the Third Reich. Next to such activities, Woolley's misdemeanour pales into insignificance. Since the galaxy of cosmic miscreants is almost as prodigious as a real galaxy, there are plenty more of them to investigate. But before we resume our quest, we might just dwell on Sir Richard a little longer.

Before he became Astronomer Royal (and, as it turned out, a most successful one), Woolley had been for 17 years Director of the Mount Stromlo Observatory in Canberra. That venerable Australian institution was, of course, in the international spotlight when all its heritage buildings – including six historic telescopes – were destroyed by the savage bushfire of 18 January 2003. But in Woolley's time, too, fire had come close to consuming the observatory. On 5 February 1952, in the middle of a particularly hot summer, lightning started a fire that eventually reached the neighbouring pine forest and swept through it to the observatory's workshop, which was completely destroyed. As in the 2003 inferno, the fire front moved with devastating speed, and it was left to the staff to fight it with whatever resources they could lay their hands on.

That Woolley was not particularly impressed with the outside help he had received was cogently revealed when he commented on the event some years later:

> When the fire had passed [through], up came a barrel of beer, and sandwiches, with the compliments of the Hotel Canberra. Finally there came the Fire Brigade, who drank the beer. Then the Minister for the Interior, who started giving the fire-fighters instructions.

Here is the suggestion of someone who uses words to devastating effect in confronting adversaries – but in a way that you can't help liking. Modern-day historians Tom Frame and the late Don Faulkner, in their history of Mount Stromlo, have uncovered a couple of other examples. They reveal that the contemptuous and, with hindsight, grossly misjudged one-liner was definitely part of Sir Richard Woolley's stock-in-trade.

In 1947, at a high-profile conference in Perth, Western Australia, he was asked where he thought the science of radio astronomy would be in ten years' time. Australia was already emerging as a major force in this new field, so Woolley's radio colleagues might have been forgiven for anticipating a few words of praise. They were decidedly unimpressed, however, when he answered, 'Forgotten.' The fall-out from that misguided remark took years to settle. And a reliable eye-witness account of a conversation, some five years later, between Woolley and the great French-American astronomer Gerard de Vaucouleurs (who worked at Mount Stromlo in the 1950s), reveals a similarly withering – though much less catastrophic – response. De Vaucouleurs had just completed his seminal work on the local super-cluster of galaxies, and excitedly asked Woolley where he thought it should be published. The *Astronomical Journal*, perhaps? '*Punch*,' replied Woolley.

THE PLANETS REDESIGNED

At the end of the day, if Woolley's contemptuous one-liners were his worst fault, they were far outweighed by his many significant contributions to astronomy. He barely qualifies as an astronomer behaving badly. However, the same cannot be said of our next cosmic hoodlum. Sixty years before Woolley's most famous debacle, this man was writing articles for the scientific press that really were utter bilge – and, on top of that, he was expressing utter outrage at the scornful response of his readers. It is thanks to the diligence of Scots historians Tristram Clarke, Alison Morrison-Low and Allen Simpson that his remarkable bad behaviour has been brought out of obscurity and into the limelight of modern scholarship.

In fact, Andrew Barclay (1814–1900) was not an astronomer by trade but an engineer – and, in his day, a very innovative one. No less than 75 patents were granted to him during the second half of the nineteenth century, a truly amazing achievement. Any reader of the *Yearbook* who is a steam buff may recognize Barclay's name, for the company he founded in Kilmarnock in the west of Scotland became world-famous for the production of colliery and shunting locomotives. By the 1870s the business was thriving and employed more than 400 people in the town.

Regrettably, Barclay's engineering expertise was not matched by his business acumen, and during the 1880s the firm underwent a lengthy and painful slide into insolvency. It was finally rescued in 1892, becoming a limited company, but the following year Barclay himself was sacked, leading to his financial ruin. Surprisingly, astronomy seems to have been part of the problem. His long-standing interest in the subject had led him to embark, in the 1850s, on a protracted venture to manufacture astronomical telescopes as a startlingly inappropriate by-product of his locomotive works. The fact that they would be totally unprofitable seems not to have occurred to him. And, instead of looking after the finances of his increasingly ailing company, he lavished his attention on their design.

Barclay produced both refracting and reflecting telescopes – though not many of either – and they were, by the standards of the time, small and old-fashioned. His reflectors, for example, used the Gregorian layout of two concave mirrors, made popular more than a century earlier by his fellow Scot, James Short (1710–68). Barclay's mirrors were still made of speculum metal, even though that had been largely supplanted by silvered glass in the 1860s. They ranged in size up to 14.5 inches (37 centimetres) in diameter, although he claimed in 1893 to be working on a 22-inch (56-centimetre) instrument. The one redeeming feature of his telescopes was that they were beautifully engineered, for Barclay had all the resources of the locomotive workshops at his disposal.

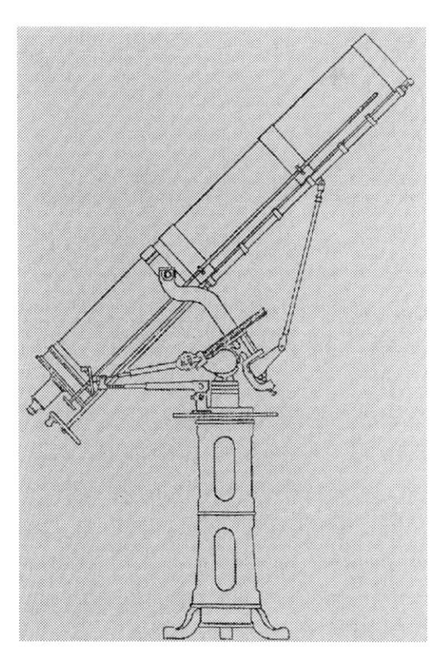

Figure 1. Beautifully engineered but optically hopeless, a 9-inch (23-centimetre) Gregorian telescope built by Andrew Barclay in the 1890s. (By courtesy of the University of New South Wales.)

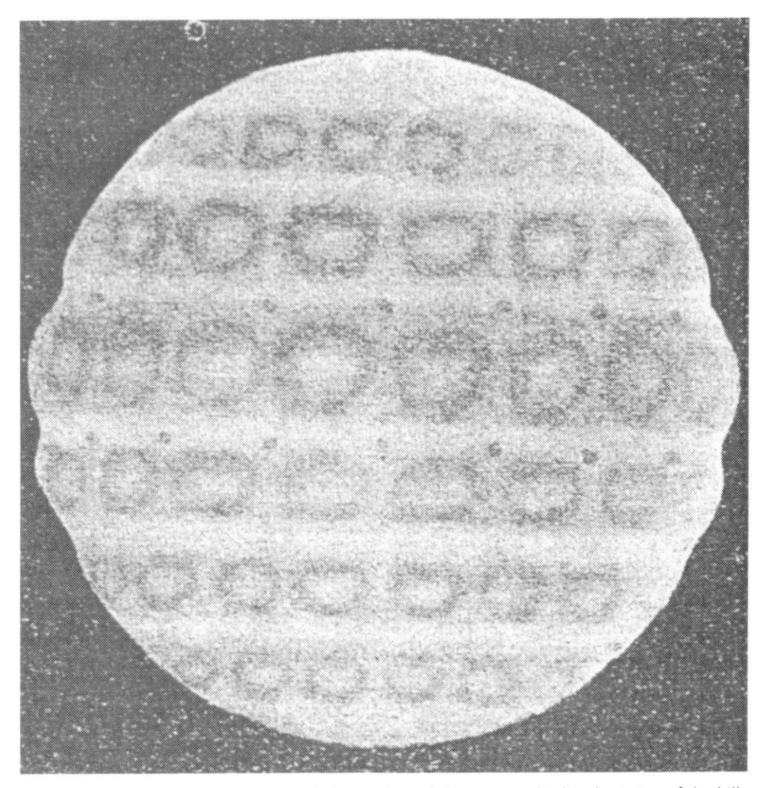

Figure 2. Among Barclay's 'Unrevealed Wonders of the Heavens' is his depiction of the hills and dales of Jupiter. It is not surprising that his work was scorned by his contemporaries. (By courtesy of the University of New South Wales.)

Although some of Barclay's earlier telescopes were reported to be of excellent optical quality, his later ones must have been questionable, to say the least. In 1893, he published the first of a number of articles in *The English Mechanic and World of Science* based on observations he had made with them. Considering that he was by then a prominent amateur astronomer, his articles were breathtakingly ill-advised. Under the heading 'The Unrevealed Wonders of the Heavens', Barclay described such absurdities as egg-shaped protuberances encircling the planet Jupiter and a Saturn-like ring around Mars – which had also grown a blue, spherical-looking mountain in its southern hemisphere. In addition, he provided some indignant comments about the Royal

Astronomical Society and the British Astronomical Association, both of which had flatly refused to publish his results. One almost has the feeling that *The English Mechanic* only agreed to carry his outrageous articles to see what effect they would have.

If that was the case, the editors must have been delighted with the immediate and largely scornful response.

> I can only say [wrote one contributor] that if I had a Gregorian telescope . . . that exhibited the great planet as depicted in Mr B's Fig.1, I would dispose of the optical part for what it would fetch, and convert the tube into a chimney cowl straightway.

A more helpful correspondent gently suggested that faulty optical polishing might have led to distortions in the image seen through the telescope. He took pains to explain how that could have led to the strange appearance of Jupiter. But the obstinate Barclay was so consumed with the idea that his were the only telescopes in the world capable of revealing the innermost secrets of the Solar System that he ignored this lifeline, pressing ahead with reports of brown smoke issuing from Jupiter's egg-like mountains, and sunspots that behaved like volcanoes.

Further tetchy correspondence followed, and then, in 1897, Barclay presented his final contribution to *The English Mechanic.* This

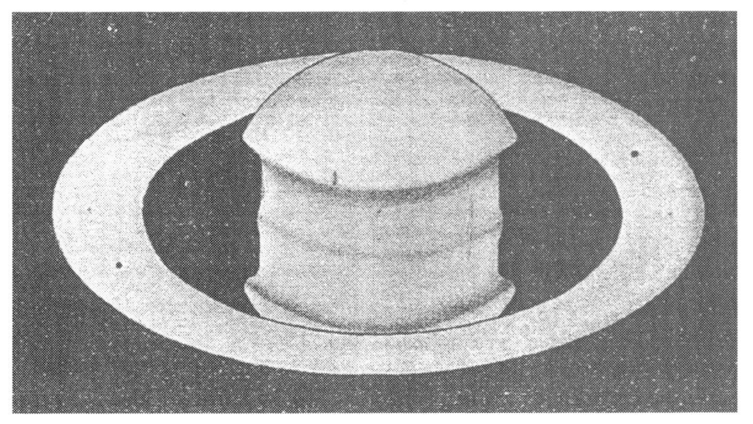

Figure 3. Andrew Barclay genuinely believed he was making a new contribution to science with his unique view of Saturn. (By courtesy of the University of New South Wales.)

contained some doubtful testimonials regarding the quality of his telescopes, besides introducing yet more 'Unrevealed Wonders'. The most dramatic of these was a sketch of Saturn that made the planet look for all the world like a half-eaten apple – an extraordinary image. The response to this was surprisingly muted compared with the derision that had greeted his earlier contributions. Perhaps the journal's readers had already written Barclay off as a fruitcake, and simply couldn't be bothered to argue any more.

In his first *English Mechanic* article, Barclay had justified his confrontation with the astronomical establishment by revealing that he had 'spent over £10,000 to find out how to finish metallic speculums [sic] and mix and cast the metals. I have made over 2,000 experiments in connection therewith.' The fact that this comment was made at a time when Barclay was in dire financial straits betrays not only that he was a fruitcake, but that he was also both stubborn and stupid – an admirable candidate for an astronomer behaving badly.

A RISKY BUSINESS

If Andrew Barclay's name is unfamiliar, the next one we encounter is known to everyone. Or, at least, everyone with half an eye on the world of astronomy. This man has been variously described as the greatest astronomer of all time, the greatest telescope maker ditto, the father of galactic astronomy, the father of infrared astronomy – and so on, all with some justification. William Herschel (1738–1822) was, indeed, one of the brightest stars of our science. His career is all the more remarkable when one considers that it was, in fact, his second career, which he didn't embark on until he was 35 years old. Before that (and, indeed, for some years beyond), he had been a professional musician.

Many readers of the *Yearbook* will be familiar with Herschel's life and work, and are no doubt searching their minds to recall what misdemeanour might qualify him for a place in this article. Perhaps it is to do with his discovery of the seventh planet of the Solar System in 1781? The fact that he had wanted to call it *Georgium Sidus* after the King might be seen as a very shrewd move to curry royal favour. Indeed, it was – and it did – but that is hardly bad behaviour. Neither is it to do with the unfortunate name the planet finally ended up with. That was Johannes Bode's fault, and even then, he can't really be blamed, as the name sounds fine in Bode's native German. No, the fact is that William Herschel the astronomer seems to have led a faultless life.

Except in one area that today we would take infinitely more seriously than he evidently did. To wit, occupational health and safety. William's behaviour in this regard was a complete disaster. It is perhaps not surprising, since he was attempting to build the largest telescopes ever conceived while using structural techniques that were rudimentary even by the standards of the late eighteenth century. His most famous instruments, the 'Large Twenty-foot' of 1783 and the giant Forty-foot completed some six years later, were monumental timber structures carrying metal mirrors that in the larger telescope, at least, weighed a significant fraction of a tonne. The observing position on both was high on the rigging, and very exposed. These were dangerous instruments to work with, and when the Large Twenty-foot was blown over by a gale in March 1784, it was only by chance that no one was injured. Herschel himself merely noted in his journal that 'fortunately, it is a cloudy evening so that I shall not lose time to repair the havock that has been made'.

Figure 4. William Herschel's cavalier attitude to occupational health and safety is highlighted in this view of his 'Large Twenty-foot' telescope. It was fortunate that no one was injured when the structure blew over in March 1784. (By courtesy of the Anglo-Australian Observatory Library.)

Herschel's sister Caroline (1750–1848), an able and accomplished astronomer in her own right, was much more aware of the hazards surrounding the family business. 'I could give a pretty long list of accidents which were near proving fatal to my brother as well as myself,' she wrote. Indeed, she had had first-hand experience of William's neglect when, in the darkness of a winter's night, she had gashed her leg badly on an iron hook hidden in the snow. Likewise, a protruding bar on the telescope caused serious injury to an eminent visiting astronomer, Giuseppe Piazzi (1746–1826), the discoverer of the first known asteroid.

William himself had several heart-stopping moments, including one in 1807 when a beam supporting the one-tonne mirror of the Forty-foot broke as the mirror was being removed from the telescope for its regular repolishing. Fortunately, it didn't have far to fall on to its handling carriage, but Caroline noted with evident shock that 'Both my brothers had a narrow escape of being crushed to death'. Perhaps the worst episode of all had occurred some 26 years earlier, however, when William was carrying out his first experiments in casting large telescope mirrors. In August 1781, he had tried to cast a mirror 36 inches (90 centimetres) in diameter for a proposed 30-foot (9.1-metre) telescope. The experiment failed when a quarter of a tonne of molten metal flooded out of a broken mould on to the stone floor of his basement workshop with explosive violence. Herschel and his workmen were lucky to escape with their lives, and the project was abandoned. Fortunately for astronomy, he later managed to get the hang of this technique.

Perhaps it is churlish to accuse William Herschel of bad behaviour when both his telescope-making and his observing pushed back the frontiers of knowledge in a way that had never been seen before – and has hardly been seen since. But it remains true that he was lucky – very lucky – that no one was killed as a result of his activities. Especially since the life most likely to have been lost would have been his own.

There is one other hint of questionable behaviour on the part of this great man, recently uncovered by the Cambridge-based Herschel specialist, Michael Hoskin. It concerns an episode that took place in 1757 when, as a 19-year-old musician, Herschel moved from his native Hanover to London. We are told in the history books that this was to pursue his ambitions as a composer – but it seems there was rather more to it than that. How much do we know about William Herschel the musician? In fact, a great deal, particularly since much of his music has survived. There is no doubt that he became a composer of great talent, and if you want to get an insight into his cheerful disposition, you can hardly do better than to listen to some of his organ works as recorded, for example, by the modern-day French astronomer–musician, Dominique Proust. Here, too, we find Herschel as a well-behaved person. But his departure from Hanover was in the midst of chaotic upheaval that stretched standards of decorum to their limits.

Herschel had been born into a musical family, the son of an oboe player in the Hanoverian Guards. It was in 1753 that he followed his father and his older brother Jacob into the regimental band, but within a few years the military implications of that had overtaken the musical ones. French ambitions against Hanover resulted in the defeat of the Hanoverian Guards at the Battle of Hastenbeck in July 1757. William, then 18, was told by his father to hotfoot it home to escape the fighting. On his arrival in Hanover, however, his mother told him he would be far better off with his regiment, since a civil defence force was being mustered in the town and he risked being conscripted into it. At least in the army he was officially a non-combatant. So, back he went, stealing unnoticed to his post.

It is a measure of the concern Herschel's father had for his two sons that he then plotted to spirit them away to Britain to escape the continual skirmishing with the French, who by now had occupied Hanover. This was not so much a problem for Jacob, whose musical talents had allowed him to revert to civilian status, but William was still in the army. Nevertheless, that was what happened, and late in 1757 the two brothers arrived safely in Hanoverian England. Back home, however, Herschel's father was promptly arrested 'by way of enforcing the return of the Deserter', as Caroline put it – although it failed to have the desired effect.

It was another two years before the Hanoverian troubles subsided with the defeat of the French at the Battle of Minden in August 1759. Jacob quickly returned home, but that option was not open to 'the Deserter', who elected to remain in England. It was not until 1762 that William received his discharge from the army (probably through Jacob's influence) and was able to visit his native city once again.

Where is the bad behaviour in all that? Most of us would have done exactly the same thing in such circumstances. Herschel's father, entirely understandably, was the instigator of these events, and he paid the price with his detention. It is easy to imagine that had he not taken the course of action he did, his gifted son might well have met an early end on the battlefields of Lower Saxony, and astronomy would have been immeasurably the poorer.

The one hint of bad behaviour, highlighted by Michael Hoskin, is that when he wrote of these events a quarter of a century later, William was rather sparing with information. He explained that the war had made his situation in Hanover 'very uncomfortable', but also that 'The known encouragement given to Music in England determined me to try my fortune abroad & accordingly about the year 1759 I came to settle in this country . . .' And who could blame him for glossing over the details?

RISKS OF A DIFFERENT KIND

Finally, it is time to bite the bullet and air some bad behaviour of a much more conventional sort, the kind that the title of this article might lead one to expect. Affairs of the heart are no respecters of profession, and astronomers are as susceptible to them as anyone else. This particular affair involves not one but three hearts (and probably many more besides), and its intricate machinations have been explored recently by US historians William Sheehan (the author of another article in this *Yearbook*) and Anthony Misch.

At the centre of the story is the astronomer, an American by the name of David Peck Todd (1855–1939). His name, like Andrew Barclay's, means little to us today, but he was prominent in the field in the late nineteenth century. As a young man he had been attracted by mechanical devices ranging from organs to steam engines. Telescopes, too, found a place there along the way. The end result was that in 1875, having completed his studies at Columbia University and Amherst College, Massachusetts, he joined the US Naval Observatory in Washington, DC, to work with the great mathematical astronomer Simon Newcomb (1835–1909).

Todd's work encompassed several areas of Solar System astronomy. Most notably, he carried out computations based on observations of the 1874 transit of Venus in order to determine the solar parallax, that elusive measurement of the Earth's distance from the Sun that made the rare Venus transits such special events. He also had a brief moment of glory in August 1877, when he confirmed Asaph Hall's discovery of Phobos, the innermost satellite of Mars, with the Naval Observatory's 26-inch (66-centimetre) refractor.

A couple of months before this event, Todd had met an attractive and vivacious young woman by the name of Mabel Loomis. Their relationship blossomed over the ensuing weeks and, in 1880, they were married. Mabel was a gifted artist and musician with a temperament that Sheehan and Misch succinctly describe as 'always in the upper ranges of the emotional register'. Nevertheless, the newlyweds got on well, and even in their twilight years half a century later, remained together. By then, though, it might have been 'just for the sake of the children . . .'

Unfortunately, one vital aspect of their relationship was clouded from the start. It is revealed by Mabel's note in her diary that 'I do not think David is what might be called a monogamous animal,' and that seems to have been the root of the problem. Her chosen astronomer's particular line of bad behaviour was inveterate philandering. Eventually, it resulted in him losing his sanity as the later stages of syphilis took hold. With that background, it is perhaps easier to understand the extraordinary situation that developed after the couple moved to Amherst College, Todd's *alma mater*, when he became professor of astronomy there in 1881. Amherst was a small town with little for Mabel to do but socialize, and that quickly led to her introduction to a prominent local family, the Dickinsons. One member of the family, Emily, subsequently became well known as a poet, and it was largely due to Mabel's later efforts that her work was preserved and recognized. But it was Emily's brother, the father figure of the family and a man much older than Mabel, with whom the astronomer's wife became most deeply involved.

Austin Dickinson was a lawyer, a married man, and clearly a person of great appeal to Mabel. The story of their developing relationship and long affair has been told in some detail in an intriguing book by modern-day scholar Polly Longsworth, but what is of interest to us is the part played by astronomy in the story. For it seems that the illicit relationship first began to flourish when Todd left Amherst in November 1882 to visit Mount Hamilton in California, home of the new Lick Observatory. Here, he was scheduled to observe the transit of Venus on 6 December – the last that would occur until 8 June 2004 – and needed to prepare the equipment to photograph the event.

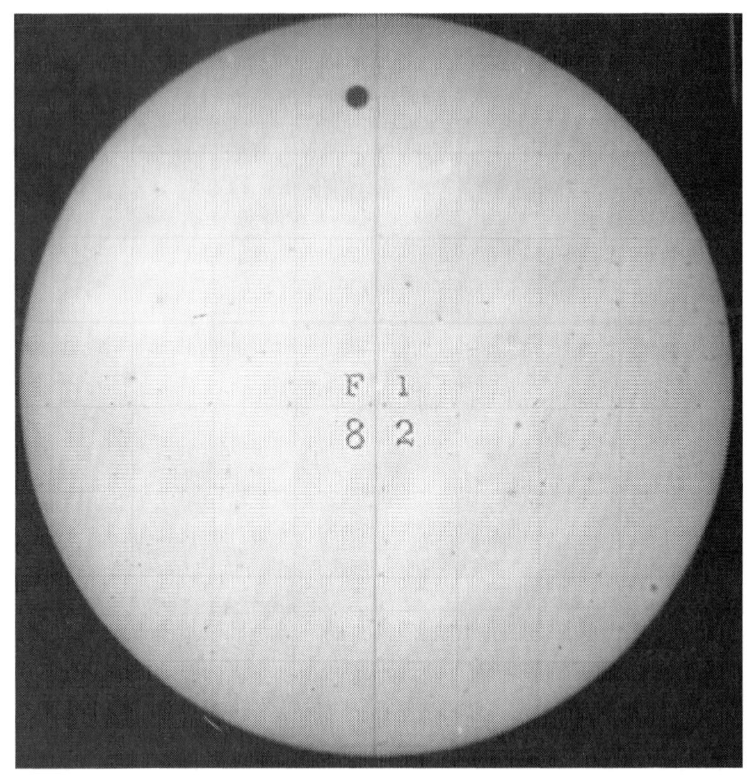

Figure 5. The transit of Venus on 6 December 1882 is recorded in this image from the US Naval Observatory. During the same event, David Todd behaved far better than he usually did by capturing a sequence of excellent photographic observations at the Lick Observatory. (By courtesy of the US Naval Observatory Library.)

That Todd was completely preoccupied with this task is evident, even though it appears he already knew of his wife's growing liaison with the Amherst lawyer. The suggestion made by Sheehan and Misch is that he quietly condoned it because it allowed him to engage in his own adventures with other women. Whatever the case, he seems eventually to have completely accepted the situation in which he shared his wife with another man, for it lasted until Austin's death in 1895.

Todd's work on the transit of Venus turned out to be excellent, with well over 100 of his photographic plates being suitable for measurement and analysis. They still exist in the archives of the Lick

Observatory. With his position at Amherst assured, David Todd remained there until his retirement due to ill health in 1917. Unfortunately, by then, he had become obsessed with the idea of trying to detect radio transmissions from the inhabitants of Mars, his mental health deteriorating as the effects of his illness overtook him. He died in 1939, some seven years after Mabel herself had passed away.

Whatever your view of the morals of the situation, it is hard to deny that this extraordinary story ranks among the more poignant in the annals of astronomy. And, as in so many cases, the heroes and villains of the piece are only indistinctly defined. Nevertheless, the important thing is quite clear. At the centre of it all, there was once again an astronomer behaving badly.

FURTHER READING (AND LISTENING)

Clarke, T.N., A.D. Morrison-Low and A.D.C. Simpson (1989), *Brass & Glass: Scientific Instrument Making Workshops in Scotland*, Edinburgh: National Museums of Scotland.

Frame, T. and D. Faulkner (2003), *Stromlo: An Australian Observatory*, Sydney: Allen & Unwin.

Hoskin, M. (2004), 'Was William Herschel a deserter?', *Journal for the History of Astronomy*, vol. 35, pp. 356–8.

Longsworth, P. (1984), *Austin and Mabel: The Amherst affair and love letters of Austin Dickinson and Mabel Loomis Todd*, New York: Farrar, Straus & Giroux.

Proust, D. (1992), *Pièces d'Orgue de William Herschel*, Vincennes: Disques Dom (DOM CD 1418).

Sheehan, W. and A. Misch (2004), '*Ménage à trois:* David Peck Todd, Mabel Loomis Todd, Austin Dickinson, and the 1882 transit of Venus', *Journal for the History of Astronomy*, vol. 35, pp. 123–34.

Watson, F. (2004), *Stargazer: The Life and Times of the Telescope*, Sydney: Allen & Unwin.

Sharpening the Sky with Adaptive Optics

MATTHEW KENWORTHY

A HISTORICAL PROBLEM

The only thing guaranteed to make an observer grind his teeth in frustration more than thin cirrus cloud is poor seeing. An otherwise crystal-clear night can draw out the most reluctant astronomer, only to find that stellar images boil and dance, planetary discs shimmer and roil and fine detail is all but impossible to resolve. Even though telescopes with apertures larger than about 12 centimetres should be able to resolve double stars with separations smaller than one arcsecond, successive generations of astronomers realized to their dismay that the stellar images did not decrease in size in accordance with expected theory.

This problem was recognized and diagnosed by Sir Isaac Newton. In his 1730 book, *Opticks*, he made the observation that

> the Air through which we look upon the Stars, is in perpetual Tremor; as may be seen by the tremulous Motion of Shadows cast from high Towers, and by the twinkling of the fix'd Stars . . . The only Remedy is a most serene and quiet Air, such as may perhaps be found on the tops of the highest Mountains above the grosser Clouds.*

What causes this? By day the Sun heats up the ground and the atmosphere in close contact with it. As night falls, these warm cells of air mingle with cooler pockets of air above. As the starlight passes

* I would like to point out that it is a tradition for any discussion about adaptive optics to start with Sir Isaac Newton's quote, and it would be remiss of me to miss this opportunity now!

through these unevenly heated pockets of air, the starlight is deflected and the star appears to shimmer and move. The same effect can be seen looking along a hot road on a summer's day, or above the flames of a hot fire. It is a problem that plagues the Earth-bound telescopes of both amateur and professional optical astronomers alike, and by moving to 'the tops of the highest Mountains' the conditions are indeed better, but still short of the images that make the Hubble Space Telescope a highly competitive telescope. To understand what is going on in the atmosphere, we need to know what we would expect if there was no atmosphere at all.

WAVES OF ENERGY

When you look at a distant star through a high-magnification eyepiece on a still night, what you see is not a tiny pinpoint of light but a small disc, with possibly a faint ring surrounding this bright core. You are not looking at the disc of the star, but rather an optical effect due to the wave-like nature of light, called diffraction. The central bright spot is called the Airy disc, and it is surrounded by successively fainter diffraction rings, of which the first one is the brightest one to be seen. The angular diameter of the Airy disc in arcseconds is equal to $25\lambda/D$, where λ is the wavelength of light (in microns) you are observing, and D is the diameter of the telescope (in centimetres). The diameter of the Airy disc represents the fundamental limit set by Nature for the resolving power of your telescope – the smaller the Airy disc, the finer the detail your telescope can resolve. To make the Airy disc smaller, you must do one of two things: observe light with a shorter wavelength (but making λ smaller requires a mirror with a correspondingly better figure), or make D bigger by building a telescope with a larger-diameter objective. For a 4-metre-diameter telescope at visible wavelengths, the diffraction limit is 0.03 arcseconds, but photographic plates stubbornly yield 1–2 arcsecond-diameter images, even with larger-diameter telescopes.

In optics, the peculiar nature of light means that it can be treated either as discrete particles ('photons') or as a continuous flow of energy. In a similar manner to waves rolling across the open ocean, light from distant stars can be thought of as being made up of a succession of large flat sheets called 'wavefronts', travelling at the speed of light and separated by roughly half a micron for visible wavelengths. As the wavefronts pass down through the atmosphere towards the telescope aperture, the temperature differences in the cells of air cause the wavefront to deform from an ideal flat surface. On a large-aperture telescope equipped with a fast video camera, the problem becomes obvious. On exposures less than a hundredth of a second, the image of a star is seen to be made up of dozens or hundreds of individual 'speckles' of light, and looking at the images in slow motion shows that these speckles move together and fall apart, and stream across the sky in the general direction of the prevailing wind. When this pattern is added up on a photographic plate or electronic detector, the familiar seeing disc takes form. Each of these speckles happens to be the same size as the Airy disc for the telescope.

The turbulence in the atmosphere is best described by Kolmogorov statistics, which relate how deformed a wavefront is for a given telescope aperture, and a parameter related to the site's seeing called the turbulence coherence length r_0 (known as the Fried parameter). For the best astronomical sites in the world with excellent seeing, r_0 can be as large as 25 centimetres in the visible, and for a bad night's seeing at more typical locations it can be as small as 5 centimetres – and this value can easily change over a matter of minutes or seconds during the night. The angular size of the seeing disc is roughly equal to $25\lambda/r_0$, meaning that, even under the best conditions, the largest telescopes in

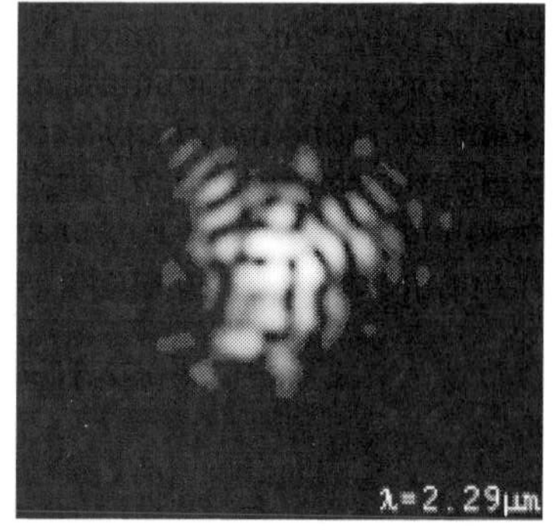

Figure 1. The effects of the atmosphere. On the left is an ideal 'diffraction-limited' image from a telescope, showing the Airy disc and the first diffraction ring. On the right is the same image, but with atmospheric turbulence for seeing of 0.5 arcseconds. The image is 1 arcsecond on a side. (All illustrations courtesy of the author, except where stated.)

the world have the same angular resolution as a 25-centimetre telescope, albeit with considerably more light-gathering power! The effects of the atmosphere are shown in Figure 1.

THE FIRST STEPS

The first steps towards adaptive optics (AO) came from the simpler need to track celestial objects accurately during long photographic exposures. Errors in the mechanical drives of telescopes would cause a periodic wobble of the celestial images, and lead to blurring of fine detail on the resultant photographs. Most modern telescopes now take the autoguider systems for granted, but in the 1940s this was a significant problem.

The simplest way to detect the motion of a star is by using a 'tip-tilt' sensor (see Figure 2). Four light-sensitive detectors are placed in a 2 × 2 square, and an image of a suitable guide star is placed on this array. When the image of the star sits in the middle of the sensor, the signal from each of the detectors is at the same level. If the pointing of the telescope changes owing to drive error or strong turbulence in the atmosphere, the image of the star moves and the signals from the detectors are no longer equal to each other. The telescope drive speed is adjusted to move the star's image and so equalize the signal from the four detectors, thereby centring the star in the tip-tilt detector again. By combining the four signals into two sets of error signals, the telescope is driven to correct errors for any direction on the sky.

Telescope autoguiders typically update the telescope motion a few times a second, but slewing the telescope at much higher speeds is very difficult because of the size and bulk of the whole telescope. By adding a small electronically steerable mirror into the telescope light path, correction rates of many hundreds of times a second are possible and the tip-tilt motion of the star due to the changing atmosphere is now removable. If the telescope diameter is one or two times the Fried length (typical for 2–4 metre telescopes observing in the near infrared) then by removing atmospheric tip-tilt motion you can get image quality close to the diffraction-limited ideal. This rapid tip-tilt system is the simplest type of adaptive optics system, used on many smaller telescopes. Large-telescope adaptive optic systems extend the idea of having one tip-tilt sensor and mirror to having many hundreds of simultaneous tip-tilt sensors and a complex deformable mirror (see Figure 2).

There are quite a few approaches to measuring the distorted wavefront from a star, but the Shack–Hartmann wavefront sensor is one of the most common in use in AO systems today. Imagine a circular tray filled edge to edge with half-filled wine glasses. As this tray is carried across a restaurant, the wine sloshes in different directions in each of the glasses, threatening to spill over the edge. By using sets of springs to counterbalance the moving liquid, the surface in each glass can be made level. A Shack–Hartmann wavefront sensor is the optical equivalent of the tray of wine glasses, splitting the primary mirror of the telescope into many small optical telescopes sitting next to each other, and then using one tip-tilt detector per mini-scope to measure the slope of that small piece of wavefront for that patch of primary mirror. A computer then takes all these tip-tilt measurements and reconstructs what the original wavefront was across the telescope aperture, and this is then fed to the deformable mirror of the AO system.

The first AO instrument design did not appear until 1953, when H.W. Babcock published a paper in the Publications of the Astronomical Society of the Pacific (referred to as PASP by astronomers and instrument-builders alike) describing a possible instrument layout that could compensate for the atmosphere's turbulence. It was never built, but the layout of the instrument has remained the same for today's AO systems (see Figure 3).

The principle of adaptive optics is simple (at least in theory!). One looks at a guide star whose light passes through the atmosphere to your telescope, measures the wavefront distortion due to the atmosphere, and then uses a deformable optic to introduce an equal but opposite distortion that cancels out the atmosphere. The maths to take the wavefront sensor data and turn it into a suitable deformation is simple, but until recently it took dedicated custom-hardware computers to perform the calculations in a short enough time for them to be useful. Since the atmosphere is being blown across the line of sight of the telescope, the measured wavefront distortion is only valid for a few milliseconds at a time, and so some powerful computer hardware is needed to perform the calculations quickly enough. The time it takes for the wavefront sensor data to be applied to the deformable mirror is called the loop update frequency. Tip-tilt AO systems run from 20 to

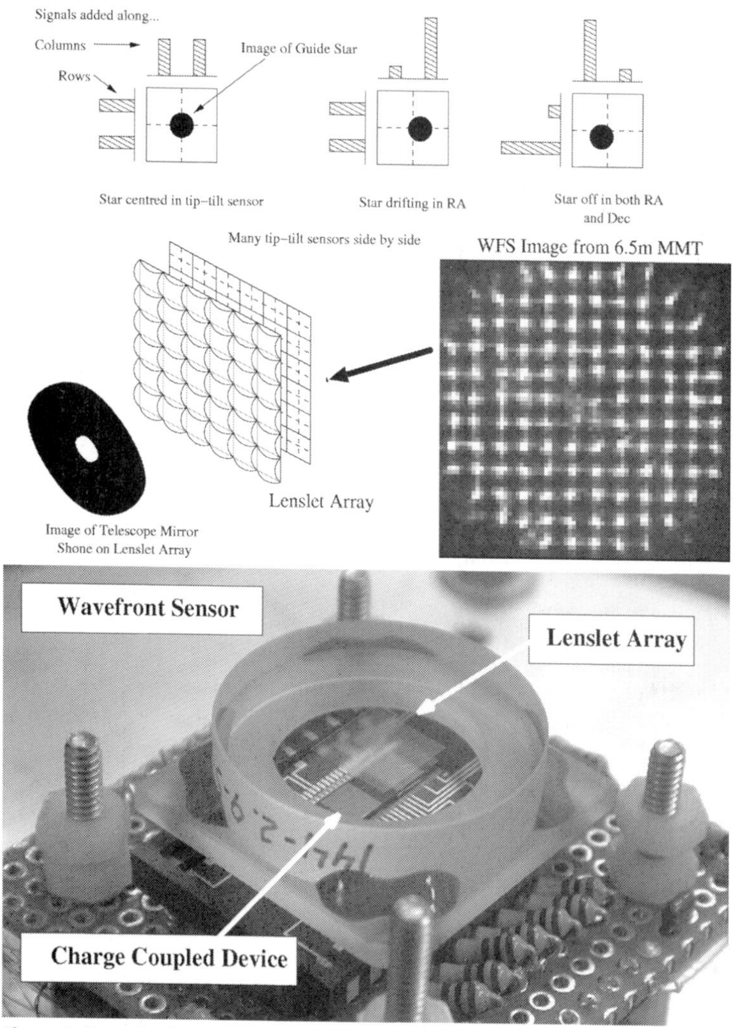

Figure 2. From tip-tilt sensors to a full wavefront sensor. A single tip-tilt sensor is shown in the top part of this figure, and an array of these tip-tilt sensors form a Shack–Hartmann sensor. A 12 × 12 wavefront sensor image from the 6.5-metre-diameter MMTO telescope shows the primary mirror divided into over a hundred subapertures, each with an image of the guide star.

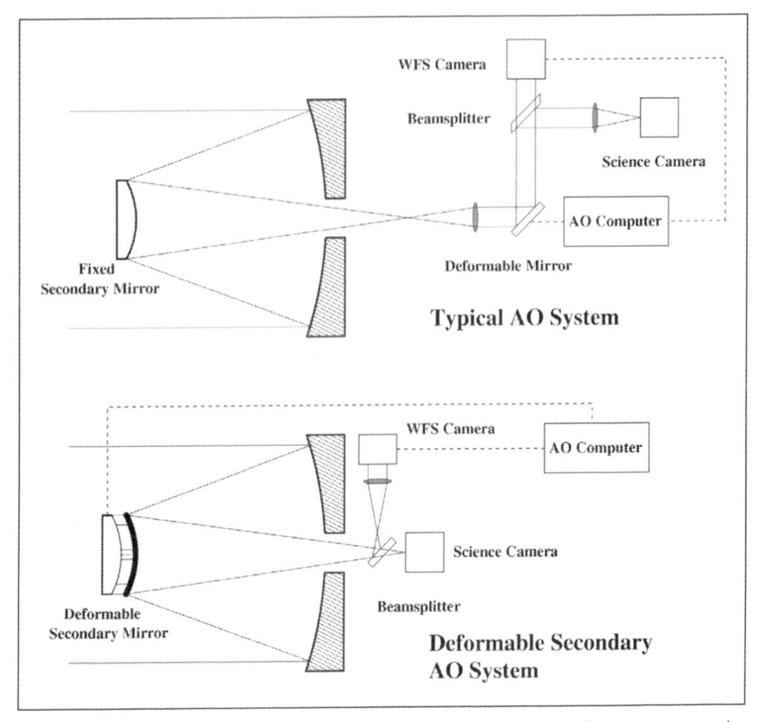

Figure 3. Two ways of installing an AO system on a telescope. Most observatories use the arrangement shown in the upper figure. Light from the telescope is reflected off a deformable mirror, off a beamsplitter and through to the science camera. In the lower figure, the rigid secondary mirror is replaced by a thin deformable mirror. The advantage is that there are fewer warm optics in the science light path, meaning that the AO system can observe scientific objects at thermal infrared wavelengths (typically 10 microns) and the fewer optical components result in higher overall efficiency.

100 Hz, but most large-telescope AO systems correct for many more modes and they run at speeds from 500 to 1,000 Hz.

Almost all telescopes equipped with AO systems use small deformable mirrors (typically 5–20 centimetres in diameter) with 20–1,000 deformable elements. Figure 3 also shows an alternative system where the secondary mirror of a Cassegrain telescope becomes the deformable optical element. This unique AO system is used at the 6.5-metre telescope at the MMT Observatory (MMTO) on Mount Hopkins in southern Arizona, as seen in Figures 4a and 4b. By building the AO system as part of the telescope, there are two big advantages. Each time light is reflected or transmitted through an optic, some of it is either absorbed or scattered out of the beam, which means that exposure times need to be longer to get the same number of photons from the astronomical object you look at. This new AO system uses the minimum number of optics possible to get science light into the science instrument – two reflections and a transmission through a beamsplitter. The other advantage is for observations at wavelengths from 3 to 20 microns, where optics at room temperature glow with thermal energy. AO systems on other telescopes have far more thermal noise at these wavelengths as the light passes through half a dozen or more lenses before reaching the science camera. By making the secondary mirror correct the science light, the sensitivity of the telescope and camera increases dramatically.

Figure 4a. The MMTO 6.5-metre telescope on top of Mount Hopkins in southern Arizona. The mirror was 'spin cast' in a special rotating furnace at the University of Arizona. The building is unusual in that the whole building rotates to track with the telescope. The MMT Observatory is a joint facility of the University of Arizona and the Smithsonian Institution. (By courtesy of Howard Lester.)

Figure 4b. The MMT AO system deformable mirror. On the left, the deformable mirror is being tested in the laboratory. This picture shows the glass prior to its aluminium coating, showing the 336 magnets and voice coils that deform the 2-millimetre-thick glass surface. In the right-hand picture the mirror is shown installed and aluminized at the front of the 6.5-metre MMTO telescope, with Mount Wrightson in the distance.

SCIENCE WITH NATURAL GUIDE STAR ADAPTIVE OPTICS (NGS AO)

The tremendous range of science coming from AO systems ranges from high-resolution images of moons in our Solar System, detecting new low-mass brown dwarf and multiple close binary systems, examining star formation regions, through to looking into the cores of globular clusters and at the core of our Galaxy and other nearby galaxies for the telltale signatures of super-massive black holes. Figure 5 shows a planetary nebula imaged by the MMTO AO system, which has a spatial resolution of approximately 0.1 arcseconds at 2 microns.

Solar astronomers also use AO systems to look at the physical phenomena in the outer surface of the Sun. Here, the natural guide stars for the WFS cameras are the darker features of the Sun's surface, which are stable enough over many minutes to provide an AO closed-loop signal for their systems. In one novel case, the disc of Mercury was used as a 'guide star' (see Figure 6).

AO can provide images that are comparable to or better than the Hubble Space Telescope, but there are two major obstacles that limit AO correction to a small fraction of the total sky.

Looking at a wide-field image taken with an AO system, the image seems to suffer from a peculiar type of blurring effect. On and near the guide star, the images are diffraction-limited and circular, but more than a few tens of arcseconds away the stellar images start stretching out into ellipses, and eventually the stellar images are back up to the

Figure 5. The Planetary Nebula IC 2149 with Adaptive Optics on the MMT. The planetary nebula IC 2149, imaged by the ARIES near-infrared imager and adaptive secondary on the 6.5-metre MMT. The central star has been allowed to saturate in order to bring out details in the surrounding nebula, which is several thousand times fainter. The inset is a narrow-band continuum image of the central bright region magnified by a factor of two. (By courtesy of Patrick A.Young, Donald W. McCarthy, Craig Kulesa, Karen A. Knierman, Jacqueline Monkiewicz, Guido Brusa and Douglas Miller.)

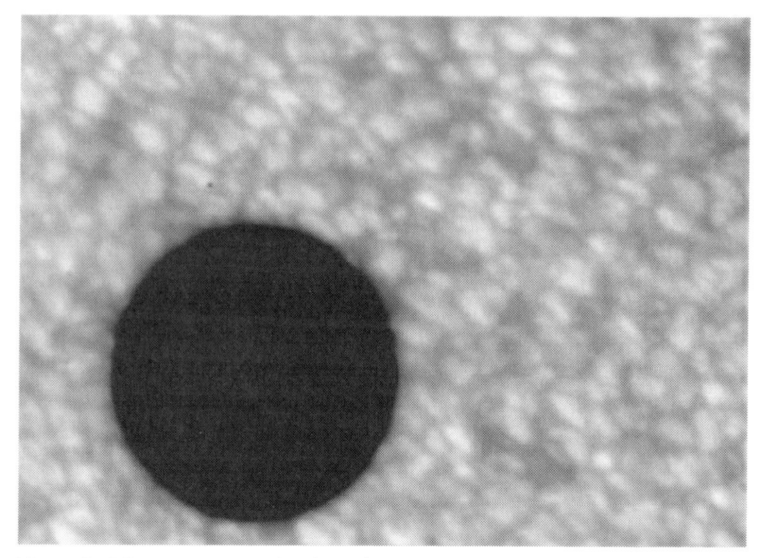

Figure 6. AO systems are not just for night-time astronomers. In this image of the solar disc, the planet Mercury acts as the 'guide star' for this solar AO instrument to acquire a closed loop. This 50-millisecond image was taken on the Vacuum Tower Telescope on Tenerife with the KAOS adaptive optics system. (By courtesy of D. Soltau and Th. Berkefeld at Kiepenheuer-Institut für Sonnenphysik, Freiburg.)

seeing disc sizes again. This is called the isoplanatic effect and it affects all AO systems (see Figure 7). When looking at the guide star, the detected guide star wavefront is actually a sum of all distortions in the column of air from the telescope aperture up through to space. The light from objects tens of arcseconds away on the sky passes through a slightly different tube of atmosphere and has a slightly different set of wavefront errors. The result is that for visible light the area of good AO correction is only a few arcseconds in diameter, and as you go to infrared wavelengths, this patch becomes larger but it is still only 30–40 arcseconds across.

The isoplanatic effect alone is not a major problem, but when combined with the second limitation, it restricts AO systems to just a small fraction of the celestial sphere. Simply put, there are not enough guide stars in the sky! Most large telescopes require a star with a magnitude brighter than 16 to provide enough photons for AO correction. One would think that a larger telescope would solve this problem, but this is not the case – as you build larger telescopes, you correspondingly need more subapertures to measure your wavefront and provide the same degree of correction (back to the tray of wine glasses, all you are doing is making the tray bigger and adding more wine glasses). With the isoplanatic effect limiting you in the near infrared to about 30 arc-second patches of sky around your guide star, the fraction of sky that can be partially AO corrected varies between 0.1 and 1 per cent of the total sky. Wouldn't it be nice to have a portable star that you could just switch on when you most needed it?

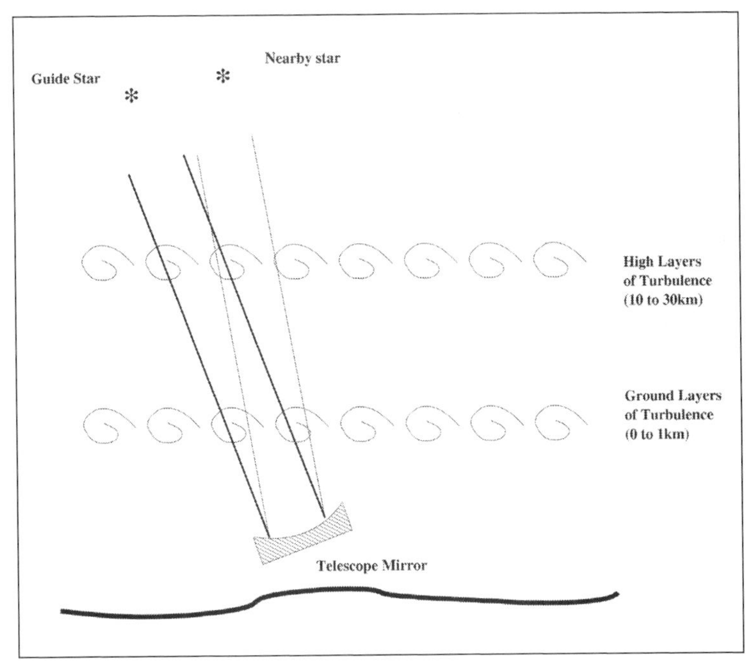

Figure 7. The isoplanatic effect. The telescope is using the guide star's wavefront for the AO system. A nearby star samples a slightly different column of atmosphere, and the difference increases with larger separations from the guide star. The degree of correction falls off with distance from the guide star. The closer the dominant layer of turbulence is to the telescope mirror, the wider the field of correction.

LASER GUIDE STARS

Early on in AO research it was realized that a portable guide star would free up the need to stay near natural guide stars, and so the rush was on to provide some form of light source that could be steered around the sky to the astronomer's content. The sodium laser guide star is one solution to this problem.

At 90 kilometres above the Earth's surface there is a thin layer of sodium atoms left by meteors burning up in the atmosphere. This layer can be excited with a carefully tuned laser and cause resonant backscattering – if the sodium atoms are illuminated with a very specific colour of light they will glow preferentially back down towards the telescope. This beacon acts like a natural guide star, by providing a directable and portable guide star for the AO system to use. The brilliant yellow laser beam is projected via a small telescope either mounted on the side of the main telescope or from behind the secondary mirror. At a wavelength of 589 nanometres, approximately 20 watts of energy are required to produce a laser guide star with enough brightness to be seen back down at the telescope and the AO system. Declassified military research from the 1980s showed the power of this technique, and one of the first astronomical observatories to use a sodium laser guide star system is the 3-metre Shane telescope on Mount Hamilton in California. After many years of development, research and hard work, these sodium laser guide star systems are just beginning to be used at some of the larger telescopes (the 10-metre Keck telescopes on Mauna Kea, and the 8-metre Very Large Telescopes on Cerro Paranal in the Atacama desert of Chile), and more are planned for other major observatories. However, because of the nature of how these specific lasers work, they are tricky and temperamental beasts at the best of times, and it is a continual challenge for the engineers working at the high-altitude observatories to persuade them to output this power level consistently and reliably. They also require a tremendous amount of electrical power to run – typical dye lasers require 50,000 watts to produce a measly 5 watts of sodium laser light! The sodium layer can also vary in concentration over the seasons, producing a further challenge of a variable brightness source for the already beleaguered engineers.

Owing to these difficulties, a previously overlooked method is now being explored. For a beam of light passing through our atmosphere, more blue light is scattered out of the beam's path than red light. For sunlight shining down on us, blue light is scattered more than red light, and this leads to the familiar blue skies we see. When the Sun is near the horizon, the sunlight travels a much longer path through the atmosphere and blue light is scattered out of the sunbeam, causing the Sun's disc to turn red. This atmospheric effect is called Rayleigh scattering. A 30-watt green laser releases a 12-nanosecond laser pulse, corresponding to a 3-metre-long tube of photons travelling at the speed of light up through the atmosphere (see Figure 8). As this tube of

Figure 8. A bright-green laser is projected from the MMTO telescope into the southern Arizona night sky. In this time-exposure picture, the green laser light scatters from the atmosphere above and back into the telescope, where a dichroic beamsplitter reflects the return signal to the wavefront sensor camera but allows infrared light into the science instrument. (By courtesy of Gabor Furész.)

light passes through the air, some light is scattered back down to the telescope and to the wavefront sensor camera. Now, imagine trying to focus on a bumble bee flying from your nose out into your garden. If you don't refocus your eyes quickly enough, you see a blurred image of the insect as your eyes try to adjust to the sudden distance change. Similarly, following the laser beam pulse requires focusing the telescope from a point about 10 kilometres up to 25 kilometres in less than a millisecond – quite a technical challenge! At the 6.5-metre MMTO telescope, a clever trick is used to refocus the telescope this rapidly. A small mirror is mounted on the end of a modified speaker cone, which moves back and forth 5,000 times a second. By carefully timing the pulse of light from the laser, the moving mirror can track the back-scattered light pulse as it travels up through the turbulent atmosphere, forming a sharply focused image on the wavefront sensor.

Rayleigh scattering does not require a specifically wavelength-tuned laser, and so far more powerful lasers can be used. With a more powerful laser system, multiple laser guide stars can be projected into the sky. Figure 9 shows the wavefront sensor image from the prototype laser system, showing five sets of images of the same telescope mirror. Each image measures the turbulence through the atmosphere for one direction in the sky. By using complex computer algorithms, a three-dimensional map of the atmosphere along the line of sight of the telescope can be modelled and reconstructed in a computer. The technology is relatively new, though, and what currently takes hours of careful data processing needs to be calculated in timescales of less than a thousandth of a second!

TO THE FUTURE

One of the most vigorous areas of research in astronomy is extrasolar planet detection. Many planetary systems are being indirectly detected by carefully measuring their gravitational influence on the motion of their parent star. With the discovery of large planets orbiting close to their parent stars, some with orbits that number in the dozens of days, there is the potential to directly observe the reflected light from their atmospheres. Detecting extrasolar planets in the nearest star systems would not be a problem if it wasn't for the light from their parent stars. If you could look back at our Solar System from a dozen parsecs away,

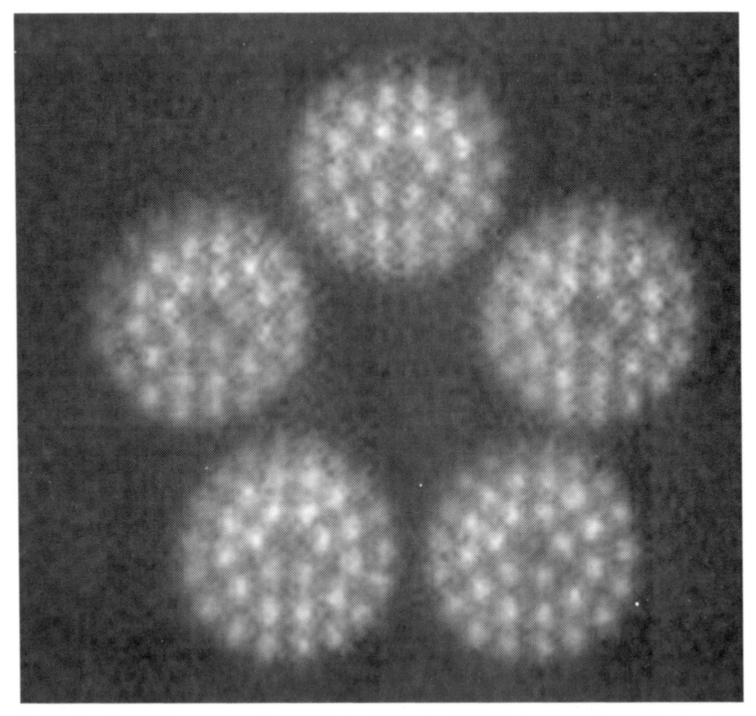

Figure 9. A wavefront sensor image of the 6.5-metre MMT telescope mirror, showing turbulence for five dynamically refocused laser beams arranged as a regular pentagon inscribed on a circle 2 arcminutes in diameter. (By courtesy of Tom Stalcup, Miguel Snyder, Christoph Baranec and Mark Milton.)

Jupiter is more than a hundred million times fainter than the Sun at visible-light wavelengths! It is similar to looking for a needle beside a burning haystack. Observing at longer wavelengths improves this ratio down to about 500,000, where the star's flux is not as bright. For the planets in close proximity to their parent stars, they are further warmed by their star's fierce heat, and for young planets there is still more energy due to their recent contraction and formation. Combining all these effects, together with their physically large size, the contrast between planet and star at 5–10-micron wavelengths can be as small as 10,000.

There are two techniques for reducing the light from the parent star while allowing the planet's light to shine through, and both rely on the planet and star being in slightly different positions on the sky. A coronagraph relies on placing a physical mask over the Airy disc of the primary star, but this requires precise positioning of the mask and careful design to prevent losing light from the planet. Nulling interferometry uses the wave properties of the light itself to build a 'mask' that resembles a picket fence, and place it over the parent star, as in Figure 10. Adaptive optics increases the efficiency of both of these

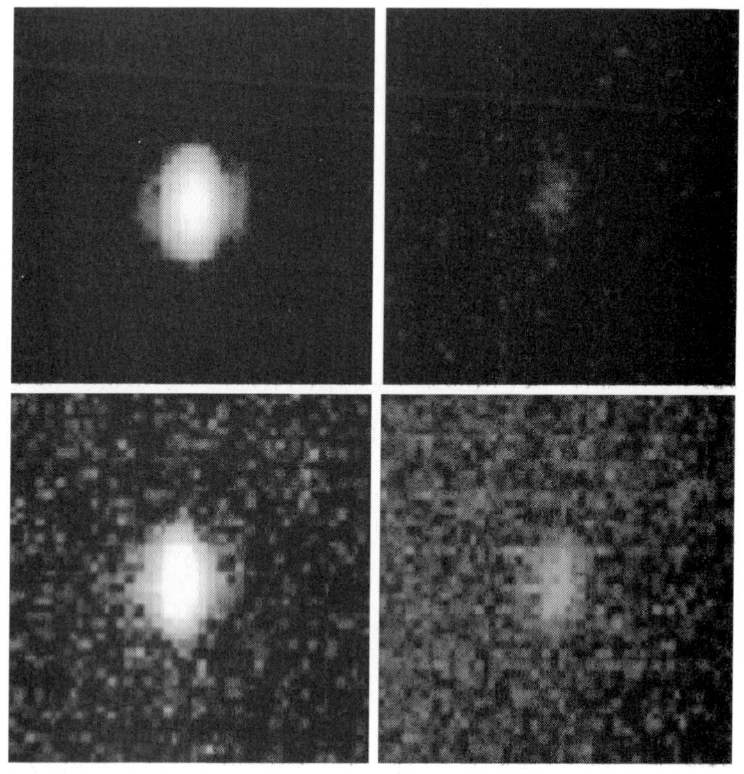

Figure 10. Nulling interferometry using an AO system. The top row shows constructive and destructive interference on a point source calibrator. The nulled image on the right shows 4.7 per cent residual flux (the elongated shape of the star is an artificial effect introduced by the interferometer). The bottom row shows the constructive and destructive interference on a Herbig Ae star. The residual flux in the nulled image of 24 per cent residual flux indicates the presence of circumstellar material. All images were taken at 10.3 microns. (By courtesy of Wilson Liu and Philip Hinz, University of Arizona.)

planet-finding techniques, and initial results from a 10-micron nulling interferometer at the MMTO is detecting large discs of dust around stars. This instrument is the prototype for a larger interferometer being built for the Large Binocular Telescope, which consists of two 8.4-metre diameter mirrors, separated by 22 metres on a common telescope mount, located on Mount Graham in southern Arizona. The light from these two telescopes will be combined with a nulling interferometer to look at dust discs and maybe even directly detect some of these planets. The VLT is also completing a large interferometer to combine light from two or more of its 8-metre telescopes in a similar quest.

The next generation of 20-metre- to 100-metre-diameter telescopes (such as the Giant Magellan Telescope and OWL) all include AO systems as part of their designs. Putting these telescopes into space would be prohibitively expensive, but with some amazing engineering we can go a long way to dealing with the 'sea of air' that we live under. Keep your eyes peeled and watch this space!

The Discovery of the Spiral-arm Structure of the Milky Way

WILLIAM SHEEHAN

The Milky Way, that splendid river of light called by the ancient Greeks 'Galaxias', consists of a powdering of faint stars, as first shown by Galileo with his telescope in the 1600s. Although today it is common astronomical knowledge that the Milky Way is a vast spiral star system, seen edgewise – one of the innumerable such systems visible in the telescope – the first clear demonstration of the fact occurred as recently as 1951. The story is not well known, even though the discovery was one of the grandest in astronomy.

THE STRUCTURE OF THE MILKY WAY: EARLY VIEWS

During the two centuries after Galileo's pioneering work with the telescope, there was, in fact, little attention paid to discerning the structure of the sidereal universe. The dominant figure in astronomy, Isaac Newton, had introduced the theory of gravitation, which he and his successors used to work out in detail the motions of the Moon and planets; from this perspective, the stars were a mere backdrop against which to register their motions. There were a few speculations by the likes of the English surveyor Thomas Wright and the German philosopher Immanuel Kant that the Milky Way might be a rotating disc of stars viewed edgewise from within. But the first observational programme to determine the outline of the star system was carried out by the German-born amateur astronomer and telescope-maker, William Herschel.

Herschel had come to England from Hanover in 1757, and at first eked out a meagre existence giving music lessons and training the band of the Durham Militia for the Earl of Darlington, but in 1766 he became organist at the Octagon Chapel in Bath. Meanwhile, he had taken up astronomy and telescope-making, and rose to sudden astronomical prominence in 1781 with the discovery of the planet Uranus from the southward-facing garden of his house at 19 New King Street.

Bequeathed a pension by George III, who appreciated Herschel's attempt to name the planet *Georgium Sidus* – the Georgian Star – a name which never found favour on the Continent, Herschel, at forty three, was able to give up his musical career and concentrate all his energies on some of the grandest astronomical problems of the age. Fanny Burney, the novelist and letter-writer, later noted: 'The King has not a happier subject than this man, who owes wholly to His Majesty that he is not wretched.'

Beginning with assumptions that faintness of stars in the Milky Way indicated distances and that all the stars were uniformly distributed (neither of which, it turns out, is actually justified) Herschel counted the number of stars in different parts of the sky in order to map the shape of the Galaxy. It seemed to extend further out in some directions than in others. In overall shape it resembled a snapping alligator. He published his famous grindstone model of the Galaxy diagram in 1785. Though it looks remarkably modern, the resemblance to modern maps of the Galaxy is somewhat misleading. In fact, he was not looking all the way to the edge of the Galaxy, as he supposed, and only mapped stars in the immediate surroundings of the Sun. But at least he got the flattened disc part right. All in all, it was a remarkable attempt.

William's studies were later extended to the southern hemisphere by his son, John Herschel, who summed up his view of the galactic structure in his *Outline of Astronomy*, which first appeared in 1849:[1]

> When we attempt to map and model out the Galaxy . . . the obvious conclusion is that its form must be, generally speaking, *flat*, and of a thickness small in comparison with its area in length and breadth, the laws of perspective affording us little further assistance in the inquiry. Probability may, it is true, here and there enlighten us as to certain features. Thus when we see, as in the Coal-sack, a sharply defined oval space free from stars, insulated in the midst of a uniform band of not much more than twice its breadth, it would seem much less probable that a conical or tubular hollow traverses the whole starry stratum, continuously extended from the eye outwards,

> than that a *distant* mass of comparatively moderate thickness should be simply perforated from side to side.

Sir John concluded that by means of the conical or tubular hollows in the starry mass he might have managed to peer right through the Galaxy into the empty space beyond. He offered an image of the Milky Way as a ring of small stars surrounding the Sun, an image that was accommodated by later astronomers to the swirls and elaborate spiral forms of other nebulae revealed by the 3rd Earl of Rosse with the giant 72-inch telescope he built in the grounds of his home at Birr Castle, County Offaly, Ireland.[2]

As late as the beginning of the twentieth century, William Herschel's view of the Galaxy continued to find some support in statistical studies of stars carried out by the Dutch astronomer Jacobus C. Kapteyn. Kapteyn regarded the Galaxy as a small disc of stars. Since he ignored the effects of absorption of starlight by interstellar dust, as had Herschel, his model included only the nearer stars. Kapteyn's disc measured a mere 13,000 light-years long by 3,000 light-years thick, and remained centred on or near the Solar System.

These provincial views were finally shattered in 1920 when Harlow Shapley, then at Mount Wilson Observatory, worked out the distances to globular clusters and showed that they formed a framework eccentrically disposed to the Sun. With the Sun now far removed from its centre, the Milky Way's disc of stars thus had to be much larger than Herschel, Kapteyn or anyone else had fathomed. By then it was also becoming increasingly clear, especially from the wide-angle Milky Way photographs of the American astronomer Edward Emerson Barnard,[3] that rather than being tubules or holes perforating a disc of stars, the dark markings of the Milky Way consisted of large dust clouds scattered along the galactic plane. John Herschel had not, as he supposed, peered through the Milky Way via tubules into the surrounding space; he had only found his view blocked in certain directions by the interstellar dust.

Nor was our local universe confined only to our own particular ring, or rings, of stars. Among the many nebulae discovered by the Herschels and others, Lord Rosse and his assistants with the great reflector at Birr Castle had discerned a spiral structure in some of them – most famously in the 'Whirlpool' nebula in Canes Venatici but also in 80 or so others. Faint and small spirals were later found in their thousands in deep photographs taken by James Keeler with the Crossley reflector at Lick Observatory at the end of the nineteenth century (Keeler died in 1900). They appeared to be almost innumerable in the regions around the galactic poles.

Many astronomers, including Keeler, believed these spirals were planetary systems in formation. A later Lick astronomer, Heber D. Curtis, studied the Crossley images more carefully and recognized that there was a family resemblance in all the spiral nebulae – in other words, they appeared to form a class of similar objects scattered at different angles and at different distances. In each case where they were seen edge-on they had dark rifts dividing them, which Curtis recognized as similar to the dark matter of the Milky Way that Barnard had photographed. By 1917, Curtis had conclusively demonstrated that the spiral nebulae were distant star systems – 'island universes' – a result that was almost immediately confirmed with the discovery of novae in the spiral nebula NGC 6946 by George Willis Ritchey using the 60-inch reflector at Mount Wilson, followed by the discovery of additional novae in other spirals by Curtis himself.[4]

The Milky Way thus took its place as but one of countless millions of star systems. Seen from an exterior vantage point, it would resemble one of these innumerable extragalactic forms. It might well be a majestic spiral in its own right, a possibility suggested as early as 1900 by the Dutch amateur astronomer Cornelis Easton. As yet, however, there was no proof. The unravelling of the windings of the Milky Way's structure, from the perspective of a star located in the midst of them, would turn out to be one of the most difficult problems of twentieth-century astronomy. Its eventual solution would depend on understanding the properties and distribution of its intrinsically most brilliant stars.

TWENTIETH-CENTURY STUDIES OF GALACTIC STRUCTURE

Kapteyn died in 1921. Largely as a result of his influence, Dutch astronomers continued his work on galactic structure. The most brilliant of them was Jan Oort who, during the 1920s, refined our knowledge of galactic rotation and modified Kapteyn's model by introducing the notion that there must be much more interstellar absorption by dust than had been realized. He noted that, because of galactic rotation, 'there was a well-defined relationship between radial velocities, distances and angles, which meant that measured systematic radial velocities could be converted to approximate distances in a straightforward way'.[5] Unfortunately, Oort did not have the telescopes to provide the kinds of data he needed – remember, the Netherlands, whose mean elevation is below sea level, is one of the worst imaginable places for observational astronomy! Moreover, his research was disrupted by the German Occupation during the Second World War.

After the war, Oort learned of the discovery of radio radiation from the Galaxy by the American engineer Grote Reber, and became the first astronomer to fully realize the great potential of a new and powerful technique that would allow penetration even of the interstellar dust clouds. Following the suggestion of a brilliant Utrecht student, Hendrik C. van de Hulst, that hydrogen gas in the ground state would emit radio at a specific frequency (the 21-centimetre line), and given there was a vast abundance of hydrogen gas in the galactic plane, he realized it was only a matter of time before radio astronomers would be able to map the structure of spiral arms, if they existed. But there were delays in getting the proper equipment. Not until the spring of 1951 did the first beneficiaries of a crash American wartime radar programme, Edward M. Purcell and H.I. McEwen at Harvard, and then Oort and radio engineer C.A. Muller at Kootwijk independently (and within six weeks of one another), succeed in detecting the 21-centimetre line. This made the mapping of the spiral arms by radio astronomers inevitable, and the first such maps would appear within a year.

Optical astronomers were, as they had been for decades, also pursuing the same goal. Though long stymied in their attempts to achieve it by means of statistical counts of stars, such as those of Herschel and Kapteyn, they had now regrouped. A different approach was needed. As Harvard historian Owen Gingerich has noted, 'the solution to this puzzle lay elsewhere, with the observational analysis of the Andromeda Nebula and other nearby galaxies'.[6] Thus, as the second half of the twentieth century began, radio and optical astronomers – neither particularly concerned with the other's methods or results – were both approaching the long-elusive goal of mapping the spiral arms of the Galaxy by using different strategies. And in an exciting race to the finish the optical astronomers were to win by the breadth of a hair.

THE GRAIL OF OPTICAL ASTRONOMERS

The breakthrough was achieved by William Wilson Morgan (Figure 1), a stellar astronomer at the Yerkes Observatory, who in turn was building on the brilliant work done by Walter Baade at Mount Wilson. Morgan put a number of leads together during the late 1940s and early 1950s and forged (from what others might have perceived as unrelated scraps) a technique that dramatically revealed the hitherto undetected pattern of the spiral arms of the Milky Way. One often hears these days of the failure of intelligence agencies to connect the dots. Morgan, in one of the most remarkable cases of intuitive creative imagination involving pattern recognition, *did* connect the dots. In his case, the dots consisted of OB star associations – groups of freshly minted, hot young stars – embedded in glowing clouds of ionized hydrogen gas (HII regions). When drawn together they at last traced the elusive outline of the spiral arms.

The reason that earlier statistical surveys failed is that, except for hot

Figure 1. William Wilson Morgan as he looked at about the time he discovered the spiral-arm structure of the Milky Way. (Image courtesy of the Yerkes Observatory.)

young stars, the other stars are so long-lived that new stars and old stars get mixed up with one another as they disperse from the vicinity of their births; thus their distribution along the spiral arms becomes diffuse over time and not even brute statistics can bring out the spiral-arm pattern. In practice, only what Walter Baade once called 'the candles and the frosting' – the hot, bright, young stars and the dust lanes – can be used to trace the spiral arms (see Figure 2). This realization was Morgan's point of departure.

Like two other galaxy pioneers, E.E. Barnard and Carl Seyfert, Morgan was a native of Tennessee. He had been born in the hamlet of

Figure 2. GALEX spacecraft image of the Andromeda Galaxy nicely showing what Walter Baade once called 'the candles and frosting', and why it was necessary to use the young, hot, bright stars to work out the spiral-arm structure of our Galaxy, not older stars such as M and K giants which, though bright enough, because of their greater age have dispersed and diffused distributions in the Galaxy. (Image courtesy of NASA and Jet Propulsion Laboratory, Caltech.)

Bethesda, a place which no longer exists, in 1906, and almost at once began to move with his parents, who were home missionaries in the Southern Methodist Church, all over the South. (A paper in the Yerkes Observatory archives noted that, from Bethesda, he moved to Crystal River, Florida, then to Starke, Florida, from where he saw Halley's Comet in 1910; to Punta Gorda, Key West; a farm near Punta Gorda; Perry, Florida; Colorado Springs, Colorado; Poplar Bluff, Missouri; Spartanburg, South Carolina; and Washington, DC. During all that developmental period, he hardly spent two successive years in the same place!) His formal education was meagre in a way, but things became more settled once he moved to Washington with his mother (his father, who was a rather domineering and unstable personality, was away much of the time). He continued on to college studies at Washington and Lee College in Virginia, and for a while aspired to become a high school English teacher, but he performed well in classes in mathematics, physics and chemistry. He was also excellent in astronomy – even persuading his professor, Benjamin Wooten, to acquire a small telescope. During his vacations he regularly dropped in at the US Naval Observatory.

In 1926, before Morgan had finished his degree, Wooten visited the Yerkes Observatory. The director, Edwin Brant Frost (Figure 3), was looking for an assistant to operate the observatory's spectroheliograph (an instrument used to obtain special images of the Sun), and Wooten recommended Morgan for the job. Morgan's father was violently opposed, thinking that he would 'end up just in a laboratory working for somebody else, [and] that's nothing'. That was the last Morgan remembered talking to his father about anything; he never saw him again. Later that year Morgan's father abandoned the family, never to return. But Morgan made the right decision, and would remain at Yerkes for 68 years.

Frost, the Yerkes director who hired Morgan, had been born with congenital myopia, a condition predisposing to retinal detachments, and by the time Morgan was hired he was legally blind. (He once told Morgan that the immediate cause of his blindness was the strain of correcting the young Edwin Hubble's first scientific paper!) He was a humane and well-rounded sort of person who held great lawn parties but was not scientifically very productive. After Frost reached retirement age in 1931, he was replaced by Otto Struve, a Russian immigrant from a very distinguished family of astronomers, a hulking man whose

Figure 3. Edwin Brant Frost at a garden party at Yerkes, the humane but rather scientifically unproductive observatory as it was when Morgan arrived in 1926. (Image courtesy of the Yerkes Observatory.)

eyes weren't quite congruent and who had a gruff bearish manner, but who was an incredibly hard worker. In those early days, Struve was a great inspiration to Morgan. He had once remarked that he had never looked at the spectrum of a star, any star, where he didn't find something important to work on. That remark made a lasting impression on Morgan. Struve was an astrophysicist – he was primarily interested in using stellar spectra as a tool to understand what was going on physically in the stars. Morgan, on the other hand, became deeply concerned with spectral classification, and in 1935 produced his first paper on classification, 'A Descriptive Study of the Spectra of the A-type Stars'.[7]

According to Struve, it was a series of lectures given by the Dutch-American astronomer Bart J. Bok at Yerkes a year later 'that first inspired Morgan to improve the distances of the hotter stars and to investigate the structure of the Milky Way with the help of these distances'.[8] These hotter stars included the stars of spectral type B and their even brighter, but much rarer, cousins, the O stars. None of the closer stars are B stars. There are only a few of them within a distance of

300 light-years. But because these stars are so intrinsically bright, they 'dominate the naked-eye sky all out of proportion to their true population'.[9] Among these B stars are such gems as Rigel, Achernar, Beta Centauri, Spica, Alpha and Beta Crucis, and Regulus. Without the B stars, the famous outline of Orion would be decimated and reduced to Betelguese and one or two others; its rival Scorpius, opposite to it in the sky so that, in keeping with legend, it might never be above the horizon at the same time as the Hunter, would be wiped out and rendered unrecognizable. In addition, the famous Seven Sisters of the Pleiades would all disappear.

The B stars are young, hot stars, very prominent in ultraviolet. They had first been grouped together in a spectral classification in the Henry Draper catalogue, developed at Harvard Observatory by Wilhelmina Fleming, Antonia Maury and Annie Jump Cannon, working under the supervision of Edward C. Pickering. The Draper catalogue had introduced the familiar categories OBAFGKM.

With the famous 40-inch refractor at Yerkes (Figure 4), since 1897 and still the largest instrument of its kind, Morgan began getting

Figure 4. The Yerkes 40-inch refractor, used by Morgan to obtain low-dispersion spectra of stars that he later used to define the spiral-arm structure of the Galaxy. (Image courtesy of the author.)

spectra by means of a low-dispersion spectrograph which had been at Yerkes since the 1920s. The instrument had been largely abandoned after failing in its first application, the measurement of radial velocities of stars. Morgan decided to upgrade it in 1939, and used it to identify from the low-dispersion spectrograms the different luminosity classes of B-type stars. Some of them were supergiants – because of surface gravity and pressure effects, their spectral lines were broadened and more diffuse (they showed 'wings'). Others, with narrower and sharper lines, were the ordinary Main Sequence stars (dwarfs). This was an important breakthrough. Since the B-type supergiants, together with their brighter but rarer cousins the O stars, are true stellar beacons, they can be seen from great distances across the Galaxy. Morgan and others realized that they could be used to map galactic structure provided one could only calibrate the luminosities of these stars to their spectral types.

In principle, this is straightforward; in practice, difficult. The main problem is that, because there are so few of these stars – and none within a few hundred light-years – they are all dimmed and reddened to some extent by interstellar dust, which is pervasive in the plane of the Galaxy. It exists as an omnipresent fog concentrated especially in the galactic plane in the dark clouds so well seen in the Milky Way photographs of E.E. Barnard (as in Taurus where the Pleiades illuminate some of the clouds at a distance of 400 light-years, and in Auriga and Perseus). This dust exists in a state of continual mixing. Being tossed about relentlessly, it shows all the telltale signs of turbulent motion, as is only to be expected in a rotating mass of gas where the rotation is not of equal angular velocity at all points. Friction and shear between the different layers produce turbulent motion, causing the dust to break into some larger structures and innumerable small ones. This mixing causes the concentrations of dust to be quite variable along different lines of sight.

Since the O and B stars also hug the galactic plane, they are all affected more or less by this dust, so one must use indirect methods to take account of the dust when attempting to determine the stars' luminosities. But it can be done. Since dust does not absorb uniformly across the spectrum – it is about twice as efficient in absorbing at the blue end as it is at the red – by measuring the brightness of stars at both ends of the spectrum (the colour index) one can determine the degree of reddening of the star and so compensate for the effect of dust. Then by combining this data with accurately measured parallax distances for some of the nearer stars one can work out the sought-for relationship of spectral type to luminosity. By 1943 – when Morgan and his colleagues Philip Keenan and Edith Kellman published *An Atlas of Stellar Spectra, with an Outline of Spectral Classification* – Morgan had established himself as the master of the field, and he spent the next several years (in collaboration with other astronomers, including Case Western University astronomer Jason J. Nassau) obtaining distances for the high-luminosity B and O stars.

BAADE'S WORK ON THE TWO STELLAR POPULATIONS

In 1944, Walter Baade at Mount Wilson, California, using the 100-inch reflector under wartime blackout conditions, published his seminal work on the two stellar populations in the Andromeda Nebula (M31) and its elliptical companions M32 and NGC 205. The two populations turned out to be young and old stars.[10] Baade submitted his paper to the *Astrophysical Journal* in 1944, and Morgan immediately recognized its importance.[11]

Baade's plates of the Andromeda Spiral showed clearly that in the spiral arms the hottest, most massive stars and open clusters were always associated with HII regions (diffuse nebulae of the Orion type), which were known to be regions of hot, ionized, interstellar hydrogen. The large complexes of nebulae and young, bright stars made up Baade's Population I, while the galactic nucleus and globular clusters were characterized by the faint red stars of Population II. In December 1947, Baade spoke about the two stellar populations at an American Astronomical Society meeting at the Perkins Observatory in Ohio. Morgan was among those in attendance. By analogy to the result Baade had announced for the Andromeda Spiral, Morgan realized that in addition to mapping the high-luminosity stars, he could also use HII regions to outline the spiral arms of the Milky Way.

At Yerkes there happened to be a wide-angle camera (Figures 5a and 5b) possessing a field of view of 140°, which had been developed by Jesse L. Greenstein and Louis G. Henyey for use as a projection system to train aerial gunners during the war. But it could equally well be adapted for use the other way around – as a camera. Under Morgan's

Figures 5a and 5b. The Greenstein–Henyey camera used by two graduate students, Donald Osterbrock and Stewart Sharpless, to obtain wide-angle photographs of the Milky Way for Morgan. (Images courtesy of the Yerkes Observatory.)

direction, two graduate students, Donald Osterbrock and Stewart Sharpless, began using this camera to photograph the Milky Way with narrow-band (hydrogen alpha) filters in the search for HII regions.[12] Many of the HII regions they mapped were already well known, but some of them were new. In both cases, because of the very wide fields of the photographs, they were identified for the first time as the important, extended objects they are (see Figure 6).

By the autumn of 1951, Morgan had been immersed in the problem of trying to find the spiral arms of the Milky Way for at least four years. He had laid out what was, essentially, the correct approach to be taken to the problem and had then pursued it in a diligent and systematic way. According to his recollection, the pieces of the puzzle finally fell into place suddenly, as he walked from his office to his house on an autumn night, some seven or eight months before the first radio observations were announced showing spiral-arm structure. His personal notebooks, which the author has been studying at the Yerkes Observatory, contain tantalizing insights into the circumstances of this brilliant discovery: 'The flash inspiration of the spiral arms [was] a creative, intuitional burst,' he records in an entry on 9 December 1956. And later that month: 'Dear Book, what a strange thing the unbridled mind is. A sequence of thoughts can develop – move rapidly from stage to stage, and end in a conclusion (a definite, unique conclusion) in a few eye-closings.'

His most complete account of what happened that evening is given

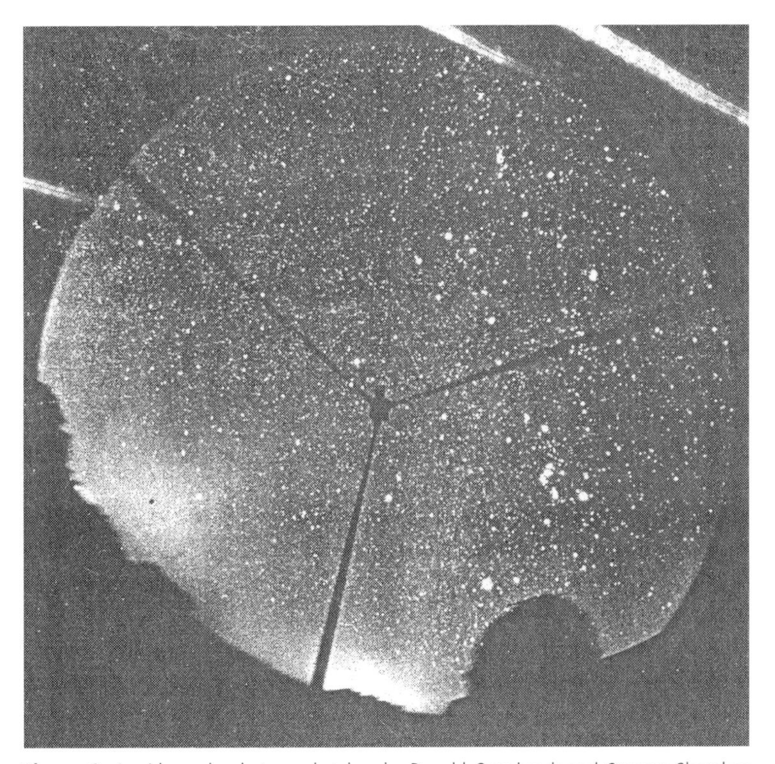

Figure 6. A wide-angle photograph taken by Donald Osterbrock and Stewart Sharpless with the 140° field Greenstein–Henyey camera. This image shows the winter Milky Way, with Orion in the lower right (above the shadow of the dome of the 40-inch refractor), while the cone of the Zodiacal Light appears at the lower left. Morgan used such photographs to map large HII regions in the Galaxy. In combination with his plots of OB stars, he was able to define the Perseus and Orion arms of the Milky Way. (Image courtesy of the Yerkes Observatory.)

in an August 1978 American Institute for Physics interview with US Air and Space Museum historian David De Vorkin:

> This was in the fall of 1951, and I was walking between the observatory and home, which is only 100 yards away. I was looking up in the sky . . . just looking up in the region of the Double Cluster [in Perseus], and I realized I had been getting distance moduli corrected the best way I could with the colors that were available, for numbers of stars in the general region . . . Anyway, I was walking. I was looking up at the sky, and it suddenly occurred to me that the double cluster in Perseus, and then a number of stars in Cassiopeia, these are not the bright stars but the distant stars, and even Cepheus, that along there I was getting distance moduli, of between 11 and 12, corrected distance moduli. Well, 11.5 is two kiloparsecs . . . and so, I couldn't wait to get over here and really plot them up. It looked like they were at the same distance . . . It looked like a concentration . . . And so, as soon as I began plotting this out, the first thing that showed up was that there was a concentration, a long narrow concentration of young stars . . . There are HII regions along there too . . . And that was the thing that broke [the problem] down.[13]

This first spiral arm – the Perseus arm – Morgan traced between galactic longitudes 70° and 140°. As he plotted the OB stars, Morgan identified another arm, the Orion arm, extending from Cygnus through Cepheus and Cassiopeia's chair past Perseus and Orion to Monoceros (from galactic longitude 20° to 180° or 190°). The so-called Great Rift of the Milky Way marked a part of the inner dark lane of this arm; the Sun lay not quite at the inner edge but 100 or 200 light-years inside it. It was the Sun's proximity to – indeed, virtual immersion in – this arm that had made it so difficult to identify. Morgan later pointed out, 'The hardest thing is to know what's going on if you're in the middle of something, or if it's going right through you.'

Morgan constructed a scale model of the spiral-arm structure of the Galaxy using old sponge rubber. Later he added some concentrations of early B stars from the southern hemisphere. This more detailed scale model, constructed using balls of cotton (Figure 7), he presented in a slide at the American Astronomical Society meeting in Cleveland the day after Christmas, 1951. It was a memorable occasion. Oort introduced Morgan, who rose and gave a 15-minute talk. But the

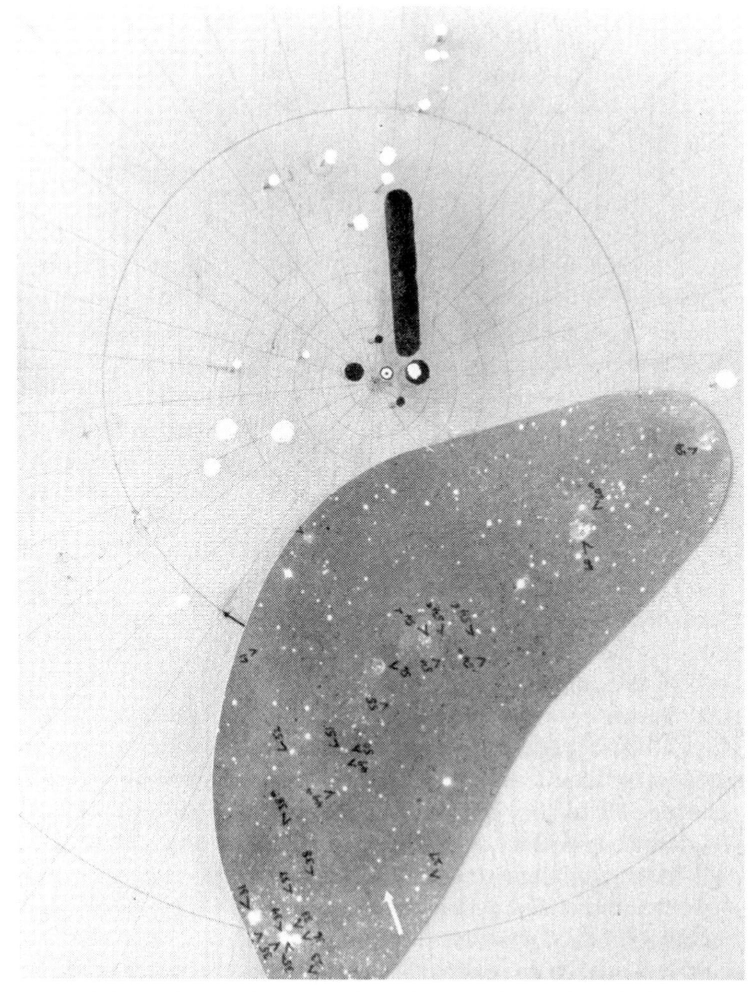

Figure 7. Morgan's cotton-ball model of the OB associations defining the Perseus and Orion arms of the Milky Way superimposed on a Walter Baade photograph of similar OB associations and HII regions in an arm of the Andromeda Galaxy, obtained with the 200-inch telescope at Mount Palomar. In the model, the cotton balls represent various OB associations and the dark, bar-like object represents the Great Rift of Cygnus. (Image courtesy of the Yerkes Observatory

importance of what he referred to as the Morgan–Sharpless–Osterbrock model was obvious, and he received a standing ovation (the only other time that had happened was when V.M. Slipher had announced the discovery of the large velocity-shifts of the nebulae at an AAS meeting in August 1914). Struve described it as 'an ovation such as I have never before witnessed. Clearly, he had in the course of a 15-minute paper presented so convincing an array of arguments that the audience for once threw caution to the wind and gave Morgan the recognition which he so fully deserved.' Ivan King, who was at the meeting and recollected it to me last year, recalled that not only was the audience clapping their hands but they also started to stomp their feet. And since Oort, after introducing Morgan, had taken the latter's seat, Morgan had nowhere to sit down!

Oddly enough, Morgan's discovery was never properly written up – the most complete account at the time was an article in the popular-astronomy magazine *Sky & Telescope*. There were various reasons for Morgan's failure to present a proper publication. He was hospitalized for manic-depressive illness at Billings Hospital at the University of Chicago in the summer of 1952. By then Oort and his team of radio astronomers had independently announced the discovery of spiral-arm structure. At the time it seemed to everyone that the radio astronomers' results were more generalizable and further-reaching than Morgan's – they were able to identify structure on a much greater scale than the optical astronomers, including even structures on the hidden far side of the Galaxy. It was only much later (about 1970) that radio astronomers began to realize they were not actually getting very accurate distances because of large-scale, systematic deviations of the hydrogen clouds from circular motion and that, although the radio maps had seemed so much more detailed than Morgan's, they were not very reliable.

Edmond Halley had said on discovering the periodicity of the comet which now bears his name, 'if it comes to be discovered, be it known that it was first seen by an Englishman'. In the same way it is fitting that the spiral-arm structure of the Milky Way was first recognized by an optical astronomer.

The Perseus arm, which is the spiral arm that Morgan first made out, marks a splendid region of the sky to explore with a small telescope. It is well placed in the winter skies of the Northern Hemisphere and furnishes one of the northerner's chief consolations for being deprived of a clear view of the centre of the Galaxy (at 20°S) and the Magellanic Clouds. The Perseus arm is 7,000 or 8,000 light-years further from the centre of the Galaxy than the Local Arm inhabited by the Sun. It appears in projection far beyond the neighbouring suns to which almost all the stars of the naked-eye constellations belong, and stretches, through condensations and star knots among its dusty lanes, from the Rosette Nebula and its OB association in Monoceros, across drifts of less well-known but equally lovely HII regions, including NGC 7762 and NGC 281, to the dazzling and unrivalled double cluster h-χ Persei, in the Sword Handle, which contains a hive of supergiant O and B stars, each a rival to the brilliant Rigel in the foot of Orion, shining with an intensity tens of thousands of times greater than that of the Sun.

It is gratifying to mark these clusters and to think of Morgan, walking from the Yerkes Observatory to his house, measuring the 7,000 light-years' distance to them with the instantaneous flight – 'the creative, intuitional burst' – of a powerful mind.

ACKNOWLEDGEMENTS

The author would like to thank Christopher Conselice, Donald E. Osterbrock, Dimitri Mihalas, Robert F. Garrison, Lew Hobbs, Ivan King, Owen Gingerich, David De Vorkin, John Mason, Joseph E. Miller, Sir Patrick Moore, Kyle Cudworth, Richard Kron, Judith Bausch and Richard Dreiser for invaluable information and assistance.

REFERENCES

1. John Herschel, *Outlines of Astronomy*, London: Longmans, Green & Co., 1887, p. 573.
2. Michael A. Hoskin, 'An Overview', in *Stellar Astronomy*, Chalfont St. Giles: Science History Publications, 1982, pp. 16–17.
3. William Sheehan, *The Immortal Fire Within: the life and work of Edward Emerson Barnard*, Cambridge: Cambridge University Press, 1995.
4. Donald E. Osterbrock, 'Astronomer for All Seasons: Heber D. Curtis', *Mercury*, May–June 2001, pp. 24–31.

5. Donald E. Osterbrock, *Walter Baade: A Life in Astrophysics*, Princeton, New Jersey: Princeton University Press, 2001, p. 147.
6. Owen Gingerich, 'The discovery of the spiral arms of the Milky Way', in *The Milky Way Galaxy*, edited by Hugo van Woerden, Ronald J. Allen and W. Butler Burton, Dordrecht: D. Reidel, 1985, p. 61.
7. W.W. Morgan, 'A Descriptive Study of the Spectra of the A-type Stars', *Publications of the Yerkes Observatory*, 7 (1935), p. 133.
8. Otto Struve, 'New Light on the Structure of the Galaxy Gained in 1952', *Astronomical Society of the Pacific*, Leaflet no. 285, January 1953, p. 282,
9. James B. Kaler, *Stars and their Spectra*, Cambridge: Cambridge University Press, 2002, p. 183.
10. Donald E. Osterbrock, *Walter Baade: A Life in Astrophysics*, Princeton, New Jersey: Princeton University Press, 2001.
11. Walter Baade, 'The Resolution of M32, NGC 205, and the Central Region of the Andromeda Galaxy', *Astrophysical Journal*, 100 (1944), pp. 137–46.
12. The camera and another of its early applications, photography of the gegenschein, are well described in Otto Struve, 'Photography of the Counterglow', *Sky & Telescope*, July 1951, pp. 215–18.
13. David De Vorkin interview, American Institute for Physics, August 1978.

How the Vikings Sought Life on Mars

DAVID M. HARLAND

Thirty years ago, in 1976, NASA put an identical pair of Viking landers on Mars to test for the presence of life on that planet.

THE ASSUMPTIONS

When NASA asked the Space Science Board of the National Academy of Sciences to assist in developing a strategy to determine whether life exists on Mars, Joshua Lederberg of Stanford University hosted a summer study in 1964 to investigate the issues. In March 1965 the draft report, *Biology and the Exploration of Mars*, said, 'Given all the evidence presently available, we believe it entirely reasonable that Mars is inhabited with living organisms, and that life independently originated there.' However, whereas if there were plants there would certainly be microbes, it was possible that there were *only* microbes, so any test for life should be aimed at microbial life. Furthermore, the report pointed out, 'We have reconciled ourselves to the fact that early missions should assume an Earth-like carbon–water type of biochemistry as the most likely basis of any Martian life'.

It might be thought that proving the presence of life would be straightforward, but this was recognized not to be the case. Given the manner in which cells function, one strategy was to seek evidence of cellular reproduction, but this is a discontinuous process, the rate of which varies greatly from species to species and even in different conditions for a given species, which made employing it as a test very difficult in the context of an exotic environment. As a continuing process that can be measured in several ways – for example, by changes in acidity or the evolution of gases – metabolism is more readily testable and more likely to produce a definitive result. The report urged a *multifaceted* test because 'no single criterion is fully satisfactory, especially in the interpretation of negative results'.

THE GO-AHEAD

In 1967 NASA established the Lunar and Planetary Mission Board to advise on the scientific objectives of missions. In October 1968 this recommended a landing on Mars in 1973 to test for life. On 4 December NASA gave this mission the go-ahead, named it Viking, and made James Martin of the Langley Research Center its manager. In January 1970 budgetary constraints obliged slipping the mission to the rather less favourable 1975 launch window, but this gave more time to design the biology package, which, since it was limited to 12 kilogrammes, would involve a stupendous exercise in miniaturization.

THE VIKING LANDER

After being ferried into Martian orbit by a Mariner spacecraft similar to that which had been inserted into orbit in 1971 to map the planet and search for landing sites, the lander was to be released to make an

Figure 1. The Viking spacecraft comprised an orbiter and lander (in the egg-like bioshield). (All illustrations courtesy of NASA.)

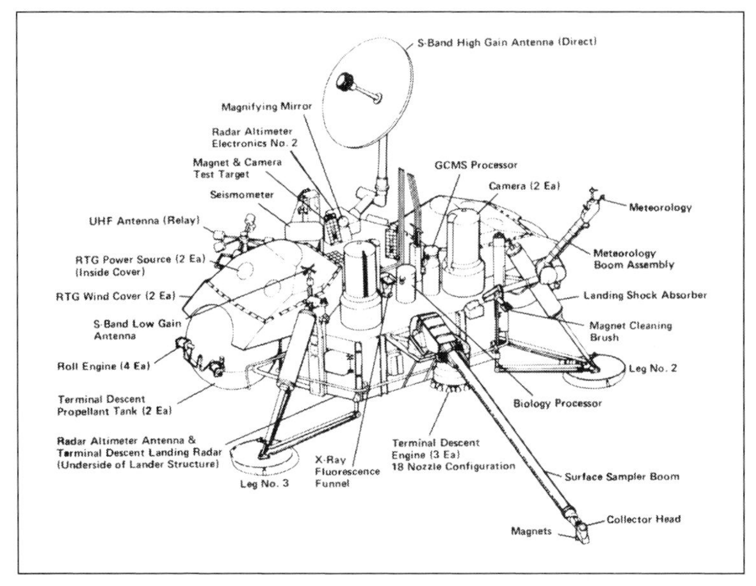

Figure 2. A schematic of the components of the Viking lander.

autonomous landing, and then operate for a minimum of 90 sols. The body was a six-sided aluminium–titanium box 3 metres wide and 0.5 metres deep, with three sides about 1 metre in length and the others, on which the legs were installed, half that length. The interior, which was insulated against heat loss, housed the computer, data storage system, tape recorder, radios, batteries, control systems, biology package, X-ray fluorescence spectrometer and molecular analysis instrument. All external apparatus was painted white to reflect insolation for thermal regulation. The primary command receiver was a low-gain antenna. A 1-metre parabolic dish on an articulated mast was electrically driven to track Earth as Mars rotated for direct S-Band transmission at 1 kilobits per second. In addition, a UHF transmitter could operate at 1, 10 or 30 watts, and send up to 16 kilobits per second to the orbiter. The activities of the lander were managed by its guidance, control and sequencing computer, which comprised two redundant units, each with a 25-bit, 18,432-word memory. In the event that the lander was unable to receive commands, it was to undertake a 60-sol mission (two-thirds of the nominal duration of the primary mission) using a sequence that would be uploaded shortly prior to separation. If all went well, the computer would be updated in 3-sol cycles with a list of activities to perform. At times when the lander was unable to transmit to either the orbiter or Earth, the data acquisition and processing unit would record engineering and science data on a recorder that had 200 metres of 4-track tape with a total capacity of 40 million bits. The lander would be able to uplink by UHF for at most 32 minutes each time the orbiter made a periapsis passage over the site, with the data either being relayed to Earth in real time or being stored on tape. The lander had two radioisotope thermal generators with a combined output of 70 watts. When more power was required, it was able to draw on four rechargeable nickel–cadmium batteries. A treaty signed in 1967 required that spacecraft sent to Mars be sterilized to preclude contaminating the planet with terrestrial microbes – and avoid the nightmare scenario of life-detecting instruments detecting pollution from their own vehicle!

TO MARS

Viking 1 was launched on 20 August 1975 and went into orbit around Mars on 19 June 1976. The operational constraint on inspecting the nominal landing sites was that, although the longitude of periapsis could be adjusted, there would be insufficient propellant to alter the latitude once this had been selected. Both the prime and the backup sites were at 22°N. The prime site was on the sedimentary plain of Chryse Planitia at 35° longitude (Martian longitudes are west), and the backup was in the Elysium volcanic province at 255° longitude. Selecting a site was not simply a matter of choosing a point, since the intrinsic uncertainties of the entry procedure meant that the target was an elliptical 'footprint' extending 120 kilometres in the direction of travel and 25 kilometres to either side of that track. If the lander were aimed at the centre of the ellipse, there was expected to be a 99 per cent chance of it reaching the surface within this boundary.

There was an imperative to 'certify' a landing site, because the plan called for Viking 1 to land on 4 July 1976 in order to mark the American Bicentennial. The spacecraft took its first picture of Chryse on 22 June, and this showed a profusion of small craters, which was bad news as impacts throw out blankets of rocky ejecta. After further imagery showed craters, channels and cliff-edged mesas all across the prime site, James Martin announced on 27 June that the landing would be postponed. The pressure was still on, however, as the landing had to be attempted before 22 July, when Viking 2 had to commit to a latitude of periapsis. A small refinement of the orbit enabled the orbiter to examine a site 250 kilometres north-west of the nominal target, because the terrain appeared to become smoother in that direction, but this also proved to be too rough. Attention switched to a site 580 kilometres further west, where there were fewer fresh-looking craters. After much deliberation, on 13 July Martin decided to attempt to land on 20 July at 22.5°N and 47.4° longitude. It was a close call, because, as the post-landing panoramic vista revealed (Figure 3), the vehicle set down within a few metres of a 3-metre-wide boulder!

Figure 3. If Viking 1 had struck this 3-metre-sized rock, nicknamed 'Big Joe', it would have been wrecked.

THE BIOLOGY EXPERIMENTS

The lander had an arm with which to retrieve soil for the experiments. The boom comprised a pair of thin ribbons of stainless steel welded together along the edges, which stiffened (in the manner of a steel tape measure) as it was unrolled, opening out to form a rigid tube. It had a reach of some 3 metres and could swivel across a horizontal arc of 300°, elevate 35° and dip 50°. At the end of the boom was the collector head. To retrieve a sample, the lid would be raised, the boom driven into the topsoil, the lid closed, the boom retracted, the head rotated to dump the sample on to the lid, and then vibrated to encourage fines to pass through the small holes into the appropriate sample inlet.

The Gas Exchange Experiment developed by Vance Oyama of NASA's Ames Research Center was initiated on 29 July. It assumed Martian life would resemble terrestrial life, and that if the planet underwent episodic climate variations then its microbes might go dormant for the long, cold, arid times, pending a resumption of more benign conditions – which the experiment aimed to offer. The objective was to determine whether metabolism caused changes in the *composition* of the gases in the test chamber. To promote metabolism, the sample was to be provided with an aqueous solution of nutrient dubbed 'chicken soup' that had almost everything a terrestrial microbe might consume: amino acids, purines, pyrimidines, organic acids, vitamins and minerals. Because water vapour was not stable at the Martian surface, the pressure in the chamber had to be significantly greater than ambient in order to prevent the nutrient breaking down.

The experiment was to proceed in two stages. First, a mix of carbon dioxide and krypton was added to the chamber and a mist of nutrient introduced to expose the sample to water vapour. Two hours later, a sample of the gases in the chamber was sent to the Gas Chromatograph and Mass Spectrometer to set the benchmark for comparison with analyses at various stages of the incubation, seeking metabolic products such as hydrogen, oxygen, nitrogen, carbon dioxide and methane. This initial measurement showed a surprisingly large peak for oxygen – fully 15 times as much as could be accounted for by adding up the known sources in the atmosphere and the added gases. Was this the result of an orgy of metabolism as the nutrient awakened dormant microbes? The onus on the scientists was not to proclaim life as soon as they saw a response that *could* imply biology, but to err in favour of chemistry until they saw something that could *only* be explained by biology. For this so-called 'humid mode' of the test, which was to last a week, the sample was suspended in a porous cup above the nutrient, and not allowed to come into direct contact with the solution. By 1 August, the release of oxygen had slowed considerably. The rapid release of oxygen, then a tailing off, suggested that there was an intense but brief inorganic reaction between the soil and the water in the nutrient. Free hydroxyl ions from ultraviolet dissociation of water vapour near the surface would build up peroxy compounds in the chilly, dry soil. Peroxides, superoxides and ozonides are all strong oxidizing agents, but in the presence of significant water vapour they would rapidly break down into water and gaseous oxygen. Was this why so much oxygen was evolved by the sample when presented with a mist of water vapour? On 5 August the experiment advanced to its 'wet mode', with the injection of nutrient directly into the sample. This caused one-third of the carbon dioxide in the chamber to be dissolved by either the sample or the water, then, as the six-month incubation proceeded, it gradually returned to its initial level and activity ceased. The *uptake* of carbon dioxide was explicable as water causing the peroxy compounds in the soil to draw in carbon dioxide to create metal oxides or hydroxides, and the later slow *release* of this gas was explained by iron oxides in the soil reacting with nutrients dissolved in the water and liberating it. Meanwhile, oxygen was reclaimed instead of being released, with the amount of oxygen taken up matching the ascorbic acid (vitamin C) in the nutrient. Evidently, the Martian soil was extremely reactive.

The Labelled Release Experiment developed by Gilbert Levin of Biospherics Incorporated, begun on 30 July, made fewer assumptions about the biochemistry of Martian life. On the assumption that life would be adapted to its environment, the nutrient was a weak 'broth' of the glycine and alanine amino acids, and the formic, glycolic and lactic acids in the form of salts in distilled water, at least one of which ingredients, it was thought, would probably be able to be metabolized by an alien carbon-based lifeform. The premise was that if microbes consumed the nutrient, their metabolism would produce gases such as carbon dioxide or methane, which would be detected by labelled carbon-14 using a Geiger counter. In contrast to the Gas Exchange Experiment, however, this experiment did not analyse *which* gases were present. A mist of nutrient was introduced to the chamber to moisten the soil, and helium injected to maintain sufficient pressure to prevent the nutrient breaking down. A rapid rise to 10,000 counts per minute indicated that a large amount of gas was evolved as soon as the nutrient was added, but by 2 August it was evident that there was no exponential increase to suggest growth. This result did not match *either* the predicted biological or chemical responses. Once it was apparent that the counts had levelled off, meaning that the release of radioactive gases had ceased, a second injection of nutrient was made. If the initial evolution of gas had been due to microbial metabolism of the nutrient then there should have been a second rise, but the rate rapidly fell to 8,000 counts per minute and levelled off, which meant either that the micobes had expired after their initial feast or that the reaction was inorganic. In view of the evidence for peroxy compounds in the sample, hydrogen peroxide could have oxidized the formic acid in the nutrient to carbon dioxide and water: the amount of radioactive carbon dioxide was only slightly less than would have been produced if all of the formic acid had been consumed in this manner. If the oxygen emitted in the Gas Exchange Experiment was due to the dissociation of peroxides in the soil by the water vapour of the nutrient mist, the water produced in the Labelled Release Experiment by the breakdown of formic acid should have decomposed *all* of the peroxy compounds at the first injection of nutrient, and the second should have produced no additional radioactive gas. The fact that the count fell when the nutrient was topped up implied that some of the carbon-14 was being reclaimed, probably by carbon dioxide being absorbed by the water in the nutrient.

The Pyrolytic Release Experiment developed by Norman Horowitz of Caltech was initiated on 28 July. It assumed that any Martian microbes would be adapted to the environment, but would also need to 'fix' carbon from the atmosphere. It was to seek evidence of *synthesis* of organic matter. The test was to be made in conditions as close as possible to the local environment. The soil was sealed into the chamber, and the air evacuated and replaced by a representative mixture of carbon monoxide and carbon dioxide labelled with carbon-14. During incubation, the chamber was illuminated by a xenon arc that simulated sunlight at the Martian surface, minus the ultraviolet. After five days, the lamp was to be turned off and the gases flushed out and analysed by a Geiger counter to produce the 'first peak' that measured the carbon-14 left in the air. To determine whether microbes had assimilated carbon, the sample was to be heated to 640°C to pyrolyse the organic molecules and thus release the carbon-14 as carbon dioxide, which would be measured as the 'second peak'. A high second peak would support a biological interpretation, but a low one would indicate few if any microbes (with the strength of this conclusion depending on how close to nonexistent the second peak was). On 7 August it was announced that the second peak was strong, but again there was ambiguity. The results argued against the peroxides that were candidates for a chemical interpretation of the Gas Exchange's response, since the Pyrolytic Release had seen a *reducing* as opposed to an *oxidizing* reaction, and peroxides would have tended to decrease the size of the second peak.

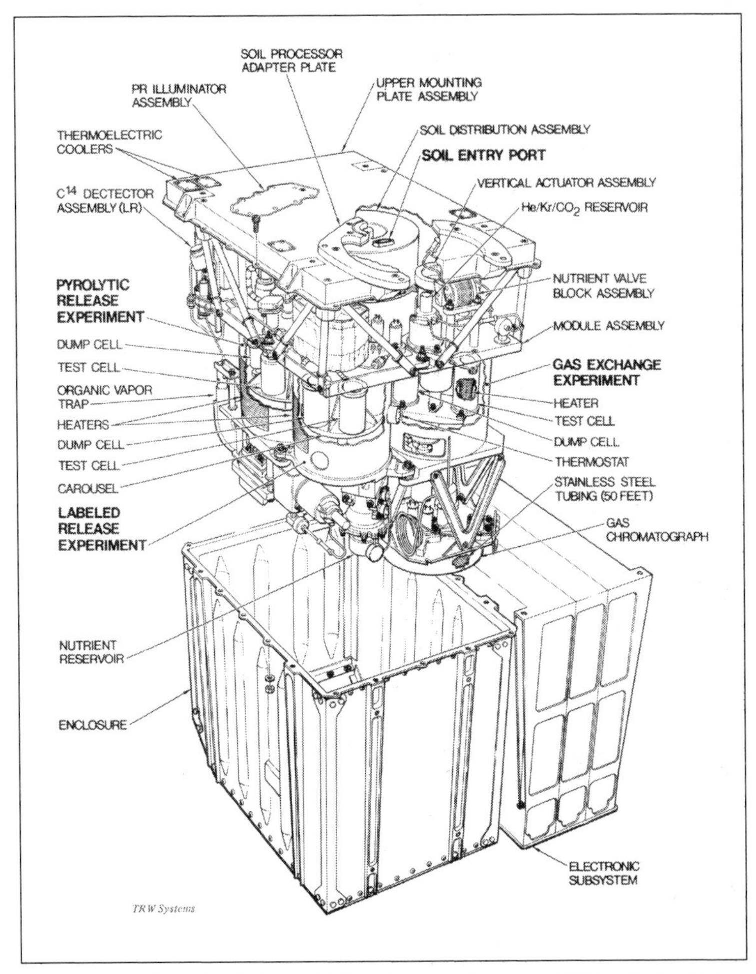

Figure 4. A schematic of the sophisticated, extremely compact Viking lander biology package.

Next, the Labelled Release and Pyrolytic Release Experiments were repeated as 'control' tests in which, prior to incubation, the samples were heated sufficiently to kill microbes but not to inhibit most chemical reactions. If the responses seen in the initial tests were the result of biology then they ought *not* to be repeated with these sterilized samples. Levin reported on 20 August that although the control test of the Labelled Release Experiment *could* have ruled out biology, it *did not do so* – the radioactivity had rapidly risen to 2,200 counts per minute, fallen back sharply, and then levelled off at 1,200. He was encouraged: 'If we'd run this experiment in the parking lot at JPL [and seen these two curves] we'd have concluded that life is present in the sample.' However, if it was a chemical reaction it was one that was disabled by heat. 'We've significantly narrowed the range of possible chemical explanations.' If the initial carbon assimilation of the Pyrolytic Release had been due to biology, the sterile sample ought to have been negative. In fact, there was assimilation, albeit at a much reduced level, which argued for a chemical reaction involving several reactants, only some of which had been inhibited by preheating. When the Gas Exchange Experiment had finished its six-month incubation, it was emptied and reloaded with fresh soil, which was sterilized before rehumidification. The fact that half of the initial amount of oxygen was released indicated that there was a non-biological reaction. As the preheating would have dissociated hydrogen peroxide, this suggested that this reaction was produced by a more thermally stable superoxide.

The first analysis by the Gas Chromatograph and Mass Spectrometer was done on 6 August. To start, the sample was heated to 200°C in order to drive most of the water out of the hydrated minerals, but surprisingly little water was released. Next, the sample was heated to the maximum 500°C to volatize organic molecules. The astonishing fact that there were *no organics* was reported on 13 August. However, the analysis had been complicated by the delayed release of water. Another sample was tested on 21 August to gain further insight. A significant amount of water was liberated at 350°C, but despite the improved sensitivity in the second stage if there were any organics they were below the 10–100 parts per billion detection limit. But as team leader Klaus Biemann of the Massachusetts Institute of Technology noted, there would have to be at least one million microbes in the sample for their organics to be detected at that sensitivity. A typical temperate sample of terrestrial soil can contain *hundreds of millions* of bacteria per cubic centimetre. If *only the living cells* were present for analysis, then one million bacteria would have been far too few for the instrument to detect. In terrestrial soil, the amount of *dead organic matter* often outweighs the living material by a factor of 10,000, and if Martian microbes were the same they *would probably* have been able to be detected by the organic wastes and dead cells they produced;

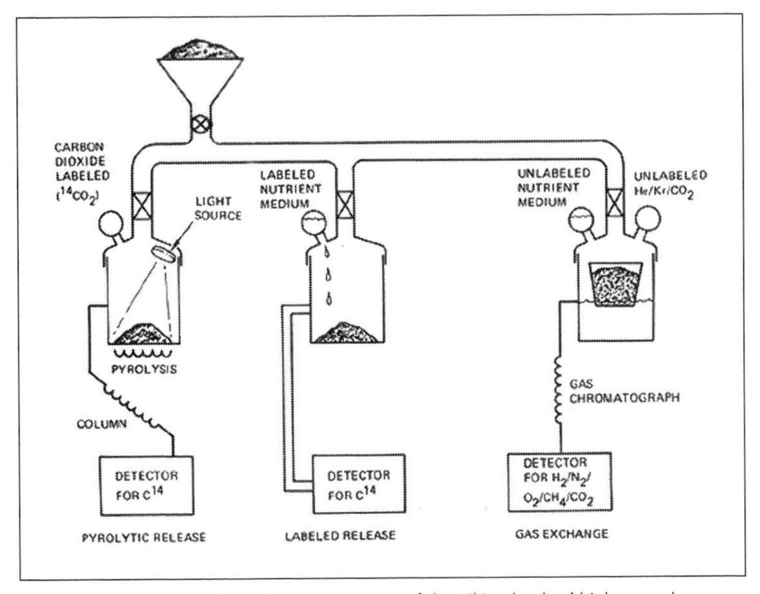

Figure 5. An overview of the three experiments of the Viking landers' biology package.

however, if they recycled their wastes and solar ultraviolet destroyed the dead cells, then microbes could have been present to produce the reactions reported by the biology package *without* their being detected by the spectrometer. Levin later processed samples from Antarctica and confirmed that soil that the Gas Chromatograph and Mass Spectrometer showed to be devoid of organics had nevertheless contained sufficient bacteria to replicate the results of the Labelled Release Experiment on Mars. Although this hypothesis *explained* the conflicting results, there was *no proof* that it was true. Viking 2, which landed further north in Utopia Planitia (at 48°N and 226° longitude) in the Elysium region on 3 September 1976, placed tighter constraints on possible inorganic chemistry, but did not resolve the debate.

WHAT WAS CONCLUDED?

Gilbert Levin opined, 'The accretion of evidence has been more compatible with biology than with chemistry – each new test result has made it more difficult to come up with a chemical explanation, but each new result has continued to allow for biology.' All other things being equal, he noted that if a terrestrial sample had given the observed results, 'we'd unhesitatingly have described [it] as biological'. Vance Oyama was sceptical: 'There was no *need* to invoke biological processes.' Norman Horowitz agreed, but admitted it was 'impossible to prove that any of the reactions . . . were *not* biological in origin'. Prior to Viking, nobody knew whether there was life on Mars; sadly, nobody knew afterwards either!

Harold Klein of Ames, leader of the biology team, later recommended that the assumption that Martian microbes would be similar to terrestrial ones should be dismissed, and that scientists ought to consider whether the Viking data suggested any clues as to 'whether there might be some less obvious kind of life on Mars'. In fact, even as the Vikings were seeking carbon-synthesizing microbes, biologists on Earth were discovering the first examples of a whole new class of microbial life which, if its existence had been known when Viking was being planned, would have prompted a wider range of experiments.

CURRENT THINKING

The 1960s premise in setting out to search for life on Mars was to ask, in essence, what kind of terrestrial life was best suited to the conditions on the surface of that planet – which were not well known – and then to presume that life there would be similar. At that time, the 'dry valleys' of Antarctica were the best terrestrial analogues for Mars. Since then, many niches that had been thought sterile have been found to host ecosystems. In fact, *extremophiles* are metabolically diverse, able to exploit almost *any* chemical energy that is abundant, including both organic and inorganic energy sources. When Viking was designed, it was believed that all life ultimately derived its energy from sunlight, that metabolism involved gaseous exchanges of carbon dioxide, and that no matter where the biology package were to be placed on Earth it would detect life. However, it is evident in hindsight that it would *not* have detected many of the extremophiles. A genetic study has shown that the 'common ancestor' for terrestrial life is a sulphur-metabolizing anaerobic autotroph found in hot springs. The lesson from Earth would therefore seem to be that life is the direct result of chemical evolution, and developed as soon as it became possible for it to exist. As

Bruce Jakosky, an astrobiologist at the University of Colorado, has put it, 'the environmental prerequisites for life include only the presence of liquid water, access to the biogenic elements, and a source of energy that can drive chemical disequilibrium; these are not terribly stringent requirements'. When terrestrial life originated, there was intense volcanism, liquid water on the surface, and the air was predominantly carbon dioxide. If early Mars was similar, then life may well have developed there. Knowing what we now know, the time is ripe to dispatch another lander specifically to test for life on Mars.

FURTHER READING

Hanlon, M. (2004), *The Real Mars*, London: Constable.

Harland, D.M. (2005), *Water and the Search for Life on Mars*, Heidelberg: Springer-Praxis.

Christaan Huygens (1629–95): The Astronomer Behind the Space Probe

ALLAN CHAPMAN

When the news came through about the safe landing of a planetary probe upon Saturn's satellite Titan, on Friday, 14 January 2005, the world held its breath about what it might find. Yet why should this particular European Space Agency spacecraft be called Huygens? Let us not forget, however, that several planetary probes have been named after illustrious astronomers from the past. There is the Hubble Space Telescope, named after Edwin Hubble. Then the names Galileo and Cassini spring to mind, while the ESA's Giotto mission to Halley's Comet in 1986 was named not so much after an astronomer as after an astronomically aware Italian painter, Giotto di Bondone, who, when painting a Nativity scene in Padua around 1303, depicted the Star of Bethlehem as possessing a tail, probably in recollection of the recent 1301 appearance of what we now call Halley's Comet. And as the Dutchman Christiaan Huygens was the first astronomer to make major telescopic discoveries regarding the planet Saturn, and was the first human being to observe and time the orbital period of its satellite Titan in 1655, it is appropriate that the Saturn–Titan mission should bear his name.

THE EARLY YEARS

Christiaan Huygens was born into a prominent Dutch family on 14 April 1629. Christiaan and Constantijn were popular family names: he had an elder brother named Constantijn (1628–97), while his father, Sir Constantijn Huygens, was a prominent Dutch diplomat, scholar, poet, musician and athlete, who had studied at Leiden and Oxford, and

Figure 1. An engraving of Christiaan Huygens based on an oil portrait. From *Systema Saturni* (The Hague, 1659).

was given an English knighthood by King James I. His grandfather, Christiaan, had also been an eminent Dutch scholar and civil servant. The Huygenses came from Zulichem, near The Hague, where they seem to have been local landowners.

Holland was, in many ways, a new country in Huygens's time. Only half a century before Christiaan's birth, the Dutch Protestants had risen up and defeated their Spanish overlords, turning the 'Spanish Netherlands' into the self-governing States General of Holland. Support for the emerging Dutch and Belgian states, moreover, had formed an important element of English foreign policy in Europe, and had constituted one of the major factors behind King Philip II sending his ill-fated Spanish Armada to 'subdue' England in 1588. And as a newly independent country, Holland had become the tiger economy of

Europe by 1610. The merchants and bankers of Amsterdam and The Hague were now undercutting Venice, Florence and the powerful trading city states of Renaissance Italy. Banking, painting, fine-art dealing, printing and the production of the world's finest maps had brought enormous wealth and cultural prestige to Holland, while the whole was underpinned by a burgeoning merchant marine which brought the trading fruits of the East Indies into the country. Leiden University, where most of the male Huygenses had been educated, had usurped Venice's Padua as Europe's premier medical school by 1640, and was to claim some of Europe's greatest scientists among its alumni.

Both of the Huygens brothers, Christiaan and Constantijn, were fascinated by the newly emerging science of the day. As Dutchmen, they must have been vividly aware of the power of geographical discovery to change our knowledge of the globe we live upon, while the problems faced by navigators and cartographers in using the heavens for practical purposes brought home to them the importance of scientific instruments when it comes to accurately measuring and quantifying the motion of astronomical bodies. Neither brother lost his passion for physics and astronomy, though for Constantijn it became second to his professional career as a Dutch diplomat and civil servant: the traditional professions, indeed, of the Huygens family. But Christiaan was to devote himself full time to science: to astronomy, horology, mechanics, gravitation theory and optics. This he did largely on the strength of independent family money, augmented in later years by pensions from the King of France.

A NEW KIND OF LENS

Without a shadow of a doubt, Christiaan Huygens was the first great observer of Saturn, and ever since Galileo in 1610 had recorded the planet's baffling changes of shape when seen through the earliest telescopes – sometimes a sphere, sometimes resembling an elongated rugby ball, or even, apparently, a large sphere with two lesser ones appended like large ears – astronomers had not known what to make of Saturn. And for 40 years after Galileo's first optical views of the planets, the refracting telescope remained an instrument of limited power. Contemporary chemical technology could not make pieces of perfectly clear glass of more than about 1.5 inches across at best, while the

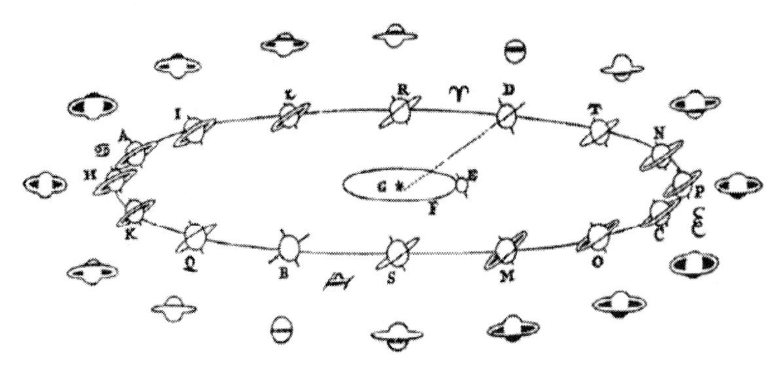

Figure 2. The changing appearance of Saturn's rings as viewed from Earth. From *Systema Saturni* (The Hague, 1659). From his *Oeuvres Completes*, 22 vols. (The Hague: Société Hollandaise des Sciences, 1888–1950), vol. 15, p. 309.

imprecise geometrical curves imparted by the spectacle-makers who made all the early telescope lenses kept the focal lengths necessarily short, and the images badly aberrated.

But object glass began to improve markedly after 1650 or so, and one notices that this happened in two places in Europe famed for the manufacture of luxury goods. Eustachio Divini and Giuseppe Campani in Italy, and the Huygens brothers in Holland, realized that the demand for glassware was rapidly increasing. In particular, the growing fashion for large and expensive mirrors had led glass manufacturers to develop a new type of thick plate glass. This was made from large balls of blown glass that were next rolled along stone tables to turn the red-hot balls into cylinders, and the glass maker only needed to slice the cylinder longitudinally, then roll it flat with marble or iron rolling pins, to have lovely thick plates of glass, maybe 18 inches square.

Then another Dutch luxury trade became of use to the lens-maker. As we know from the paintings of Vermeer and other artists of the seventeenth century, well-to-do houses, churches and town halls often had their floors covered with highly polished black and white marble slabs to create a chequerboard effect. Christiaan Huygens studied the machines used to cut and polish these floor marbles, and realized that they could also be employed for polishing large pieces of glass. By having several slabs from the glass manufacturer polished flat in this way, he was able to select very transparent regions within the larger slabs that could then be cut out with a diamond, to form blanks for telescope object glasses. Blanks of up to 8 or 9 inches in diameter were sometimes possible, and the Royal Society of London, to which Christiaan was elected a Fellow in 1663, still has three Huygens object glasses of large size preserved in its collections. When one looks at fine print through these lenses, one is immediately struck by the overall clarity of the glass, in spite of some striated or bubbled regions. They also tend to have a greenish tinge for, as Christiaan recorded, it was often easier to get perfectly clear greenish or yellowish glass than it was pure white.

To work these blanks into lenses, the Huygens brothers designed and had constructed a figuring and polishing machine. The glass blank was made to move inside a concave tool, under the combined actions of a handle and a foot treadle. A ratchet wheel ensured the evenness of each stroke of the rotating mirror blank upon the tool. In this way, it became possible for a relatively unskilled workman to impart convex curves of a predictable focal length to glasses moving inside the concave tool. To polish one side of a lens, it was necessary for the workman to impart over 3,000 strokes by combined hand and foot operations – but what wonderful lenses resulted!

What Christiaan and Constantijn Huygens were trying to make, just like Campani and Divini, and Johannes Hevelius in the rich merchant city of Danzig, Poland, were lenses of very long focal length. Such lenses were ideal for planetary studies, because the longer the focal length of the object glass, the larger the resulting prime focus image. A 2-inch focal length eyepiece, therefore, would give twice as much magnification when applied to a 24-foot-focus object glass than it would to one of twelve feet. Long-focus lenses also reduced chromatic aberration, though the real goal of all Europe's new breed of planetary observers was to get the biggest possible prime focus image.

When one looks at telescope object glasses after 1650, one sees an almost year-by-year lengthening of focal length, as opticians came to master the evolving technology that could produce almost flat, perfectly symmetrical curves that threw the focus back 12, 23, 36, 60, 100 or more feet. By March 1655, Huygens had figured an excellent 2-inch-diameter object glass with a focus of 12 feet, though by the end of 1655 he had a larger-diameter glass which formed an image at 23 feet. It was with these two telescopes that he made his epoch-making discoveries of Saturn.

A SERIES OF DISCOVERIES

Although the 12-foot-focus telescope could still not settle the true cause of Saturn's distended appearance, it did reveal a satellite rotating around the planet. Huygens timed the satellite's period of revolution to 16 days. This was the body later named Titan, and was the first Solar System satellite to be discovered since Galileo had seen the four moons of Jupiter in January 1610. And while Huygens had no idea that Titan was the frozen world we now know it to be, he recognized that it possessed important cosmological significance: by rotating around Saturn – as Galileo's four 'Medicean Stars' rotated around Jupiter – the new satellite added extra weight to the Copernican theory by showing that the Earth was not the only centre of rotation in the Universe.

Then later in that wonderfully productive year, 1655, the Huygens brothers brought a new telescope into operation. It was the 23-foot focal length instrument mentioned above, and with it Christiaan at last solved the riddle of Saturn's curious shape. Though it was not until 1659 that the discovery was laid before the astronomers of Europe, in Christiaan's *Systema Saturni* of that year, he had discovered that whereas Saturn was in itself a sphere, it was surrounded by (in English translation) 'a ring, thin, plane nowhere attached, and inclined to the ecliptic'. Huygens now realized why Saturn assumed a lenticular shape at such times as it was inclined obliquely to the Earth, and why the lenticular shape disappeared altogether when the ring was viewed edge-on. The true interpretation of Saturn's ring, along with his observation of Titan, was one of the great discoveries of modern astronomy, solving a long-standing puzzle, yet presenting a new one – what could such a ring be made of? Then, as telescope technology continued to stride ahead, 20 years later and using a superior telescope with Italian lenses paid for by King Louis XIV of France, Giovanni Domenico Cassini discovered that Huygens's ring actually had a division of clear sky shining through it: Cassini's Division. Cassini also found that Saturn had four additional moons, as well as Titan, that had not been visible in earlier telescopes.

THE FIRST VIABLE PENDULUM CLOCK

When Huygens discovered Titan in the spring of 1655, he still lacked a precision clock with which to measure its exact period of rotation around the planet. Indeed, high-precision clocks did not exist in 1655, and although clockwork had been around since about 1300, the lack of a perfectly regular 'escapement' mechanism, whereby the energy of the driving weight or spring was released in perfectly equal bursts, meant that clocks were rarely accurate to more than 20 minutes a day. Yet back in 1583, the young Galileo had realized that a swinging pendulum of a given length always swung at exactly the same rate, no matter whether it described a large or a small arc. Later in life Galileo had made drawings of ways in which a pendulum, with its perfectly *isochronal* (Greek, for 'equal time') swings, could be harnessed to clockwork, though nothing enduring came of it.

It was Christiaan Huygens in 1656 who devised and constructed the world's first viable pendulum clock in The Hague. It was built by Solomon Coster. The weight drive, gear and finger work were conventional for a domestic wall clock of the period, but what was radically different was the way in which Huygens had designed a mechanism – known technically as a *verge* – whereby each swing of the pendulum released an exact burst of energy through the gear train to the fingers on the dial. And as the pendulum's swings were controlled by the constant force of gravity for a given location, it meant that the escapement worked 'isochronally', resulting in an unprecedented high level of accuracy.

All of a sudden, the pendulum produced an exponential increase in timekeeping accuracy, transforming the long-familiar mechanical clock from a domestic or public utility into a precision scientific instrument. For Huygens's designs were now able to measure time reliably to within a few *seconds* per day. And in the fast-moving world of commerce, technology and potential profits that was Europe by 1658, the new invention was rapidly developed and improved. Astronomers, for instance, realized that one could measure celestial angles to a new level of accuracy by making critical timings of stars as they passed the meridian, while Huygens, and Robert Hooke in London, experimented with spring-driven, short-pendulum clocks to see if they could be mounted in ships as a way of finding longitude at sea – though in practice the idea would take another century, and John Harrison, to render it truly practicable.

And soon after Huygens announced his pendulum mechanism, English astronomers found that a pendulum that was exactly 39.25 inches long beat dead seconds in London, though *not* in South America, St Helena or Siam. Could it possibly have something to do with the fact that the Earth is not a perfect sphere, but has an equatorial diameter that is greater than its polar diameter, so that tropical Brazil and Siam are slightly further from the Earth's centre than are London, Paris and Amsterdam? Within 20 years of its invention, indeed, the pendulum clock had even become a *geophysical* instrument, capable of detecting slight regional changes in the Earth's gravity field.

I would also suggest that the pendulum clock was the first piece of pure science-based technology for, although the mechanics of gears, weights and springs had been known for centuries, this was perhaps the first time that a piece of pure physics had been harnessed to control a hitherto purely empirical invention.

OTHER CONTRIBUTIONS TO SCIENCE

During the course of his life, Christiaan Huygens made major contributions to various branches of physics. Gravitation physics, for instance, was a subject of intense interest to European scientists long before Sir Isaac Newton drew everything together in the *Principia* (1687). Indeed, ever since Johannes Kepler had announced his three Laws of Planetary Motion in 1619, scientists had been enquiring into the force that bound the Sun, Moon and planets with such exactitude. The Englishman Jeremiah Horrocks had made major contributions before his tragically early death in 1641 at the age of only 22, while Robert Hooke, the Frenchman Pierre Gassendi and others had come to understand that mathematical ratios existed between the masses, orbital periods and distances from the Sun of the planets that seemed to be connected to the rate of descent of terrestrial falling bodies and the oscillation times of pendulums of different lengths.

In 1673 and 1690 Huygens published major studies in what we would call gravitational dynamics. As one of Europe's most creative experimental scientists and mathematicians, he explored the nature of the force that governed the motions of the planets and pendulums, and produced orbits of particular shapes. He was, in many ways, the first person to identify and study centrifugal force as part of a dynamical system, though in fact he never really thought in terms of abstract *forces* in the way that Newton did. Newton came to concentrate on finding precise mathematical descriptions of physical phenomena while not being interested in the nature of forces in an absolute sense: he was only interested in the quantifiable *effects* they had on bodies. Huygens, however, was in the tradition of René Descartes' mechanical philosophy, which also tried to explain phenomena in an absolute sense. And as a mechanist, Huygens believed that things only moved if they were pushed, rather in the manner in which railway wagons only move when other wagons collide with them. To Huygens, therefore, as it had been to Descartes 40 years before, space was filled with an infinity of minute particles, constituting the ether, and it was the swirls or vortices through which this ether moved which caused the planets to rotate around the Sun. The mathematics described the motions, but the ethereal vortices were the absolute *causes* of gravitation.

Christiaan Huygens's other major area of research was optics. Unlike Newton, but like Robert Hooke, Huygens developed a wave theory of light. Whereas Newton (who considered the nature of absolute space to be knowable only by God) was less concerned with mechanical ethers, and saw light as moving as bullet-like 'corpuscles' in straight lines through a void, Huygens saw it as a mechanical wave vibrating through the ether. Just as shock waves moved through air or water, so Huygens saw light travelling through the fundamental particles of the ether.

A FASCINATION WITH TELESCOPES

Yet while his researches into gravity and light were of a very theoretical kind, Christiaan Huygens never lost his practical fascination with telescopes. As the focal length of telescopic object glasses increased and diameters got larger as the technology improved between 1650 and 1690, the business of mounting the object glasses adequately became more and more of a problem. Indeed, we can only marvel at how it was possible to manipulate tubes mounting 60- or 80-foot focal length lenses, let alone hold the image steady enough for long enough to detect surface details on Jupiter or the rings and satellites of Saturn.

Yet these astronomers did, and the proof of that fact lies in those discoveries we can verify for ourselves today.

In 1684, however, Christiaan Huygens' ingenuity led him to a much simpler way of mounting long-focus lenses than the long, flimsy wooden tubes used until that time. For his 'aerial telescopes' had no tube at all. The object lens was mounted in a ball-swivel cell on the top of a tall mast. Focus was obtained by the simple expedient of pulling a piece of string of the correct length to bring the eyepiece and objective into collimation, and by steadying the apparatus with a stand placed before the observer.

By 1684, however, the big object glasses made from mirror plate glass had been developed pretty well as far as they could go. Although the technology available by this time had enabled Christiaan and Constantijn Huygens (or employees working under their supervision) to impart 210-foot-focus curves upon a 9-inch-diameter piece of glass (for such are the specifications of the largest Huygens lens preserved in the Royal Society collection), such lenses were not really practicable for sustained research. Quite simply, by the 1690s these giant object glasses had more or less reached their limit. They had, in their collective usage across Europe by Huygens, Cassini, Hooke, Hevelius and others, produced a wonderful harvest of discoveries and added enormously to our knowledge of the Solar System. Indeed, Huygens had even used his giant telescope to make the first drawing of a deep-space object when, in 1656, he had drawn the Orion Nebula. But no more major observational researches of planetary or deep-space objects could be undertaken until Sir William Herschel began to develop the large-aperture reflecting telescope. For between 1690 and the 1780s, European observational astronomy had become overwhelmingly concerned not with planetary surfaces, but with mapping the stellar heavens anew with telescopic quadrants, with the intention partly of substantiating Newton's Laws of Gravitation, and partly of perfecting our knowledge of the lunar orbit as a way of finding longitude at sea. But there were no new technological breakthroughs that showed anything fresh on the surfaces of the planets that could not have been seen with the telescopes of Huygens's day.

Finally, we should never forget that the astronomers of the seventeenth century were very optimistic about the Solar System being inhabited, and in 1695 Christiaan Huygens wrote his last book, *Cosmotheoros*, which dealt with this subject. Huygens's line of reasoning, like that of many of his contemporaries, ran thus: telescopes have revealed the planets to be *worlds* in space; is it then likely that God would have left such potentially habitable worlds uninhabited? And if there are Saturnians, or Jovians, should they not be clever creatures? And just as clever men on Earth had devised tools, instruments and, indeed, powerful telescopes, was it not within the bounds of possibility that there were astronomers on Saturn looking at *us*? Of course, all of this was pure speculation, as Huygens was well aware; but it was nevertheless careful speculation, advanced within the best technical knowledge and widely held social assumptions of the age, and would have seemed eminently sensible to contemporaries.

Constantijn Huygens, though becoming a leading Dutch civil servant, never lost his fascination with astronomy, and the brothers remained close throughout their lives. In 1688, however, when William of Orange of Holland succeeded to the British throne, Constantijn came with him, as Secretary to His Majesty King William III, so that the Anglo-Dutch connection of the Huygens family took a new and highly influential direction. Seven years later, after having lived some time in France at the court of King Louis XIV, Christiaan returned to The Hague, where he died in 1695.

Christiaan Huygens was one of the greatest telescopic astronomers of all time. And as the news of the safe landing of the Titan probe began to come through on 14 January 2005, and as I later observed Titan with my own telescope, I could not help wondering what Huygens would have made of the wonderful spacecraft that so proudly bears his name.

ACKNOWLEDGEMENTS

I wish to express my thanks to Dr Robert van Gent of Universiteit Utrecht, Netherlands, and to Valerie Lawrence of the Faculty of Modern History Library, Oxford.

FURTHER READING

Chapman, A. (1995), 'Christiaan Huygens (1629–1695), Astronomer and Mechanician', *Endeavour*, pp. 140–5.

Helden, A. Van (1974), 'The Telescope in the Seventeenth Century', *Isis*, 65, no. 226, pp. 38–57.

Huygens, Christiaan, *Oeuvres Complètes*, 22 vols (The Hague, 1880–1950), reprints all of Huygens's books, correspondence and documents in the original languages, mainly Latin, Dutch and French.

—— *Horologium* (The Hague, 1658). An English translation was printed in *Antiquarian Horology* VII (1970), pp. 33–54.

—— *Cosmotheoros* (The Hague, 1695). English translations, as *Cosmotheoros, The Celestial Worlds Discover'd*, or *Conjectures concerning the Inhabitants, Plants, and productions of the World in the Planets* (London, 1695, 1698).

—— *Systema Saturni* (The Hague, 1659), reprinted in the original Latin with French translation in Huygens, *Oeuvres Complètes* (above), vol. XX, pp. 208–353.

King, Henry C. (1955), 'The History of the Telescope', London: Charles Griffin.

Part III

Miscellaneous

Some Interesting Variable Stars

JOHN ISLES

All variable stars are of potential interest, and hundreds of them can be observed with minimal optical aid – even with a pair of binoculars. The stars in the list that follows include many that are popular with amateur observers, as well as some less well-known objects that are nevertheless suitable for study visually. The periods and ranges of many variables are not constant from one cycle to another, and some are completely irregular.

Finder charts are given after the list for those stars marked with an asterisk. These charts are adapted with permission from those issued by the Variable Star Section of the British Astronomical Association. Apart from the eclipsing variables and others in which the light changes are purely a geometrical effect, variable stars can be divided broadly into two classes: the pulsating stars, and the eruptive or cataclysmic variables.

Mira (Omicron Ceti) is the best-known member of the long-period subclass of pulsating red-giant stars. The chart is suitable for use in estimating the magnitude of Mira when it reaches naked-eye brightness – typically from about a month before the predicted date of maximum until two or three months after maximum. Predictions for Mira and other stars of its class follow the section of finder charts.

The semi-regular variables are less predictable, and generally have smaller ranges. V Canum Venaticorum is one of the more reliable ones, with steady oscillations in a six-month cycle. Z Ursae Majoris, easily found with binoculars near Delta, has a large range, and often shows double maxima owing to the presence of multiple periodicities in its light changes. The chart for Z is also suitable for observing another semi-regular star, RY Ursae Majoris. These semi-regular stars are mostly red giants or supergiants.

The RV Tauri stars are of earlier spectral class than the semi-regulars, and in a full cycle of variation they often show deep minima and double maxima that are separated by a secondary minimum. U Monocerotis is one of the brightest RV Tauri stars.

Among eruptive variable stars is the carbon-rich supergiant R Coronae Borealis. Its unpredictable eruptions cause it not to brighten, but to fade. This happens when one of the sooty clouds that the star throws out from time to time happens to come in our direction and blots out most of the star's light from our view. Much of the time R Coronae is bright enough to be seen with binoculars, and the chart can be used to estimate its magnitude. During the deepest minima, however, the star needs a telescope of 25-centimetre or larger aperture to be detected.

CH Cygni is a symbiotic star – that is, a close binary comprising a red giant and a hot dwarf star that interact physically, giving rise to outbursts. The system also shows semi-regular oscillations, and sudden fades and rises that may be connected with eclipses.

Observers can follow the changes of these variable stars by using the comparison stars whose magnitudes are given below each chart. Observations of variable stars by amateurs are of scientific value, provided they are collected and made available for analysis. This is done by several organizations, including the British Astronomical Association (see the list of astronomical societies in this volume), the American Association of Variable Star Observers (25 Birch Street, Cambridge, Mass. 02138), and the Royal Astronomical Society of New Zealand (PO Box 3181, Wellington).

Star	RA		Declination		Range	Type	Period	Spectrum
	h	m	°	′			(days)	
R Andromedae	00	24.0	+38	35	5.8–14.9	Mira	409	S
W Andromedae	02	17.6	+44	18	6.7–14.6	Mira	396	S
U Antliae	10	35.2	−39	34	5–6	Irregular	—	C
Theta Apodis	14	05.3	−76	48	5–7	Semi-regular	119	M
R Aquarii	23	43.8	−15	17	5.8–12.4	Symbiotic	387	M+Pec
T Aquarii	20	49.9	−05	09	7.2–14.2	Mira	202	M
R Aquilae	19	06.4	+08	14	5.5–12.0	Mira	284	M
V Aquilae	19	04.4	−05	41	6.6–8.4	Semi-regular	353	C
Eta Aquilae	19	52.5	+01	00	3.5–4.4	Cepheid	7.2	F–G
U Arae	17	53.6	−51	41	7.7–14.1	Mira	225	M
R Arietis	02	16.1	+25	03	7.4–13.7	Mira	187	M
U Arietis	03	11.0	+14	48	7.2–15.2	Mira	371	M
R Aurigae	05	17.3	+53	35	6.7–13.9	Mira	458	M
Epsilon Aurigae	05	02.0	+43	49	2.9–3.8	Algol	9892	F+B
R Boötis	14	37.2	+26	44	6.2–13.1	Mira	223	M

Star	RA		Declination		Range	Type	Period	Spectrum
	h	m	°	′			(days)	
X Camelopardalis	04	45.7	+75	06	7.4–14.2	Mira	144	K–M
R Cancri	08	16.6	+11	44	6.1–11.8	Mira	362	M
X Cancri	08	55.4	+17	14	5.6–7.5	Semi-regular	195?	C
R Canis Majoris	07	19.5	−16	24	5.7–6.3	Algol	1.1	F
VY Canis Majoris	07	23.0	−25	46	6.5–9.6	Unique	—	M
S Canis Minoris	07	32.7	+08	19	6.6–13.2	Mira	333	M
R Canum Ven.	13	49.0	+39	33	6.5–12.9	Mira	329	M
*V Canum Ven.	13	19.5	+45	32	6.5–8.6	Semi-regular	192	M
R Carinae	09	32.2	−62	47	3.9–10.5	Mira	309	M
S Carinae	10	09.4	−61	33	4.5–9.9	Mira	149	K–M
l Carinae	09	45.2	−62	30	3.3–4.2	Cepheid	35.5	F–K
Eta Carinae	10	45.1	−59	41	−0.8–7.9	Irregular	—	Pec
R Cassiopeiae	23	58.4	+51	24	4.7–13.5	Mira	430	M
S Cassiopeiae	01	19.7	+72	37	7.9–16.1	Mira	612	S
W Cassiopeiae	00	54.9	+58	34	7.8–12.5	Mira	406	C
Gamma Cas.	00	56.7	+60	43	1.6–3.0	Gamma Cas.	—	B
Rho Cassiopeiae	23	54.4	+57	30	4.1–6.2	Semi-regular	—	F–K
R Centauri	14	16.6	−59	55	5.3–11.8	Mira	546	M
S Centauri	12	24.6	−49	26	7–8	Semi-regular	65	C
T Centauri	13	41.8	−33	36	5.5–9.0	Semi-regular	90	K–M
S Cephei	21	35.2	+78	37	7.4–12.9	Mira	487	C
T Cephei	21	09.5	+68	29	5.2–11.3	Mira	388	M
Delta Cephei	22	29.2	+58	25	3.5–4.4	Cepheid	5.4	F–G
Mu Cephei	21	43.5	+58	47	3.4–5.1	Semi-regular	730	M
U Ceti	02	33.7	−13	09	6.8–13.4	Mira	235	M
W Ceti	00	02.1	−14	41	7.1–14.8	Mira	351	S
*Omicron Ceti	02	19.3	−02	59	2.0–10.1	Mira	332	M
R Chamaeleontis	08	21.8	−76	21	7.5–14.2	Mira	335	M
T Columbae	05	19.3	−33	42	6.6–12.7	Mira	226	M
R Comae Ber.	12	04.3	+18	47	7.1–14.6	Mira	363	M
*R Coronae Bor.	15	48.6	+28	09	5.7–14.8	R Coronae Bor.	—	C
S Coronae Bor.	15	21.4	+31	22	5.8–14.1	Mira	360	M
T Coronae Bor.	15	59.6	+25	55	2.0–10.8	Recurrent nova	—	M+Pec
V Coronae Bor.	15	49.5	+39	34	6.9–12.6	Mira	358	C
W Coronae Bor.	16	15.4	+37	48	7.8–14.3	Mira	238	M
R Corvi	12	19.6	−19	15	6.7–14.4	Mira	317	M
R Crucis	12	23.6	−61	38	6.4–7.2	Cepheid	5.8	F–G
R Cygni	19	36.8	+50	12	6.1–14.4	Mira	426	S
U Cygni	20	19.6	+47	54	5.9–12.1	Mira	463	C
W Cygni	21	36.0	+45	22	5.0–7.6	Semi-regular	131	M

Star	RA		Declination		Range	Type	Period	Spectrum
	h	m	°	′			(days)	
RT Cygni	19	43.6	+48	47	6.0–13.1	Mira	190	M
SS Cygni	21	42.7	+43	35	7.7–12.4	Dwarf nova	50±	K+Pec
*CH Cygni	19	24.5	+50	14	5.6–9.0	Symbiotic	—	M+B
Chi Cygni	19	50.6	+32	55	3.3–14.2	Mira	408	S
R Delphini	20	14.9	+09	05	7.6–13.8	Mira	285	M
U Delphini	20	45.5	+18	05	5.6–7.5	Semi-regular	110?	M
EU Delphini	20	37.9	+18	16	5.8–6.9	Semi-regular	60	M
Beta Doradûs	05	33.6	–62	29	3.5–4.1	Cepheid	9.8	F–G
R Draconis	16	32.7	+66	45	6.7–13.2	Mira	246	M
T Eridani	03	55.2	–24	02	7.2–13.2	Mira	252	M
R Fornacis	02	29.3	–26	06	7.5–13.0	Mira	389	C
R Geminorum	07	07.4	+22	42	6.0–14.0	Mira	370	S
U Geminorum	07	55.1	+22	00	8.2–14.9	Dwarf nova	105±	Pec+M
Zeta Geminorum	07	04.1	+20	34	3.6–4.2	Cepheid	10.2	F–G
Eta Geminorum	06	14.9	+22	30	3.2–3.9	Semi-regular	233	M
S Gruis	22	26.1	–48	26	6.0–15.0	Mira	402	M
S Herculis	16	51.9	+14	56	6.4–13.8	Mira	307	M
U Herculis	16	25.8	+18	54	6.4–13.4	Mira	406	M
Alpha Herculis	17	14.6	+14	23	2.7–4.0	Semi-regular	—	M
68, u Herculis	17	17.3	+33	06	4.7–5.4	Algol	2.1	B+B
R Horologii	02	53.9	–49	53	4.7–14.3	Mira	408	M
U Horologii	03	52.8	–45	50	6–14	Mira	348	M
R Hydrae	13	29.7	–23	17	3.5–10.9	Mira	389	M
U Hydrae	10	37.6	–13	23	4.3–6.5	Semi-regular	450?	C
VW Hydri	04	09.1	–71	18	8.4–14.4	Dwarf nova	27±	Pec
R Leonis	09	47.6	+11	26	4.4–11.3	Mira	310	M
R Leonis Minoris	09	45.6	+34	31	6.3–13.2	Mira	372	M
R Leporis	04	59.6	–14	48	5.5–11.7	Mira	427	C
Y Librae	15	11.7	–06	01	7.6–14.7	Mira	276	M
RS Librae	15	24.3	–22	55	7.0–13.0	Mira	218	M
Delta Librae	15	01.0	–08	31	4.9–5.9	Algol	2.3	A
R Lyncis	07	01.3	+55	20	7.2–14.3	Mira	379	S
R Lyrae	18	55.3	+43	57	3.9–5.0	Semi-regular	46?	M
RR Lyrae	19	25.5	+42	47	7.1–8.1	RR Lyrae	0.6	A–F
Beta Lyrae	18	50.1	+33	22	3.3–4.4	Eclipsing	12.9	B
U Microscopii	20	29.2	–40	25	7.0–14.4	Mira	334	M
*U Monocerotis	07	30.8	–09	47	5.9–7.8	RV Tauri	91	F–K
V Monocerotis	06	22.7	–02	12	6.0–13.9	Mira	340	M
R Normae	15	36.0	–49	30	6.5–13.9	Mira	508	M
T Normae	15	44.1	–54	59	6.2–13.6	Mira	241	M

Star	RA h	m	Declination °	′	Range	Type	Period (days)	Spectrum
R Octantis	05	26.1	−86	23	6.3–13.2	Mira	405	M
S Octantis	18	08.7	−86	48	7.2–14.0	Mira	259	M
V Ophiuchi	16	26.7	−12	26	7.3–11.6	Mira	297	C
X Ophiuchi	18	38.3	+08	50	5.9–9.2	Mira	329	M
RS Ophiuchi	17	50.2	−06	43	4.3–12.5	Recurrent nova	—	OB+M
U Orionis	05	55.8	+20	10	4.8–13.0	Mira	368	M
W Orionis	05	05.4	+01	11	5.9–7.7	Semi-regular	212	C
Alpha Orionis	05	55.2	+07	24	0.0–1.3	Semi-regular	2335	M
S Pavonis	19	55.2	−59	12	6.6–10.4	Semi-regular	381	M
Kappa Pavonis	18	56.9	−67	14	3.9–4.8	W Virginis	9.1	G
R Pegasi	23	06.8	+10	33	6.9–13.8	Mira	378	M
X Persei	03	55.4	+31	03	6.0–7.0	Gamma Cas.	—	O9.5
Beta Persei	03	08.2	+40	57	2.1–3.4	Algol	2.9	B
Zeta Phoenicis	01	08.4	−55	15	3.9–4.4	Algol	1.7	B+B
R Pictoris	04	46.2	−49	15	6.4–10.1	Semi-regular	171	M
RS Puppis	08	13.1	−34	35	6.5–7.7	Cepheid	41.4	F–G
L^2 Puppis	07	13.5	−44	39	2.6–6.2	Semi-regular	141	M
T Pyxidis	09	04.7	−32	23	6.5–15.3	Recurrent nova	7000±	Pec
U Sagittae	19	18.8	+19	37	6.5–9.3	Algol	3.4	B+G
WZ Sagittae	20	07.6	+17	42	7.0–15.5	Dwarf nova	1900±	A
R Sagittarii	19	16.7	−19	18	6.7–12.8	Mira	270	M
RR Sagittarii	19	55.9	−29	11	5.4–14.0	Mira	336	M
RT Sagittarii	20	17.7	−39	07	6.0–14.1	Mira	306	M
RU Sagittarii	19	58.7	−41	51	6.0–13.8	Mira	240	M
RY Sagittarii	19	16.5	−33	31	5.8–14.0	R Coronae Bor.	—	G
RR Scorpii	16	56.6	−30	35	5.0–12.4	Mira	281	M
RS Scorpii	16	55.6	−45	06	6.2–13.0	Mira	320	M
RT Scorpii	17	03.5	−36	55	7.0–15.2	Mira	449	S
Delta Scorpii	16	00.3	−22	37	1.6–2.3	Irregular	—	B
S Sculptoris	00	15.4	−32	03	5.5–13.6	Mira	363	M
R Scuti	18	47.5	−05	42	4.2–8.6	RV Tauri	146	G–K
R Serpentis	15	50.7	+15	08	5.2–14.4	Mira	356	M
S Serpentis	15	21.7	+14	19	7.0–14.1	Mira	372	M
T Tauri	04	22.0	+19	32	9.3–13.5	T Tauri	—	F–K
SU Tauri	05	49.1	+19	04	9.1–16.9	R Coronae Bor.	—	G
Lambda Tauri	04	00.7	+12	29	3.4–3.9	Algol	4.0	B+A
R Trianguli	02	37.0	+34	16	5.4–12.6	Mira	267	M
R Ursae Majoris	10	44.6	+68	47	6.5–13.7	Mira	302	M
T Ursae Majoris	12	36.4	+59	29	6.6–13.5	Mira	257	M
*Z Ursae Majoris	11	56.5	+57	52	6.2–9.4	Semi-regular	196	M

Star	RA		Declination		Range	Type	Period	Spectrum
	h	m	°	′			(days)	
*RY Ursae Majoris	12	20.5	+61	19	6.7–8.3	Semi-regular	310?	M
U Ursae Minoris	14	17.3	+66	48	7.1–13.0	Mira	331	M
R Virginis	12	38.5	+06	59	6.1–12.1	Mira	146	M
S Virginis	13	33.0	–07	12	6.3–13.2	Mira	375	M
SS Virginis	12	25.3	+00	48	6.0–9.6	Semi-regular	364	C
R Vulpeculae	21	04.4	+23	49	7.0–14.3	Mira	137	M
Z Vulpeculae	19	21.7	+25	34	7.3–8.9	Algol	2.5	B+A

V CANUM VENATICORUM 13h 19.5m +45° 32′ (2000)

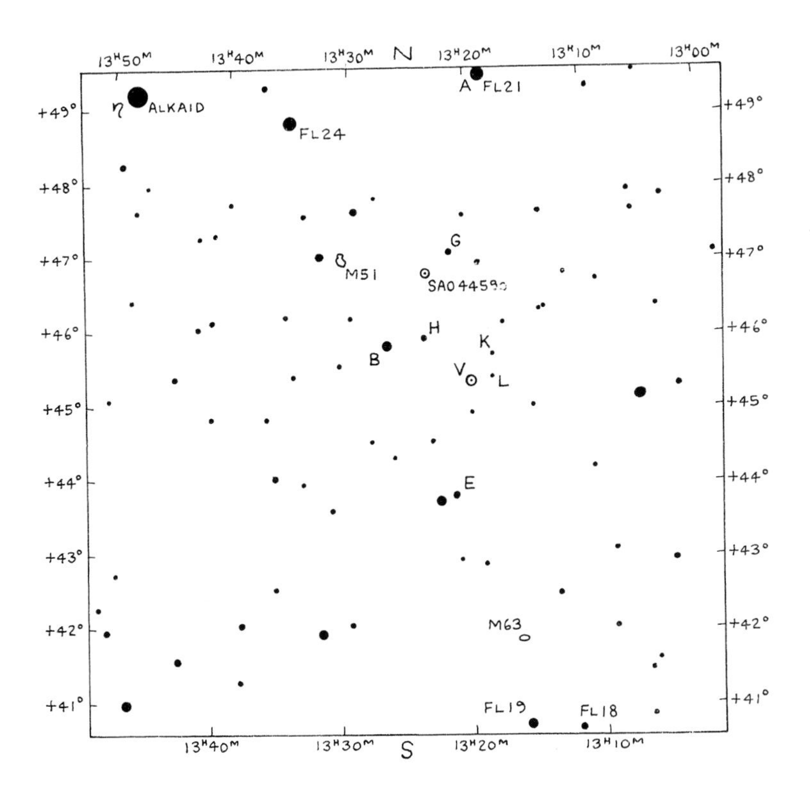

A 5.1 H 7.8
B 5.9 K 8.4
E 6.5 L 8.6
G 7.1

o (MIRA) CETI 02h 19.3m –02° 59′ (2000)

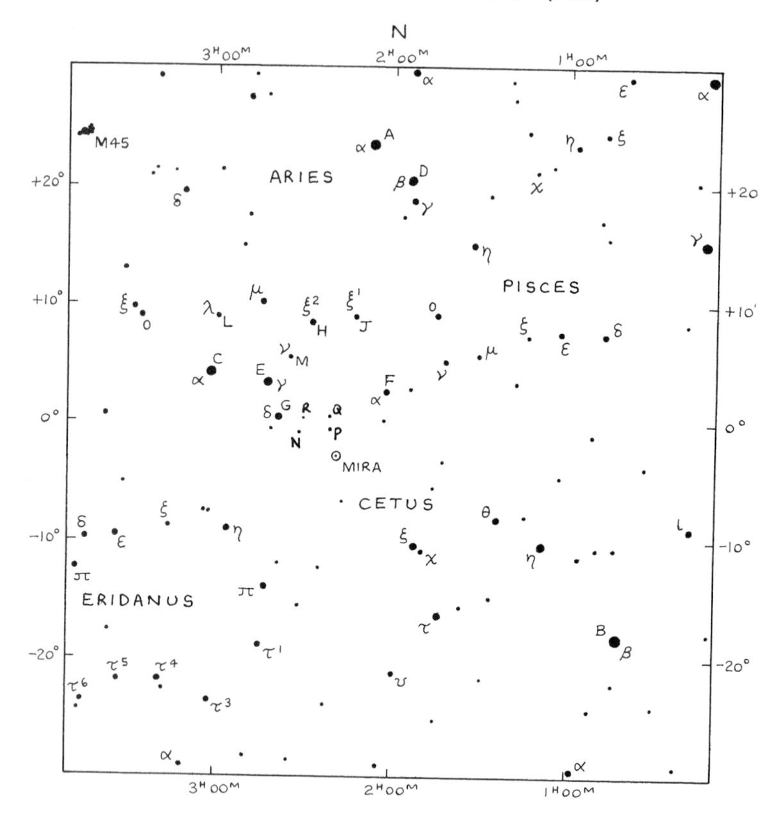

A 2.2	J 4.4
B 2.4	L 4.9
C 2.7	M 5.1
D 3.0	N 5.4
E 3.6	P 5.5
F 3.8	Q 5.7
G 4.1	R 6.1
H 4.3	

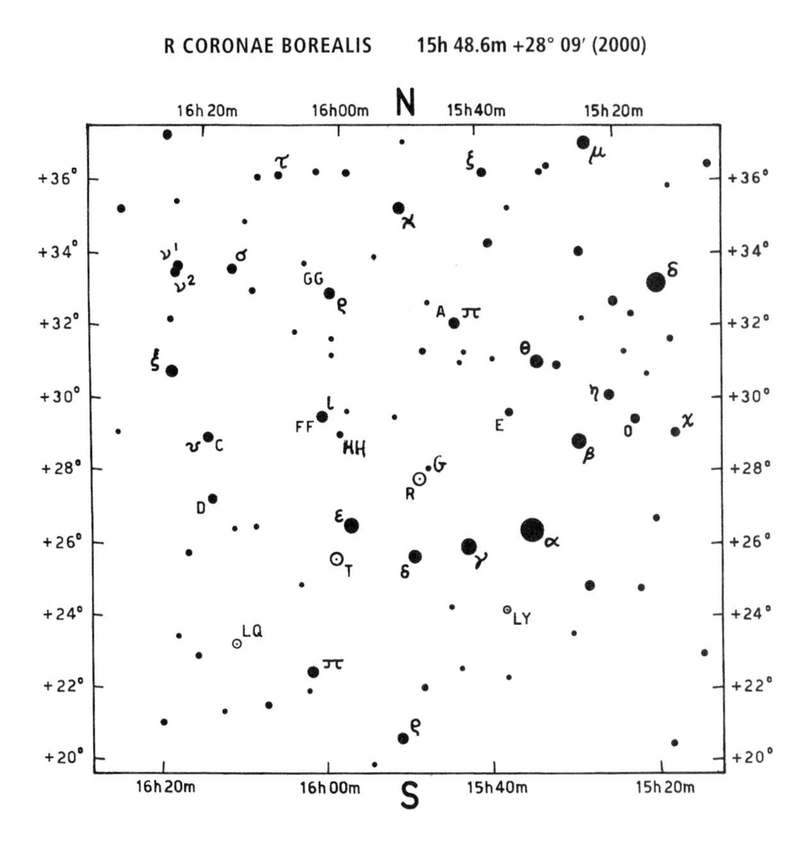

FF	5.0	C	5.8
GG	5.4	D	6.2
A	5.6	E	6.5
		HH	7.1
		G	7.4

CH CYGNI 19h 24.5m +50° 14′ (2000)

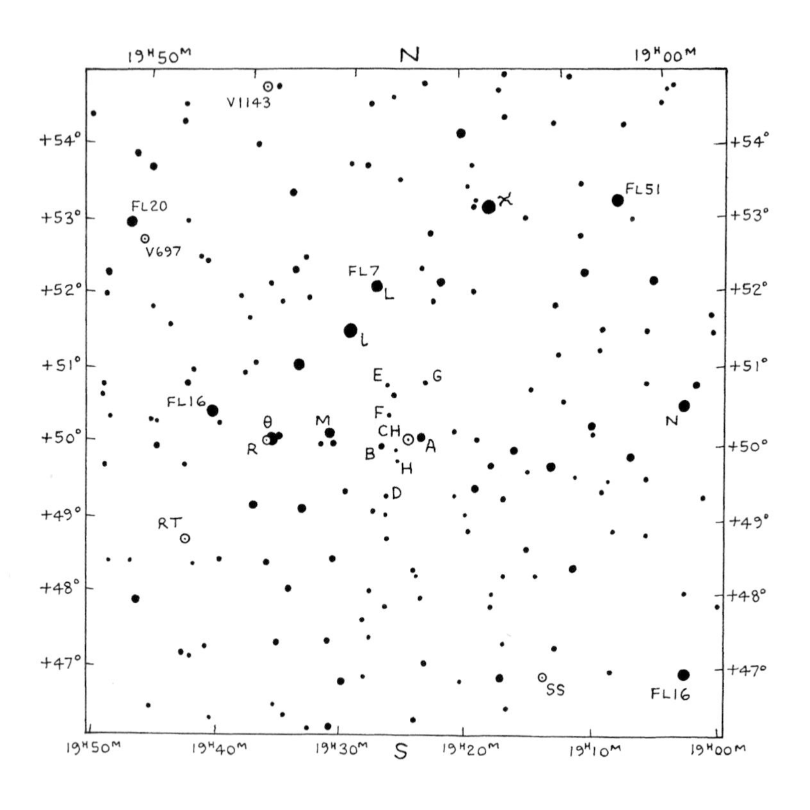

N 5.4	D 8.0
M 5.5	E 8.1
L 5.8	F 8.5
A 6.5	G 8.5
B 7.4	H 9.2

U MONOCEROTIS 07h 30.8m −09° 47′ (2000)

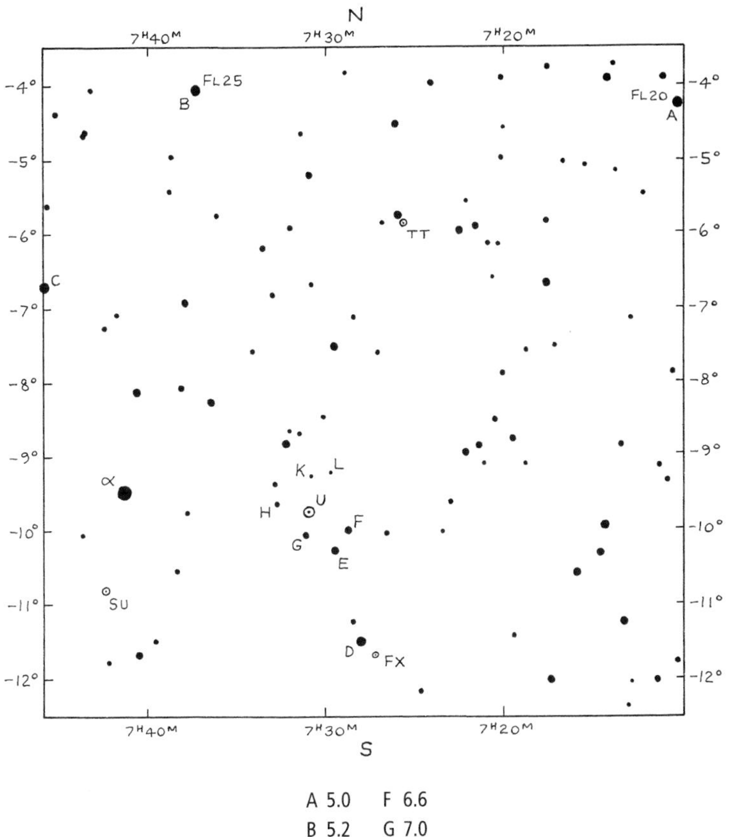

A 5.0	F 6.6
B 5.2	G 7.0
C 5.7	H 7.5
D 5.9	K 7.8
E 6.0	L 8.0

RY URSAE MAJORIS 12h 20.5m +61° 19′ (2000)
Z URSAE MAJORIS 11h 56.5m +57° 52′ (2000)

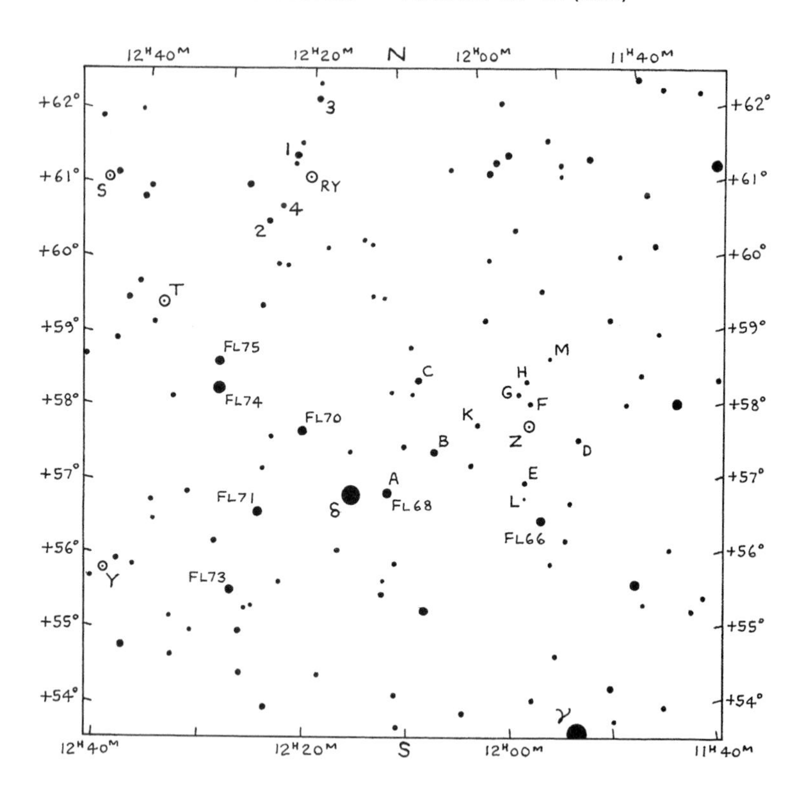

A	6.5	F	8.6	M	9.1
B	7.2	G	8.7	1	6.9
C	7.6	H	8.8	2	7.4
D	8.0	K	8.9	3	7.7
E	8.3	L	9.0	4	7.8

Mira Stars: Maxima, 2006

JOHN ISLES

Below are the predicted dates of maxima for Mira stars that reach magnitude 7.5 or brighter at an average maximum. Individual maxima can in some cases be brighter or fainter than average by a magnitude or more, and all dates are only approximate. The positions, extreme ranges and mean periods of these stars can be found in the preceding list of interesting variable stars.

Star	Mean Magnitude at Maximum	Dates of Maxima
R Andromedae	6.9	31 Mar
W Andromedae	7.4	17 Mar
R Aquarii	6.5	28 Oct
R Aquilae	6.1	15 Sep
R Bootis	7.2	10 Aug
R Cancri	6.8	23 Sep
S Canis Minoris	7.5	23 Apr
R Carinae	4.6	22 Sep
S Carinae	5.7	14 Feb, 13 Jul, 20 Dec
R Cassiopeiae	7.0	16 Aug
R Centauri	5.8	4 May
T Cephei	6.0	27 Nov
U Ceti	7.5	27 May
Omicron Ceti	3.4	7 Apr
T Columbae	7.5	11 Aug
S Coronae Borealis	7.3	25 Sep
V Coronae Borealis	7.5	16 Mar
R Corvi	7.5	20 Jun
R Cygni	7.5	4 Aug
U Cygni	7.2	1 May
RT Cygni	7.3	11 Jun, 19 Dec

Star	Mean Magnitude at Maximum	Dates of Maxima
Chi Cygni	5.2	19 Aug
R Geminorum	7.1	14 Dec
U Herculis	7.5	23 Jul
R Horologii	6.0	28 Sep
R Hydrae	4.5	20 Oct
R Leonis	5.8	12 Apr
R Leonis Minoris	7.1	2 Dec
R Leporis	6.8	18 May
RS Librae	7.5	26 Jul
V Monocerotis	7.0	6 Sep
R Normae	7.2	26 Feb
T Normae	7.4	6 Apr, 2 Dec
V Ophiuchi	7.5	20 Oct
X Ophiuchi	6.8	13 Mar
U Orionis	6.3	10 Jan
R Sagittarii	7.3	6 Apr
RR Sagittarii	6.8	3 Apr
RT Sagittarii	7.0	6 Feb, 9 Dec
RU Sagittarii	7.2	11 Jul
RR Scorpii	5.9	12 Feb, 20 Nov
RS Scorpii	7.0	19 Aug
S Sculptoris	6.7	15 Dec
R Serpentis	6.9	24 Nov
R Trianguli	6.2	16 Jan, 10 Oct
R Ursae Majoris	7.5	16 Oct
R Virginis	6.9	11 Jan, 6 Jun, 29 Oct
S Virginis	7.0	17 Jan

Some Interesting Double Stars

BOB ARGYLE

The positions, angles and separations given below correspond to epoch 2006.0.

No.	RA		Declination		Star	Magnitudes	Separation	PA	Catalogue	Comments
	h	m	°	′			arcsec	°		
1	00	31.5	–62	58	β Tuc	4.4, 4.8	27.1	169	LCL 119	Both again difficult doubles.
2	00	49.1	+57	49	η Cas	3.4, 7.5	13.1	320	Σ60	Easy. Creamy, bluish.
3	00	55.0	+23	38	36 And	6.0, 6.4	1.0	318	Σ73	P = 168 years. Both yellow. Slowly opening.
4	01	13.7	+07	35	ζ Psc	5.6, 6.5	23.1	63	Σ100	Yellow, reddish-white.
5	01	39.8	–56	12	p Eri	5.8, 5.8	11.6	189	Δ5	Period = 483 years.
6	01	53.5	+19	18	γ Ari	4.8, 4.8	7.5	1	Σ180	Very easy. Both white.
7	02	02.0	+02	46	α Psc	4.2, 5.1	1.8	268	Σ202	Binary, period = 933 years.
8	02	03.9	+42	20	γ And	2.3, 5.0	9.6	63	Σ205	Yellow, blue. Relatively fixed.
					γ2 And	5.1, 6.3	0.3	100	OΣ38	BC. Needs 30 cm. Closing.
9	02	29.1	+67	24	ι Cas AB	4.9, 6.9	2.6	230	Σ262	AB is long-period binary. P = 620 years.
					ι Cas AC	4.9, 8.4	7.2	118		
10	02	33.8	–28	14	ω For	5.0, 7.7	10.8	245	HJ 3506	Common proper motion.
11	02	43.3	+03	14	γ Cet	3.5, 7.3	2.6	298	Σ299	Not too easy.

No.	RA		Declination		Star	Magnitudes	Separation	PA	Catalogue	Comments
	h	m	°	′			arcsec	°		
12	02	58.3	−40	18	θ Eri	3.4, 4.5	8.3	90	PZ 2	Both white.
13	02	59.2	+21	20	ε Ari	5.2, 5.5	1.5	208	Σ333	Binary. Little motion. Both white.
14	03	00.9	+52	21	Σ331 Per	5.3, 6.7	12.0	85	–	Fixed.
15	03	12.1	−28	59	α For	4.0, 7.0	5.1	299	HJ 3555	P = 269 years. B variable?
16	03	48.6	−37	37	f Eri	4.8, 5.3	8.2	215	Δ16	Pale yellow. Fixed.
17	03	54.3	−02	57	32 Eri	4.8, 6.1	6.9	348	Σ470	Fixed.
18	04	32.0	+53	55	1 Cam	5.7, 6.8	10.3	308	Σ550	Fixed.
19	04	50.9	−53	28	ι Pic	5.6, 6.4	12.4	58	Δ18	Good object for small apertures. Fixed.
20	05	13.2	−12	56	κ Lep	4.5, 7.4	2.2	357	Σ661	Visible in 7.5 cm.
21	05	14.5	−08	12	β Ori	0.1, 6.8	9.5	204	Σ668	Companion once thought to be close double.
22	05	21.8	−24	46	41 Lep	5.4, 6.6	3.4	93	HJ 3752	Deep-yellow pair in a rich field.
23	05	24.5	−02	24	η Ori	3.8, 4.8	1.7	78	DA 5	Slow-moving binary.
24	05	35.1	+09	56	λ Ori	3.6, 5.5	4.3	44	Σ738	Fixed.
25	05	35.3	−05	23	θ Ori AB	6.7, 7.9	8.6	32	Σ748	Trapezium in M42.
					θ Ori CD	5.1, 6.7	13.4	61		
26	05	38.7	−02	36	σ Ori AC	4.0, 10.3	11.4	238	Σ762	Quintuple. A is a close double.
					σ Ori ED	6.5, 7.5	30.1	231		
27	05	40.7	−01	57	ζ Ori	1.9, 4.0	2.4	164	Σ774	Can be split in 7.5 cm. Long-period binary.
28	06	14.9	+22	30	η Gem	var, 6.5	1.6	255	β1008	Well seen with 20 cm. Primary orange.
29	06	46.2	+59	27	12 Lyn AB	5.4, 6.0	1.7	67	Σ948	AB is binary, P = 706 years.
					12 Lyn AC	5.4, 7.3	8.7	309		

No.	RA		Declination		Star	Magnitudes	Separation	PA	Catalogue	Comments
	h	m	°	′			arcsec	°		
30	07	08.7	−70	30	γ Vol	3.9, 5.8	14.1	298	Δ42	Very slow binary.
31	07	16.6	−23	19	h3945 CMa	4.8, 6.8	26.8	51	–	Contrasting colours.
32	07	20.1	+21	59	δ Gem	3.5, 8.2	5.7	226	Σ1066	Not too easy. Yellow, pale blue.
33	07	34.6	+31	53	α Gem	1.9, 2.9	4.3	60	Σ1110	Widening. Easy with 7.5 cm.
34	07	38.8	−26	48	κ Pup	4.5, 4.7	9.8	318	H III 27	Both white.
35	08	12.2	+17	39	ζ Cnc AB	5.6, 6.0	1.0	52	Σ1196	Period (AB) = 60 years. Near maximum separation.
					ζ Cnc AB-C	5.0, 6.2	5.9	72	Σ1196	Period (AB-C) = 1,150 years.
36	08	44.7	−54	43	δ Vel	2.1, 5.1	0.8	328	I 10	Difficult close pair. Period 142 years.
37	08	46.8	+06	25	ε Hyd	3.3, 6.8	2.9	302	Σ1273	PA slowly increasing. A is a very close pair.
38	09	18.8	+36	48	38 Lyn	3.9, 6.6	2.8	230	Σ1338	Almost fixed.
39	09	47.1	−65	04	μ Car	3.1, 6.1	5.0	128	RMK 11	Fixed. Fine in small telescopes.
40	10	20.0	+19	50	γ Leo	2.2, 3.5	4.4	125	Σ1424	Binary, period = 619 years. Both orange.
41	10	32.0	−45	04	s Vel	6.2, 6.5	13.5	218	PZ 3	Fixed.
42	10	46.8	−49	26	μ Vel	2.7, 6.4	2.5	54	R 155	P = 138 years. Near widest separation.
43	10	55.6	+24	45	54 Leo	4.5, 6.3	6.6	111	Σ1487	Slowly widening. Pale yellow and white.

No.	RA		Declin-ation		Star	Magni-tudes	Separa-tion	PA	Cata-logue	Comments
	h	m	°	′			arcsec	°		
44	11	18.2	+31	32	ξ UMa	4.3, 4.8	1.7	239	Σ1523	Binary, 60 years. Needs 7.5 cm.
45	11	21.0	–54	29	π Cen	4.3, 5.0	0.2	160	I 879	Binary, 38.7 years. Very close. Needs 40 cm.
46	11	23.9	+10	32	ι Leo	4.0, 6.7	1.9	104	Σ1536	Binary, period = 186 years..
47	11	32.3	–29	16	N Hya	5.8, 5.9	9.5	210	H III 96	Fixed.
48	12	14.0	–45	43	D Cen	5.6, 6.8	2.8	243	RMK 14	Orange and white. Closing.
49	12	26.6	–63	06	α Cru	1.4, 1.9	4.0	112	Δ252	Third star in a low-power field.
50	12	41.5	–48	58	γ Cen	2.9, 2.9	0.6	339	HJ 4539	Period = 84 years. Closing. Both yellow.
51	12	41.7	–01	27	γ Vir	3.5, 3.5	0.4	86	Σ1670	Periastron in 2005. Now widening..
52	12	46.3	–68	06	β Mus	3.7, 4.0	1.3	47	R 207	Both white. Closing slowly. P = 383 years.
53	12	54.6	–57	11	μ Cru	4.3, 5.3	34.9	17	Δ126	Fixed. Both white.
54	12	56.0	+38	19	α CVn	2.9, 5.5	19.3	229	Σ1692	Easy. Yellow, bluish.
55	13	22.6	–60	59	J Cen	4.6, 6.5	60.0	343	Δ133	Fixed. A is a close pair.
56	13	24.0	+54	56	ζ UMa	2.3, 4.0	14.4	152	Σ1744	Very easy. Naked-eye pair with Alcor.
57	13	51.8	–33	00	3 Cen	4.5, 6.0	7.9	106	H III 101	Both white. Closing slowly.
58	14	39.6	–60	50	α Cen	0.0, 1.2	9.8	232	RHD 1	Finest pair in the sky. P = 80 years. Closing.
59	14	41.1	+13	44	ζ Boo	4.5, 4.6	0.7	297	Σ1865	Both white. Closing – highly inclined orbit.

No.	RA		Declination		Star	Magnitudes	Separation	PA	Catalogue	Comments
	h	m	°	′			arcsec	°		
60	14	45.0	+27	04	ε Boo	2.5, 4.9	2.9	345	Σ1877	Yellow, blue. Fine pair.
61	14	46.0	−25	27	54 Hya	5.1, 7.1	8.3	122	H III 97	Closing slowly.
62	14	49.3	−14	09	μ Lib	5.8, 6.7	1.9	2	β106	Becoming wider. Fine in 7.5 cm.
63	14	51.4	+19	06	ξ Boo	4.7, 7.0	6.3	312	Σ1888	Fine contrast. Easy.
64	15	03.8	+47	39	44 Boo	5.3, 6.2	1.9	57	Σ1909	Period = 206 years. Beginning to close.
65	15	05.1	−47	03	π Lup	4.6, 4.7	1.7	64	HJ 4728	Widening.
66	15	18.5	−47	53	μ Lup AB	5.1, 5.2	0.8	120	HJ 4753	AB closing. Underobserved.
					μ Lup AC	4.4, 7.2	24.0	129	Δ180	AC almost fixed.
67	15	23.4	−59	19	γ Cir	5.1, 5.5	0.8	352	HJ 4757	Closing. Needs 20 cm. Long-period binary.
68	15	32.0	+32	17	η CrB	5.6, 5.9	0.5	126	Σ1937	Both yellow. P = 41 yrs. Widening until 2013.
69	15	34.8	+10	33	δ Ser	4.2, 5.2	4.3	176	Σ1954	Long-period binary.
70	15	35.1	−41	10	γ Lup	3.5, 3.6	0.8	277	HJ 4786	Binary. Period = 190 years. Needs 15 cm.
71	15	56.9	−33	58	ξ Lup	5.3, 5.8	10.2	49	PZ 4	Fixed.
72	16	14.7	+33	52	σ CrB	5.6, 6.6	7.1	237	Σ2032	Long-period binary. Both white.
73	16	29.4	−26	26	α Sco	1.2, 5.4	2.6	274	GNT 1	Red, green. Difficult from mid northern latitudes.
74	16	30.9	+01	59	λ Oph	4.2, 5.2	1.6	35	Σ2055	P = 129 years. Fairly difficult in small apertures.

No.	RA		Declination		Star	Magnitudes	Separation	PA	Catalogue	Comments
	h	m	°	′			arcsec	°		
75	16	41.3	+31	36	ζ Her	2.9, 5.5	1.0	214	Σ2084	Period 34 years. Now widening. Needs 20 cm.
76	17	05.3	+54	28	μ Dra	5.7, 5.7	2.3	11	Σ2130	Period 672 years.
77	17	14.6	+14	24	α Her	var, 5.4	4.6	104	Σ2140	Red, green. Long-period binary.
78	17	15.3	–26	35	36 Oph	5.1, 5.1	4.9	326	SHJ 243	Period = 471 years.
79	17	23.7	+37	08	ρ Her	4.6, 5.6	4.1	318	Σ2161	Slowly widening.
80	18	01.5	+21	36	95 Her	5.0, 5.1	6.4	257	Σ2264	Colours thought variable in C19.
81	18	05.5	+02	30	70 Oph	4.2, 6.0	5.1	137	Σ2272	Opening. Easy in 7.5 cm.
82	18	06.8	–43	25	h5014 CrA	5.7, 5.7	1.7	4	–	Period = 450 years. Needs 10 cm.
83	18	35.9	+16	58	OΣ358 Her	6.8, 7.0	1.6	151	–	Period = 380 years.
84	18	44.3	+39	40	ε^1 Lyr	5.0, 6.1	2.5	349	Σ2382	Quadruple system with ε^2. Both pairs
85	18	44.3	+39	40	ε^2 Lyr	5.2, 5.5	2.3	79	Σ2383	visible in 7.5 cm.
86	18	56.2	+04	12	θ Ser	4.5, 5.4	22.4	104	Σ2417	Fixed. Very easy.
87	19	06.4	–37	04	γ CrA	4.8, 5.1	1.3	32	HJ 5084	Beautiful pair. Period = 122 years.
88	19	30.7	+27	58	β Cyg AB	3.1, 5.1	34.3	54	Σ I 43	Glorious. Yellow, blue-greenish.
					β Cyg Aa	3.1, 5.2	0.3	105	MCA 55	Aa. Period = 97 years. Closing.
89	19	45.0	+45	08	δ Cyg	2.9, 6.3	2.6	222	Σ2579	Slowly widening. Period = 780 years.
90	19	48.2	+70	16	ε Dra	3.8, 7.4	3.2	17	Σ2603	Slow binary.

No.	RA		Declin-ation		Star	Magni-tudes	Separa-tion	PA	Cata-logue	Comments
	h	m	°	′			arcsec	°		
91	20	46.7	+16	07	γ Del	4.5, 5.5	9.2	266	Σ2727	Easy. Yellowish. Long-period binary.
92	20	47.4	+36	29	λ Cyg	4.8, 6.1	0.9	10	OΣ413	Difficult binary in small apertures.
93	20	59.1	+04	18	ε Equ AB	6.0, 6.3	0.7	284	Σ2737	Fine triple. AB is closing.
					ε Equ AC	6.0, 7.1	10.3	66		
94	21	06.9	+38	45	61 Cyg	5.2, 6.0	31.0	151	Σ2758	Nearby binary. Both orange. Period = 722 years.
95	21	19.9	−53	27	θ Ind	4.5, 7.0	6.8	271	HJ 5258	Pale yellow and reddish. Long-period binary.
96	21	44.1	+28	45	μ Cyg	4.8, 6.1	1.8	313	Σ2822	Period = 713 years.
97	22	03.8	+64	37	ξ Cep	4.4, 6.5	8.1	275	Σ2863	White and blue. Long-period binary.
98	22	26.6	−16	45	53 Aqr	6.4, 6.6	1.4	24	SHJ 345	Long-period binary, approaching periastron.
99	22	28.8	−00	01	ζ Aqr	4.3, 4.5	2.1	177	Σ2909	Slowly widening.
100	23	59.4	+33	43	Σ3050 And	6.6, 6.6	2.1	333	–	Period = 350 years.

Some Interesting Nebulae, Clusters and Galaxies

Object	RA		Declination		Remarks
	h	m	°	′	
M31 Andromedae	00	40.7	+41	05	Andromeda Galaxy, visible to naked eye.
H VIII 78 Cassiopeiae	00	41.3	+61	36	Fine cluster, between Gamma and Kappa Cassiopeiae.
M33 Trianguli	01	31.8	+30	28	Spiral. Difficult with small apertures.
H VI 33–4 Persei, C14	02	18.3	+56	59	Double cluster; Sword-handle.
Δ142 Doradus	05	39.1	–69	09	Looped nebula round 30 Doradus. Naked eye. In Large Magellanic Cloud.
M1 Tauri	05	32.3	+22	00	Crab Nebula, near Zeta Tauri.
M42 Orionis	05	33.4	–05	24	Orion Nebula. Contains the famous Trapezium, Theta Orionis.
M35 Geminorum	06	06.5	+24	21	Open cluster near Eta Geminorum.
H VII 2 Monocerotis, C50	06	30.7	+04	53	Open cluster, just visible to naked eye.
M41 Canis Majoris	06	45.5	–20	42	Open cluster, just visible to naked eye.
M47 Puppis	07	34.3	–14	22	Mag. 5.2. Loose cluster.
H IV 64 Puppis	07	39.6	–18	05	Bright planetary in rich neighbourhood.
M46 Puppis	07	39.5	–14	42	Open cluster.
M44 Cancri	08	38	+20	07	Praesepe. Open cluster near Delta Cancri. Visible to naked eye.
M97 Ursae Majoris	11	12.6	+55	13	Owl Nebula, diameter 3′. Planetary.
Kappa Crucis, C94	12	50.7	–60	05	'Jewel Box'; open cluster, with stars of contrasting colours.
M3 Can. Ven.	13	40.6	+28	34	Bright globular.
Omega Centauri, C80	13	23.7	–47	03	Finest of all globulars. Easy with naked eye.
M80 Scorpii	16	14.9	–22	53	Globular, between Antares and Beta Scorpii.
M4 Scorpii	16	21.5	–26	26	Open cluster close to Antares.

Object	RA		Declina-tion		Remarks
	h	m	°	′	
M13 Herculis	16	40	+36	31	Globular. Just visible to naked eye.
M92 Herculis	16	16.1	+43	11	Globular. Between Iota and Eta Herculis.
M6 Scorpii	17	36.8	−32	11	Open cluster; naked eye.
M7 Scorpii	17	50.6	−34	48	Very bright open cluster; naked eye.
M23 Sagittarii	17	54.8	−19	01	Open cluster nearly 50′ in diameter.
H IV 37 Draconis, C6	17	58.6	+66	38	Bright planetary.
M8 Sagittarii	18	01.4	−24	23	Lagoon Nebula. Gaseous. Just visible with naked eye.
NGC 6572 Ophiuchi	18	10.9	+06	50	Bright planetary, between Beta Ophiuchi and Zeta Aquilae.
M17 Sagittarii	18	18.8	−16	12	Omega Nebula. Gaseous. Large and bright.
M11 Scuti	18	49.0	−06	19	Wild Duck. Bright open cluster.
M57 Lyrae	18	52.6	+32	59	Ring Nebula. Brightest of planetaries.
M27 Vulpeculae	19	58.1	+22	37	Dumb-bell Nebula, near Gamma Sagittae.
H IV 1 Aquarii, C55	21	02.1	−11	31	Bright planetary, near Nu Aquarii.
M15 Pegasi	21	28.3	+12	01	Bright globular, near Epsilon Pegasi.
M39 Cygni	21	31.0	+48	17	Open cluster between Deneb and Alpha Lacertae. Well seen with low powers.

(M = Messier number; NGC = New General Catalogue number; C = Caldwell number.)

Our Contributors

Professor Garry E. Hunt has been a leading international space scientist for many decades with Viking (Mars), Voyager, where he was the only UK scientist involved with the mission, and an adviser to NASA and ESA. He has held senior appointments at Imperial College, London, UCL and JPL/CalTech, as well as many visiting professorships in the USA, Canada and Australia. He is now Managing Partner of Elbury Enterprises. Garry continues to be a regular contributor to BBC TV and *The Sky at Night*, as well as the *Yearbook of Astronomy*.

Martin Mobberley is one of the UK's most active imagers of comets, planets, novae and supernovae, and served as President of the British Astronomical Association from 1997 to 1999. In 2000, he was awarded the Association's Walter Goodacre Award. He is the author of two major astronomy books, *Astronomical Equipment for Amateurs* and *The New Amateur Astronomer*, as well as a children's astronomy book, *Space Navigator*.

Dr Stephen J. Wainwright is a biologist by training and is a retired Senior Lecturer in Environmental Biology from the University of Wales, Swansea, UK. He has been an amateur astronomer for 40 years and has been an active member of the Cardiff and Swansea Astronomical Societies. He was a writer of the 'Night Sky News', a monthly astronomical column in the *South Wales Evening Post*, for 10 years. He is a Fellow of the Royal Astronomical Society, and the founder of QCUIAG, a 7,000+ strong international astronomical imaging group that converts unconventional devices for astronomical imaging (www.qcuiag.co.uk).

Professor Fred Watson is Astronomer-in-Charge of the Anglo-Australian Observatory at Coonabarabran in north-western New South Wales. He is an adjunct Professor in the School of Physical and Chemical Sciences of Queensland University of Technology, and an honorary Professor of Astronomy in the University of Southern

Queensland. A regular contributor to the *Yearbook of Astronomy*, his new book, *Stargazer: The Life and Times of the Telescope*, is published by Allen & Unwin.

Dr Matthew Kenworthy is an Instrument Scientist at the Steward Observatory in Tucson, Arizona. As an amateur astronomer growing up near London, his fascination with telescopes and optics led to a career building astronomical instruments of all shapes and sizes.

Dr William Sheehan has been an amateur astronomer since the age of nine. He has written several books, including *The Immortal Fire Within* (1995), a biography of pioneer Milky Way photographer Edward Emerson Barnard, and was named a 2001 Guggenheim Fellow for his research on the structure and evolution of the Galaxy. He lives in Willmar, Minnesota, USA.

Dr David M. Harland gained his BSc in astronomy in 1977 and a doctorate in computational science. Subsequently, he has taught computer science, worked in industry and managed academic research. In 1995 he 'retired' and has since published many books on space themes.

Dr Allan Chapman, of Wadham College, Oxford, is probably Britain's leading authority on the history of astronomy. He has published many research papers and several books, as well as numerous popular accounts. He is a frequent and welcome contributor to the *Yearbook*.

Astronomical Societies in the British Isles

British Astronomical Association
Assistant Secretary: Burlington House, Piccadilly, London W1V 9AG.
Meetings: Lecture Hall of Scientific Societies, Civil Service Commission Building, 23 Savile Row, London W1. Last Wednesday each month (Oct.–June), 5 p.m. and some Saturday afternoons.

Association for Astronomy Education
Secretary: Teresa Grafton, The Association for Astronomy Education, c/o The Royal Astronomical Society, Burlington House, Piccadilly, London W1V 0NL.

Astronomical Society of Edinburgh
Secretary: Graham Rule, 105/19 Causewayside, Edinburgh EH9 1QG.
Website: www.roe.ac.uk/asewww/; *Email:* asewww@roe.ac.uk
Meetings: City Observatory, Calton Hill, Edinburgh. 1st Friday each month, 8 p.m.

Astronomical Society of Glasgow
Secretary: Mr David Degan, 5 Hillside Avenue, Alexandria, Dunbartonshire G83 0BB.
Website: www.astronomicalsocietyofglasgow.org.uk
Meetings: Royal College, University of Strathclyde, Montrose Street, Glasgow. 3rd Thursday each month, Sept.–Apr., 7.30 p.m.

Astronomical Society of Haringey
Secretary: Jerry Workman, 91 Greenslade Road, Barking, Essex IG11 9XF.
Meetings: Palm Court, Alexandra Palace, 3rd Wednesday each month, 8 p.m.

Astronomy Ireland
Secretary: Tony Ryan, PO Box 2888, Dublin 1, Eire.
Website: www.astronomy.ie; *Email:* info@astronomy.ie
Meetings: 2nd Monday of each month. Telescope meetings every clear Saturday.

Federation of Astronomical Societies
Secretary: Clive Down, 10 Glan-y-Llyn, North Cornelly, Bridgend, County Borough CF33 4EF.
Email: clivedown@btinternet.com

Junior Astronomical Society of Ireland
Secretary: K. Nolan, 5 St Patrick's Crescent, Rathcoole, Co. Dublin.
Meetings: The Royal Dublin Society, Ballsbridge, Dublin 4. Monthly.

Society for Popular Astronomy
Secretary: Guy Fennimore, 36 Fairway, Keyworth, Nottingham NG12 5DU.
Website: www.popastro.com; *Email:* SPAstronomy@aol.com
Meetings: Last Saturday in Jan., Apr., July, Oct., 2.30 p.m. in London.

Webb Society
Secretary: M.B. Swan, Carrowreagh, Kilshanny, Kilfenora, Co. Clare, Eire.

Aberdeen and District Astronomical Society
Secretary: Ian C. Giddings, 95 Brentfield Circle, Ellon, Aberdeenshire AB41 9DB.
Meetings: Robert Gordon's Institute of Technology, St Andrew's Street, Aberdeen. Fridays, 7.30 p.m.

Abingdon Astronomical Society (was **Fitzharry's Astronomical Society**)
Secretary: Chris Holt, 9 Rutherford Close, Abingdon, Oxon OX14 2AT.
Website: www.abingdonastro.org.uk; *Email:* info@abingdonastro.co.uk
Meetings: All Saints' Methodist Church Hall, Dorchester Crescent, Abingdon, Oxon. 2nd Monday Sept.–June, 8 p.m. and additional beginners' meetings and observing evenings as advertised.

Altrincham and District Astronomical Society
Secretary: Derek McComiskey, 33 Tottenham Drive, Manchester M23 9WH.
Meetings: Timperley Village Club. 1st Friday Sept.–June, 8 p.m.

Andover Astronomical Society
Secretary: Mrs S. Fisher, Staddlestones, Aughton, Kingston, Marlborough, Wiltshire SN8 3SA.
Meetings: Grately Village Hall. 3rd Thursday each month, 7.30 p.m.

Astra Astronomy Section
Secretary: c/o Duncan Lunan, Flat 65, Dalraida House, 56 Blythswood Court, Anderston, Glasgow G2 7PE.
Meetings: Airdrie Arts Centre, Anderson Street, Airdrie. Weekly.

Astrodome Mobile School Planetarium
Contact: Peter J. Golding, 53 City Way, Rochester, Kent ME1 2AX.
Website: www.astrodome.clara.co.uk; *Email:* astrodome@clara.co.uk

Aylesbury Astronomical Society
Secretary: Alan Smith, 182 Marley Fields, Leighton Buzzard, Bedfordshire LU7 8WN.
Meetings: 1st Monday in month at 8 p.m., venue in Aylesbury area. Details from Secretary.

Bassetlaw Astronomical Society
Secretary: Andrew Patton, 58 Holding, Worksop, Notts S81 0TD.
Meetings: Rhodesia Village Hall, Rhodesia, Worksop, Notts. 2nd and 4th Tuesdays of month at 7.45 p.m.

Batley & Spenborough Astronomical Society
Secretary: Robert Morton, 22 Links Avenue, Cleckheaton, West Yorks BD19 4EG.
Meetings: Milner K. Ford Observatory, Wilton Park, Batley. Every Thursday, 8 p.m.

Bedford Astronomical Society
Secretary: Mrs L. Harrington, 24 Swallowfield, Wyboston, Bedfordshire MK44 3AE.
Website: www.observer1.freeserve.co.uk/bashome.html
Meetings: Bedford School, Burnaby Rd, Bedford. Last Wednesday each month.

Bingham & Brooks Space Organization
Secretary: N. Bingham, 15 Hickmore's Lane, Lindfield, West Sussex.

Birmingham Astronomical Society
Contact: P. Bolas, 4 Moat Bank, Bretby, Burton-on-Trent DE15 0QJ.
Website: www.birmingham-astronomical.co.uk; *Email:* pbolas@aol.com
Meetings: Room 146, Aston University. Last Tuesday of month. Sept.–June (except Dec., moved to 1st week in Jan.).

Blackburn Leisure Astronomy Section
Secretary: Mr H. Murphy, 20 Princess Way, Beverley, East Yorkshire HU17 8PD.
Meetings: Blackburn Leisure Welfare. Mondays, 8 p.m.

Blackpool & District Astronomical Society
Secretary: Terry Devon, 30 Victory Road, Blackpool, Lancashire FY1 3JT.
Acting Secretary: Tony Evanson, 25 Aintree Road, Thornton, Lancashire FY5 5HW.
Website: www.geocities.com/bad_astro/index.html; *Email:* bad_astro@yahoo.co.uk
Meetings: St Kentigens Social Centre, Blackpool. 1st Wednesday of the month, 8 p.m.

Bolton Astronomical Society
Secretary: Peter Miskiw, 9 Hedley Street, Bolton, Lancashire BL1 3LE.
Meetings: Ladybridge Community Centre, Bolton. 1st and 3rd Tuesdays Sept.–May, 7.30 p.m.

Border Astronomy Society
Secretary: David Pettitt, 14 Sharp Grove, Carlisle, Cumbria CA2 5QR.
Website: www.members.aol.com/P3pub/page8.html;
Email: davidpettitt@supanet.com
Meetings: The Observatory, Trinity School, Carlisle. Alternate Thursdays, 7.30 p.m., Sept.–May.

Boston Astronomers
Secretary: Mrs Lorraine Money, 18 College Park, Horncastle, Lincolnshire LN9 6RE.
Meetings: Blackfriars Arts Centre, Boston. 2nd Monday each month, 7.30 p.m.

Bradford Astronomical Society
Contact: Mrs J. Hilary Knaggs, 6 Meadow View, Wyke, Bradford BD12 9LA.
Website: www.bradford-astro.freeserve.co.uk/index.htm
Meetings: Eccleshill Library, Bradford. Alternate Mondays, 7.30 p.m.

Braintree, Halstead & District Astronomical Society
Secretary: Mr J. R. Green, 70 Dorothy Sayers Drive, Witham, Essex CM8 2LU.
Meetings: BT Social Club Hall, Witham Telephone Exchange. 3rd Thursday each month, 8 p.m.

Breckland Astronomical Society (was **Great Ellingham and District Astronomy Club**)
Contact: Martin Wolton, Willowbeck House, Pulham St Mary, Norfolk IP21 4QS.
Meetings: Great Ellingham Recreation Centre, Watton Road (B1077), Great Ellingham, 2nd Friday each month, 7.15 p.m.

Bridgend Astronomical Society
Secretary: Clive Down, 10 Glan-y-Llyn, Broadlands, North Cornelly, Bridgend County CF33 4EF.
Email: clivedown@btinternet.com
Meetings: Bridgend Bowls Centre, Bridgend. 2nd Friday, monthly, 7.30 p.m.

Bridgwater Astronomical Society
Secretary: Mr G. MacKenzie, Watergore Cottage, Watergore, South Petherton, Somerset TA13 5JQ.
Website: www.ourworld.compuserve.com/hompages/dbown/Bwastro.htm
Meetings: Room D10, Bridgwater College, Bath Road Centre, Bridgwater. 2nd Wednesday each month, Sept.–June.

Bridport Astronomical Society
Secretary: Mr G.J. Lodder, 3 The Green, Walditch, Bridport, Dorset DT6 4LB.
Meetings: Walditch Village Hall, Bridport. 1st Sunday each month, 7.30 p.m.

Brighton Astronomical and Scientific Society
Secretary: Ms T. Fearn, 38 Woodlands Close, Peacehaven, East Sussex BN10 7SF.
Meetings: St John's Church Hall, Hove. 1st Tuesday each month, 7.30 p.m.

Bristol Astronomical Society
Secretary: Dr John Pickard, 'Fielding', Easter Compton, Bristol BS35 5SJ.
Meetings: Frank Lecture Theatre, University of Bristol Physics Dept., alternate Fridays in term time, and Westbury Park Methodist Church Rooms, North View, other Fridays.

Callington Community Astronomy Group
Secretary: Beccy Watson. *Tel:* 07732 945671
Email: Beccyboo@kimwatson99.fsnet.co.uk
Website: www.callington-astro.org.uk
Meetings: Callington Space Centre, Callington Community College, Launceston Road, Callington, Cornwall PL17 7DR. 1st and 3rd Saturday of each month, 7.30 p.m., Sept.–July.

Cambridge Astronomical Society
Secretary: Brian Lister, 80 Ramsden Square, Cambridge CB4 2BL.
Meetings: Institute of Astronomy, Madingley Road. 3rd Friday each month.

Cardiff Astronomical Society
Secretary: D.W.S. Powell, 1 Tal-y-Bont Road, Ely, Cardiff CF5 5EU.
Meetings: Dept. of Physics and Astronomy, University of Wales, Newport Road, Cardiff. Alternate Thursdays, 8 p.m.

Castle Point Astronomy Club
Secretary: Andrew Turner, 3 Canewdon Hall Close, Canewdon, Rochford, Essex SS4 3PY.
Meetings: St Michael's Church Hall, Daws Heath. Wednesdays, 8 p.m.

Chelmsford Astronomers
Secretary: Brendan Clark, 5 Borda Close, Chelmsford, Essex.
Meetings: Once a month.

Chester Astronomical Society
Secretary: Mrs S. Brooks, 39 Halton Road, Great Sutton, South Wirral LL66 2UF.
Meetings: All Saints' Parish Church, Chester. Last Wednesday each month except Aug. and Dec., 7.30 p.m.

Chester Society of Natural Science, Literature and Art
Secretary: Paul Braid, 'White Wing', 38 Bryn Avenue, Old Colwyn, Colwyn Bay LL29 8AH.
Email: p.braid@virgin.net
Meetings: Once a month.

Chesterfield Astronomical Society
President: Mr D. Blackburn, 71 Middlecroft Road, Stavely, Chesterfield, Derbyshire S41 3XG. Tel: 07909 570754.
Website: www.chesterfield-as.org.uk
Meetings: Barnet Observatory, Newbold, each Friday.

Clacton & District Astronomical Society
Secretary: C. L. Haskell, 105 London Road, Clacton-on-Sea, Essex.

Cleethorpes & District Astronomical Society
Secretary: C. Illingworth, 38 Shaw Drive, Grimsby, South Humberside.
Meetings: Beacon Hill Observatory, Cleethorpes. 1st Wednesday each month.

Cleveland & Darlington Astronomical Society
Contact: Dr John McCue, 40 Bradbury Rd., Stockton-on-Tees, Cleveland TS20 1LE.
Meetings: Grindon Parish Hall, Thorpe Thewles, near Stockton-on-Tees. 2nd Friday, monthly.

Cork Astronomy Club
Secretary: Charles Coughlan, 12 Forest Ridge Crescent, Wilton, Cork, Eire.
Meetings: 1st Monday, Sept.–May (except bank holidays).

Cornwall Astronomical Society
Secretary: J.M. Harvey, 1 Tregunna Close, Porthleven, Cornwall TR13 9LW.
Meetings: Godolphin Club, Wendron Street, Helston, Cornwall. 2nd and 4th Thursday of each month, 7.30 for 8 p.m.

Cotswold Astronomical Society
Secretary: Rod Salisbury, Grove House, Christchurch Road, Cheltenham, Gloucestershire GL50 2PN.
Website: www.members.nbci.com/CotswoldAS
Meetings: Shurdington Church Hall, School Lane, Shurdington, Cheltenham. 2nd Saturday each month, 8 p.m.

Coventry & Warwickshire Astronomical Society
Secretary: Steve Payne, 68 Stonebury Avenue, Eastern Green, Coventry CV5 7FW.
Website: www.cawas.freeserve.co.uk; *Email:* sjp2000@thefarside57.freeserve.co.uk
Meetings: The Earlsdon Church Hall, Albany Road, Earlsdon, Coventry. 2nd Friday, monthly, Sept.–June.

Crawley Astronomical Society
Secretary: Ron Gamer, 1 Pevensey Close, Pound Hill, Crawley, West Sussex RH10 7BL.
Meetings: Ifield Community Centre, Ifield Road, Crawley. 3rd Friday each month, 7.30 p.m.

Crayford Manor House Astronomical Society
Secretary: Roger Pickard, 28 Appletons, Hadlow, Kent TM1 0DT.
Meetings: Manor House Centre, Crayford. Monthly during term time.

Crewkerne and District Astronomical Society (CADAS)
Chairman: Kevin Dodgson, 46 Hermitage Street, Crewkerne, Somerset TA18 8ET.
Email: crewastra@aol.com

Croydon Astronomical Society
Secretary: John Murrell, 17 Dalmeny Road, Carshalton, Surrey.
Meetings: Lecture Theatre, Royal Russell School, Combe Lane, South Croydon. Alternate Fridays, 7.45 p.m.

Derby & District Astronomical Society
Secretary: Ian Bennett, Freers Cottage, Sutton Lane, Etwall.
Web site: www.derby-astro-soc.fsnet/index.html;
Email: bennett.lovatt@btinternet.com
Meetings: Friends Meeting House, Derby. 1st Friday each month, 7.30 p.m.

Doncaster Astronomical Society
Secretary: A. Anson, 15 Cusworth House, St James Street, Doncaster DN1 3AY
Web site: www.donastro.freeserve.co.uk; *Email:* space@donastro.freeserve.co.uk
Meetings: St George's Church House, St George's Church, Church Way, Doncaster. 2nd and 4th Thursday of each month, commencing at 7.30 p.m.

Dumfries Astronomical Society
Secretary: Mr J. Sweeney, 3 Lakeview, Powfoot, Annan DG13 5PG.
Meetings: Gracefield Arts Centre, Edinburgh Road, Dumfries. 3rd Tuesday Aug.–May, 7.30 p.m.

Dundee Astronomical Society

Secretary: G. Young, 37 Polepark Road, Dundee, Tayside DD1 5QT.

Meetings: Mills Observatory, Balgay Park, Dundee. 1st Friday each month, 7.30 p.m. Sept.–Apr.

Easington and District Astronomical Society

Secretary: T. Bradley, 52 Jameson Road, Hartlepool, Co. Durham.

Meetings: Easington Comprehensive School, Easington Colliery. Every 3rd Thursday throughout the year, 7.30 p.m.

Eastbourne Astronomical Society

Secretary: Peter Gill, 18 Selwyn House, Selwyn Road, Eastbourne, East Sussex BN21 2LF.

Meetings: Willingdon Memorial Hall, Church Street, Willingdon. One Saturday per month, Sept.–July, 7.30 p.m.

East Riding Astronomers

Secretary: Tony Scaife, 15 Beech Road, Elloughton, Brough, North Humberside HU15 1JX.

Meetings: As arranged.

East Sussex Astronomical Society

Secretary: Marcus Croft, 12 St Mary's Cottages, Ninfield Road, Bexhill-on-Sea, East Sussex.

Website: www.esas.org.uk

Meetings: St Marys School, Wrestwood Road, Bexhill. 1st Thursday of each month, 8 p.m.

Edinburgh University Astronomical Society

Secretary: c/o Dept. of Astronomy, Royal Observatory, Blackford Hill, Edinburgh.

Ewell Astronomical Society

Secretary: Richard Gledhill, 80 Abinger Avenue, Cheam SM2 7LW.

Website: www.ewell-as.co.uk

Meetings: St Mary's Church Hall, London Road, Ewell. 2nd Friday of each month except August, 7.45 p.m.

Exeter Astronomical Society

Secretary: Tim Sedgwick, Old Dower House, Half Moon, Newton St Cyres, Exeter, Devon EX5 5AE.

Meetings: The Meeting Room, Wynards, Magdalen Street, Exeter. 1st Thursday of month.

Farnham Astronomical Society

Secretary: Laurence Anslow, 'Asterion', 18 Wellington Lane, Farnham, Surrey GU9 9BA.

Meetings: Central Club, South Street, Farnham. 2nd Thursday each month, 8 p.m.

Foredown Tower Astronomy Group

Secretary: M. Feist, Foredown Tower Camera Obscura, Foredown Road, Portslade, East Sussex BN41 2EW.

Meetings: At the above address, 3rd Tuesday each month. 7 p.m. (winter), 8 p.m. (summer).

Fylde Astronomical Society

Secretary: 28 Belvedere Road, Thornton, Lancashire.

Meetings: Stanley Hall, Rossendale Avenue South. 1st Wednesday each month.

Greenock Astronomical Society
Secretary: Carl Hempsey, 49 Brisbane Street, Greenock.
Meetings: Greenock Arts Guild, 3 Campbell Street, Greenock.

Grimsby Astronomical Society
Secretary: R. Williams, 14 Richmond Close, Grimsby, South Humberside.
Meetings: Secretary's home. 2nd Thursday each month, 7.30 p.m.

Guernsey: La Société Guernesiasie Astronomy Section
Secretary: Debby Quertier, Lamorna, Route Charles, St Peter Port, Guernsey GY1 1QS and Jessica Harris, Keanda, Les Sauvagees, St Sampson's, Guernsey GY2 4XT.
Meetings: Observatory, Rue du Lorier, St Peter's. Tuesdays, 8 p.m.

Guildford Astronomical Society
Secretary: A. Langmaid, 22 West Mount, The Mount, Guildford, Surrey GU2 5HL.
Meetings: Guildford Institute, Ward Street, Guildford. 1st Thursday each month, except Aug., 7.30 p.m.

Gwynedd Astronomical Society
Secretary: Mr Ernie Greenwood, 18 Twrcelyn Street, Llanerchymedd, Anglesey LL74 8TL.
Meetings: Dept. of Electronic Engineering, Bangor University. 1st Thursday each month except Aug., 7.30 p.m.

The Hampshire Astronomical Group
Secretary: Geoff Mann, 10 Marie Court, 348 London Road, Waterlooville, Hampshire PO7 7SR.
Website: www.hantsastro.demon.co.uk; *Email:* Geoff.Mann@hazleton97.fsnet.co.uk
Meetings: 2nd Friday, Clanfield Memorial Hall, all other Fridays Clanfield Observatory.

Hanney & District Astronomical Society
Secretary: Bob Church, 47 Upthorpe Drive, Wantage, Oxfordshire OX12 7DG.
Meetings: Last Thursday each month, 8 p.m.

Harrogate Astronomical Society
Secretary: Brian Bonser, 114 Main Street, Little Ouseburn TO5 9TG.
Meetings: National Power HQ, Beckwith Knowle, Harrogate. Last Friday each month.

Hastings and Battle Astronomical Society
Secretary: K.A. Woodcock, 24 Emmanuel Road, Hastings, East Sussex TN34 3LB.
Email: keith@habas.freeserve.co.uk
Meetings: Herstmonceux Science Centre. 2nd Saturday of each month, 7.30 p.m.

Havering Astronomical Society
Secretary: Frances Ridgley, 133 Severn Drive, Upminster, Essex RM14 1PP.
Meetings: Cranham Community Centre, Marlborough Gardens, Upminster, Essex. 3rd Wednesday each month (except July and Aug.), 7.30 p.m.

Heart of England Astronomical Society
Secretary: John Williams, 100 Stanway Road, Shirley, Solihull B90 3JG.
Website: www.members.aol.com/hoeas/home.html; *Email:* hoeas@aol.com
Meetings: Furnace End Village, over Whitacre, Warwickshire. Last Thursday each month, except June, July & Aug., 8 p.m.

Hebden Bridge Literary & Scientific Society, Astronomical Section
Secretary: Peter Jackson, 44 Gilstead Lane, Bingley, West Yorkshire BD16 3NP.
Meetings: Hebden Bridge Information Centre. Last Wednesday, Sept.–May.

Herschel Astronomy Society

Secretary: Kevin Bishop, 106 Holmsdale, Crown Wood, Bracknell, Berkshire RG12 3TB.

Meetings: Eton College. 2nd Friday each month, 7.30 p.m.

Highlands Astronomical Society

Secretary: Richard Green, 11 Drumossie Avenue, Culcabock, Inverness IV2 3SJ.

Meetings: The Spectrum Centre, Inverness. 1st Tuesday each month, 7.30 p.m.

Hinckley & District Astronomical Society

Secretary: Mr S. Albrighton, 4 Walnut Close, The Bridleways, Hartshill, Nuneaton, Warwickshire CV10 0XH.

Meetings: Burbage Common Visitors Centre, Hinckley. 1st Tuesday Sept.–May, 7.30 p.m.

Horsham Astronomy Group (was **Forest Astronomical Society**)

Secretary: Dan White, 32 Burns Close, Horsham, West Sussex RH12 5PF.

Email: secretary@horshamastronomy.com

Meetings: 1st Wednesday each month.

Howards Astronomy Club

Secretary: H. Ilett, 22 St George's Avenue, Warblington, Havant, Hampshire.

Meetings: To be notified.

Huddersfield Astronomical and Philosophical Society

Secretary: Lisa B. Jeffries, 58 Beaumont Street, Netherton, Huddersfield, West Yorkshire HD4 7HE.

Email: l.b.jeffries@hud.ac.uk

Meetings: 4a Railway Street, Huddersfield. Every Wednesday and Friday, 7.30 p.m.

Hull and East Riding Astronomical Society

President: Rob Overfield, 125 Marlborough Avenue, Princes Avenue, Hull HU5 3JU.

Email: rob.overfield@btinternet.com

Meetings: The Wilberforce Building, Room SR110, University of Hull, Cottingham Road, Hull. 1st Monday each month, Sept.–Apr., 7.30–10.00 p.m.

Ilkeston & District Astronomical Society

Secretary: Mark Thomas, 2 Elm Avenue, Sandiacre, Nottingham NG10 5EJ.

Meetings: The Function Room, Erewash Museum, Anchor Row, Ilkeston. 2nd Tuesday monthly, 7.30 p.m.

Ipswich, Orwell Astronomical Society

Secretary: R. Gooding, 168 Ashcroft Road, Ipswich.

Meetings: Orwell Park Observatory, Nacton, Ipswich. Wednesdays, 8 p.m.

Irish Astronomical Association

President: Terry Moseley, 31 Sunderland Road, Belfast BT6 9LY, Northern Ireland.

Email: terrymosel@aol.com

Meetings: Ashby Building, Stranmillis Road, Belfast. Alternate Wednesdays, 7.30 p.m.

Irish Astronomical Society

Secretary: James O'Connor, PO Box 2547, Dublin 15, Eire.

Meetings: Ely House, 8 Ely Place, Dublin 2. 1st and 3rd Monday each month.

Isle of Man Astronomical Society

Secretary: James Martin, Ballaterson Farm, Peel, Isle of Man IM5 3AB.

Email: ballaterson@manx.net

Meetings: Isle of Man Observatory, Foxdale. 1st Thursday of each month, 8 p.m.

Isle of Wight Astronomical Society
Secretary: J. W. Feakins, 1 Hilltop Cottages, High Street, Freshwater, Isle of Wight.
Meetings: Unitarian Church Hall, Newport, Isle of Wight. Monthly.

Keele Astronomical Society
Secretary: Natalie Webb, Department of Physics, University of Keele, Keele, Staffordshire ST5 5BG.
Meetings: As arranged during term time.

Kettering and District Astronomical Society
Asst. Secretary: Steve Williams, 120 Brickhill Road, Wellingborough, Northamptonshire.
Meetings: Quaker Meeting Hall, Northall Street, Kettering, Northamptonshire. 1st Tuesday each month, 7.45 p.m.

King's Lynn Amateur Astronomical Association
Secretary: P. Twynman, 17 Poplar Avenue, RAF Marham, King's Lynn.
Meetings: As arranged.

Lancaster and Morecambe Astronomical Society
Secretary: Mrs E. Robinson, 4 Bedford Place, Lancaster LA1 4EB.
Email: ehelenerob@btinternet.com
Meetings: Church of the Ascension, Torrisholme. 1st Wednesday each month, except July and Aug.

Lancaster University Astronomical Society
Secretary: c/o Students' Union, Alexandra Square, University of Lancaster.
Meetings: As arranged.

Laymans Astronomical Society
Secretary: John Evans, 10 Arkwright Walk, The Meadows, Nottingham.
Meetings: The Popular, Bath Street, Ilkeston, Derbyshire. Monthly.

Leeds Astronomical Society
Secretary: Mark A. Simpson, 37 Roper Avenue, Gledhow, Leeds LS8 1LG.
Meetings: Centenary House, North Street. 2nd Wednesday each month, 7.30 p.m.

Leicester Astronomical Society
Secretary: Dr P.J. Scott, 21 Rembridge Close, Leicester LE3 9AP.
Meetings: Judgemeadow Community College, Marydene Drive, Evington, Leicester. 2nd and 4th Tuesdays each month, 7.30 p.m.

Letchworth and District Astronomical Society
Secretary: Eric Hutton, 14 Folly Close, Hitchin, Hertfordshire.
Meetings: As arranged.

Lewes Amateur Astronomers
Secretary: Christa Sutton, 8 Tower Road, Lancing, West Sussex BN15 9HT.
Meetings: The Bakehouse Studio, Lewes. Last Wednesday each month.

Limerick Astronomy Club
Secretary: Tony O'Hanlon, 26 Ballycannon Heights, Meelick, Co. Clare, Eire.
Meetings: Limerick Senior College, Limerick. Monthly (except June and Aug.), 8 p.m.

Lincoln Astronomical Society
Secretary: David Swaey, 'Everglades', 13 Beaufort Close, Lincoln LN2 4SF.
Meetings: The Lecture Hall, off Westcliffe Street, Lincoln. 1st Tuesday each month.

Liverpool Astronomical Society
Secretary: Mr K. Clark, 31 Sandymount Drive, Wallasey, Merseyside L45 0LJ.
Meetings: Lecture Theatre, Liverpool Museum. 3rd Friday each month, 7 p.m.

Norman Lockyer Observatory Society
Secretary: G.E. White, PO Box 9, Sidmouth EX10 0YQ.
Website: www.ex.ac.uk/nlo/; *Email:* g.e.white@ex.ac.uk
Meetings: Norman Lockyer Observatory, Sidmouth. Fridays and 2nd Monday each month, 7.30 p.m.

Loughton Astronomical Society
Secretary: Charles Munton, 14a Manor Road, Wood Green, London N22 4YJ.
Meetings: 1st Theydon Bois Scout Hall, Loughton Lane, Theydon Bois. Weekly.

Lowestoft and Great Yarmouth Regional Astronomers (LYRA) Society
Secretary: Simon Briggs, 28 Sussex Road, Lowestoft, Suffolk.
Meetings: Community Wing, Kirkley High School, Kirkley Run, Lowestoft. 3rd Thursday each month, 7.30 p.m.

Luton Astronomical Society
Secretary: Mr G. Mitchell, Putteridge Bury, University of Luton, Hitchin Road, Luton.
Website: www.lutonastrosoc.org.uk; *Email:* user998491@aol.com
Meetings: Putteridge Bury, Luton. Last Friday each month, 7.30 p.m.

Lytham St Annes Astronomical Association
Secretary: K.J. Porter, 141 Blackpool Road, Ansdell, Lytham St Anne's, Lancashire.
Meetings: College of Further Education, Clifton Drive South, Lytham St Anne's. 2nd Wednesday monthly Oct.–June.

Macclesfield Astronomical Society
Secretary: Mr John H. Thomson, 27 Woodbourne Road, Sale, Cheshire M33 3SY
Website: www.maccastro.com; *Email:* jhandlc@yahoo.com
Meetings: Jodrell Bank Science Centre, Goostrey, Cheshire. 1st Tuesday of every month, 7 p.m.

Maidenhead Astronomical Society
Secretary: Tim Haymes, Hill Rise, Knowl Hill Common, Knowl Hill, Reading RG10 9YD.
Meetings: Stubbings Church Hall, near Maidenhead. 1st Friday Sept.–June.

Maidstone Astronomical Society
Secretary: Stephen James, 4 The Cherry Orchard, Haddow, Tonbridge, Kent.
Meetings: Nettlestead Village Hall. 1st Tuesday in the month except July and Aug., 7.30 p.m.

Manchester Astronomical Society
Secretary: Mr Kevin J. Kilburn FRAS, Godlee Observatory, UMIST, Sackville Street, Manchester M60 1QD.
Website: www.u-net.com/ph/mas/; *Email:* kkilburn@globalnet.co.uk
Meetings: At the Godlee Observatory. Thursdays, 7 p.m., except below.
Free Public Lectures: Renold Building UMIST, third Thursday Sept.–Mar., 7.30 p.m.

Mansfield and Sutton Astronomical Society
Secretary: Angus Wright, Sherwood Observatory, Coxmoor Road, Sutton-in-Ashfield, Nottinghamshire NG17 5LF.
Meetings: Sherwood Observatory, Coxmoor Road. Last Tuesday each month, 7.30 p.m.

Mexborough and Swinton Astronomical Society
Secretary: Mark R. Benton, 14 Sandalwood Rise, Swinton, Mexborough, South Yorkshire S64 8PN.
Website: www.msas.org.uk; *Email:* mark@masas.f9.co.uk
Meetings: Swinton WMC. Thursdays, 7.30 p.m.

Mid-Kent Astronomical Society
Secretary: Peter Bassett, 167 Shakespeare Road, Gillingham, Kent ME7 5QB.
Meetings: Riverside Country Park, Lower Rainham Road, Gillingham. 2nd and last Fridays each month, 7.45 p.m.

Milton Keynes Astronomical Society
Secretary: Mike Leggett, 19 Matilda Gardens, Shenley Church End, Milton Keynes MK5 6HT.
Website: www.mkas.org.uk; *Email:* mike-pat-leggett@shenley9.fsnet.co.uk
Meetings: Rectory Cottage, Bletchley. Alternate Fridays.

Moray Astronomical Society
Secretary: Richard Pearce, 1 Forsyth Street, Hopeman, Elgin, Moray, Scotland.
Meetings: Village Hall Close, Co. Elgin.

Newbury Amateur Astronomical Society
Secretary: Miss Nicola Evans, 'Romaron', Bunces Lane, Burghfield Common, Reading RG7 3DG.
Meetings: United Reformed Church Hall, Cromwell Place, Newbury. 2nd Friday of month, Sept.–June.

Newcastle-on-Tyne Astronomical Society
Secretary: C.E. Willits, 24 Acomb Avenue, Seaton Delaval, Tyne and Wear.
Meetings: Zoology Lecture Theatre, Newcastle University. Monthly.

North Aston Space & Astronomical Club
Secretary: W.R. Chadburn, 14 Oakdale Road, North Aston, Sheffield.
Meetings: To be notified.

Northamptonshire Natural History Society (Astronomy Section)
Secretary: R.A. Marriott, 24 Thirlestane Road, Northampton NN4 8HD.
Email: ram@hamal.demon.co.uk
Meetings: Humfrey Rooms, Castilian Terrace, Northampton. 2nd and last Mondays, most months, 7.30 p.m.

Northants Amateur Astronomers
Secretary: Mervyn Lloyd, 76 Havelock Street, Kettering, Northamptonshire.
Meetings: 1st and 3rd Tuesdays each month, 7.30 p.m.

North Devon Astronomical Society
Secretary: P.G. Vickery, 12 Broad Park Crescent, Ilfracombe, Devon EX34 8DX.
Meetings: Methodist Hall, Rhododendron Avenue, Sticklepath, Barnstaple. 1st Wednesday each month, 7.15 p.m.

North Dorset Astronomical Society
Secretary: J.E.M. Coward, The Pharmacy, Stalbridge, Dorset.
Meetings: Charterhay, Stourton, Caundle, Dorset. 2nd Wednesday each month.

North Downs Astronomical Society
Secretary: Martin Akers, 36 Timber Tops, Lordswood, Chatham, Kent ME5 8XQ.
Meetings: Vigo Village Hall. 3rd Thursday each month. 7.30 p.m.

North-East London Astronomical Society
Secretary: Mr B. Beeston, 38 Abbey Road, Bush Hill Park, Enfield EN1 2QN.
Meetings: Wanstead House, The Green, Wanstead. 3rd Sunday each month (except Aug.), 3 p.m.

North Gwent and District Astronomical Society
Secretary: Jonathan Powell, 14 Lancaster Drive, Gilwern, nr Abergavenny, Monmouthshire NP7 0AA.
Meetings: Gilwern Community Centre. 15th of each month, 7.30 p.m.

North Staffordshire Astronomical Society
Secretary: Duncan Richardson, Halmerend Hall Farm, Halmerend, Stoke-on-Trent, Staffordshire ST7 8AW.
Email: dwr@enterprise.net
Meetings: 21st Hartstill Scout Group HQ, Mount Pleasant, Newcastle-under-Lyme ST5 1DR. 1st Tuesday each month (except July and Aug.), 7–9.30 p.m.

North Western Association of Variable Star Observers
Secretary: Jeremy Bullivant, 2 Beaminster Road, Heaton Mersey, Stockport, Cheshire.
Meetings: Four annually.

Norwich Astronomical Society
Secretary: Dave Balcombe, 52 Folly Road, Wymondham, Norfolk NR18 0QR.
Website: www.norwich.astronomical.society.org.uk
Meetings: Seething Observatory, Toad Lane, Thwaite St Mary, Norfolk. Every Friday, 7.30 p.m.

Nottingham Astronomical Society
Secretary: C. Brennan, 40 Swindon Close, The Vale, Giltbrook, Nottingham NG16 2WD.
Meetings: Djanogly City Technology College, Sherwood Rise (B682). 1st and 3rd Thursdays each month, 7.30 p.m.

Oldham Astronomical Society
Secretary: P.J. Collins, 25 Park Crescent, Chadderton, Oldham.
Meetings: Werneth Park Study Centre, Frederick Street, Oldham. Fortnightly, Friday.

Open University Astronomical Society
Secretary: Dr Andrew Norton, Department of Physics and Astronomy, The Open University, Walton Hall, Milton Keynes MK7 6AA.
Website: www.physics.open.ac.uk/research/astro/a_club.html
Meetings: Open University, Milton Keynes. 1st Tuesday of every month, 7.30 p.m.

Orpington Astronomical Society
Secretary: Dr Ian Carstairs, 38 Brabourne Rise, Beckenham, Kent BR3 2SG.
Meetings: High Elms Nature Centre, High Elms Country Park, High Elms Road, Farnborough, Kent. 4th Thursday each month, Sept.–July, 7.30 p.m.

Papworth Astronomy Club
Contact: Keith Tritton, Magpie Cottage, Fox Street, Great Gransden, Sandy, Bedfordshire SG19 3AA.
Email: kpt2@tutor.open.ac.uk
Meetings: Bradbury Progression Centre, Church Lane, Papworth Everard, nr Huntingdon. 1st Wednesday each month, 7 p.m.

Peterborough Astronomical Society
Secretary: Sheila Thorpe, 6 Cypress Close, Longthorpe, Peterborough.
Meetings: 1st Thursday every month, 7.30 p.m.

Plymouth Astronomical Society
Secretary: Alan G. Penman, 12 St Maurice View, Plympton, Plymouth, Devon PL7 1FQ.
Email: oakmount12@aol.com
Meetings: Glynis Kingham Centre, YMCA Annex, Lockyer Street, Plymouth. 2nd Friday each month, 7.30 p.m.

PONLAF
Secretary: Matthew Hepburn, 6 Court Road, Caterham, Surrey CR3 5RD.
Meetings: Room 5, 6th floor, Tower Block, University of North London. Last Friday each month during term time, 6.30 p.m.

Port Talbot Astronomical Society (formerly **Astronomical Society of Wales**)
Secretary: Mr J. Hawes, 15 Lodge Drive, Baglan, Port Talbot, West Glamorgan SA12 8UD.
Meetings: Port Talbot Arts Centre. 1st Tuesday each month, 7.15 p.m.

Portsmouth Astronomical Society
Secretary: G.B. Bryant, 81 Ringwood Road, Southsea.
Meetings: Monday, fortnightly.

Preston & District Astronomical Society
Secretary: P. Sloane, 77 Ribby Road, Wrea Green, Kirkham, Preston, Lancashire.
Meetings: Moor Park (Jeremiah Horrocks) Observatory, Preston. 2nd Wednesday, last Friday each month, 7.30 p.m.

Reading Astronomical Society
Secretary: Mrs Ruth Sumner, 22 Anson Crescent, Shinfield, Reading RG2 8JT.
Meetings: St Peter's Church Hall, Church Road, Earley. 3rd Friday each month, 7 p.m.

Renfrewshire Astronomical Society
Secretary: Ian Martin, 10 Aitken Road, Hamilton, South Lanarkshire ML3 7YA.
Website: www.renfrewshire-as.co.uk; *Email:* RenfrewAS@aol.com
Meetings: Coats Observatory, Oakshaw Street, Paisley. Fridays, 7.30 p.m.

Rower Astronomical Society
Secretary: Mary Kelly, Knockatore, The Rower, Thomastown, Co. Kilkenny, Eire.

St Helens Amateur Astronomical Society
Secretary: Carl Dingsdale, 125 Canberra Avenue, Thatto Heath, St Helens, Merseyside WA9 5RT.
Meetings: As arranged.

Salford Astronomical Society
Secretary: Mrs Kath Redford, 2 Albermarle Road, Swinton, Manchester M27 5ST.
Meetings: The Observatory, Chaseley Road, Salford. Wednesdays.

Salisbury Astronomical Society
Secretary: Mrs R. Collins, 3 Fairview Road, Salisbury, Wiltshire SP1 1JX.
Meetings: Glebe Hall, Winterbourne Earls, Salisbury. 1st Tuesday each month.

Sandbach Astronomical Society
Secretary: Phil Benson, 8 Gawsworth Drive, Sandbach, Cheshire.
Meetings: Sandbach School, as arranged.

Sawtry & District Astronomical Society
Secretary: Brooke Norton, 2 Newton Road, Sawtry, Huntingdon, Cambridgeshire PE17 5UT.
Meetings: Greenfields Cricket Pavilion, Sawtry Fen. Last Friday each month.

Scarborough & District Astronomical Society
Secretary: Mrs S. Anderson, Basin House Farm, Sawdon, Scarborough, North Yorkshire.
Meetings: Scarborough Public Library. Last Saturday each month, 7–9 p.m.

Scottish Astronomers Group
Secretary: Dr Ken Mackay, Hayford House, Cambusbarron, Stirling FK7 9PR.
Meetings: North of Hadrian's Wall, twice yearly.

Sheffield Astronomical Society
Secretary: Mr Andrew Green, 11 Lyons Street, Ellesmere, Sheffield S4 7QS.
Website: www.saqqara.demon.co.uk/sas/sashome.htm
Meetings: Twice monthly at Mayfield Environmental Education Centre, David Lane, Fulwood, Sheffield S10, 7.30–10 p.m.

Shetland Astronomical Society
Secretary: Peter Kelly, The Glebe, Fetlar, Shetland ZE2 9DJ.
Email: theglebe@zetnet.co.uk
Meetings: Fetlar, Fridays, Oct.–Mar.

Shropshire Astronomical Society
Secretary: Mrs Jacqui Dodds, 35 Marton Drive, Wellington, Telford TF1 3HL.
Website: www.astro.cf.ac.uk/sas/sasmain.html; *Email:* jacquidodds@ntlworld.com
Meetings: Gateway Arts and Education Centre, Chester Street, Shrewsbury. Occasional Fridays plus monthly observing meetings, Rodington Village Hall.

Sidmouth and District Astronomical Society
Secretary: M. Grant, Salters Meadow, Sidmouth, Devon.
Meetings: Norman Lockyer Observatory, Salcombe Hill. 1st Monday in each month.

Skipton & Craven Astronomical Society
Contact: Tony Ireland, 14 Cross Bank, Skipton, North Yorkshire BD23 6AH.
Email: scas@beeb.net
Meetings: Monthly, Oct.–April. For venue and times contact Mr Ireland.

Solent Amateur Astronomers
Secretary: Ken Medway, 443 Burgess Road, Swaythling, Southampton SO16 3BL.
Web site: www.delscope.demon.co.uk;
Email: kenmedway@kenmedway.demon.co.uk
Meetings: Room 8, Oaklands, Community School, Fairisle Road, Lordshill, Southampton. 3rd Tuesday each month, 7.30 p.m.

Southampton Astronomical Society
Secretary: John Thompson, 4 Heathfield, Hythe, Southampton SO45 5BJ.
Web site: www.home.clara.net/lmhobbs/sas.html;
Email: John.G.Thompson@Tesco.net
Meetings: Conference Room 3, The Civic Centre, Southampton. 2nd Thursday each month (except Aug.), 7.30 p.m.

South Downs Astronomical Society
Secretary: J. Green, 46 Central Avenue, Bognor Regis, West Sussex PO21 5HH.
Website: www.southdowns.org.uk
Meetings: Chichester High School for Boys. 1st Friday in each month (except Aug.).

South-East Essex Astronomical Society
Secretary: C.P. Jones, 29 Buller Road, Laindon, Essex.
Website: www.seeas.dabsol.co.uk/; *Email:* cpj@cix.co.uk
Meetings: Lecture Theatre, Central Library, Victoria Avenue, Southend-on-Sea. Generally 1st Thursday in month, Sept.–May, 7.30 p.m.

South-East Kent Astronomical Society
Secretary: Andrew McCarthy, 25 St Paul's Way, Sandgate, near Folkestone, Kent CT20 3NT.
Meetings: Monthly.

South Lincolnshire Astronomical & Geophysical Society
Secretary: Ian Farley, 12 West Road, Bourne, Lincolnshire PE10 9PS.
Meetings: Adult Education Study Centre, Pinchbeck. 3rd Wednesday each month, 7.30 p.m.

Southport Astronomical Society
Secretary: Patrick Brannon, Willow Cottage, 90 Jacksmere Lane, Scarisbrick, Ormskirk, Lancashire L40 9RS.
Meetings: Monthly Sept.–May, plus observing sessions.

Southport, Ormskirk and District Astronomical Society
Secretary: J.T. Harrison, 92 Cottage Lane, Ormskirk, Lancashire L39 3NJ.
Meetings: Saturday evenings, monthly, as arranged.

South Shields Astronomical Society
Secretary: c/o South Tyneside College, St George's Avenue, South Shields.
Meetings: Marine and Technical College. Each Thursday, 7.30 p.m.

South Somerset Astronomical Society
Secretary: G. McNelly, 11 Laxton Close, Taunton, Somerset.
Meetings: Victoria Inn, Skittle Alley, East Reach, Taunton, Somerset. Last Saturday each month, 7.30 p.m.

South-West Hertfordshire Astronomical Society
Secretary: Tom Walsh, 'Finches', Coleshill Lane, Winchmore Hill, Amersham, Buckinghamshire HP7 0NP.
Meetings: Rickmansworth. Last Friday each month, Sept.–May.

Stafford and District Astronomical Society
Secretary: Miss L. Hodkinson, 6 Elm Walk, Penkridge, Staffordshire ST19 5NL.
Meetings: Weston Road High School, Stafford. Every 3rd Thursday, Sept.–May, 7.15 p.m.

Stirling Astronomical Society
Secretary: Hamish MacPhee, 10 Causewayhead Road, Stirling FK9 5ER.
Meetings: Smith Museum & Art Gallery, Dumbarton Road, Stirling. 2nd Friday each month, 7.30 p.m.

Stoke-on-Trent Astronomical Society
Secretary: M. Pace, Sundale, Dunnocksfold, Alsager, Stoke-on-Trent.
Meetings: Cartwright House, Broad Street, Hanley. Monthly.

Stratford-upon-Avon Astronomical Society
Secretary: Robin Swinbourne, 18 Old Milverton, Leamington Spa, Warwickshire CV32 6SA.
Meetings: Tiddington Home Guard Club. 4th Tuesday each month, 7.30 p.m.

Sunderland Astronomical Society
Contact: Don Simpson, 78 Stratford Avenue, Grangetown, Sunderland SR2 8RZ.
Meetings: Friends Meeting House, Roker. 1st, 2nd and 3rd Sundays each month.

Sussex Astronomical Society
Secretary: Mrs C.G. Sutton, 75 Vale Road, Portslade, Sussex.
Meetings: English Language Centre, Third Avenue, Hove. Every Wednesday, 7.30–9.30 p.m., Sept.–May.

Swansea Astronomical Society
Secretary: Dr Michael Morales, 238 Heol Dulais, Birch Grove, Swansea SA7 9LH.
Website: www.crysania.co.uk/sas/astro/star
Meetings: Lecture Room C, Science Tower, University of Swansea. 2nd and 4th Thursday each month from Sept.–June, 7 p.m.

Tavistock Astronomical Society
Secretary: Mrs Ellie Coombes, Rosemount, Under Road, Gunnislake, Cornwall PL18 9JL.
Meetings: Science Laboratory, Kelly College, Tavistock. 1st Wednesday each month, 7.30 p.m.

Thames Valley Astronomical Group
Secretary: K.J. Pallet, 82a Tennyson Street, South Lambeth, London SW8 3TH.
Meetings: As arranged.

Thanet Amateur Astronomical Society
Secretary: P.F. Jordan, 85 Crescent Road, Ramsgate.
Meetings: Hilderstone House, Broadstairs, Kent. Monthly.

Torbay Astronomical Society
Secretary: Tim Moffat, 31 Netley Road, Newton Abbot, Devon TQ12 2LL.
Meetings: Torquay Boys' Grammar School, 1st Thursday in month; and Town Hall, Torquay, 3rd Thursday in month, Oct.–May, 7.30 p.m.

Tullamore Astronomical Society
Secretary: Tom Walsh, 25 Harbour Walk, Tullamore, Co. Offaly, Eire.
Website: www.iol.ie/seanmck/tas.htm; *Email:* tcwalsh25@yahoo.co.uk
Meetings: Order of Malta Lecture Hall, Tanyard, Tullamore, Co. Offaly, Eire. Mondays at 8 p.m., every fortnight.

Tyrone Astronomical Society
Secretary: John Ryan, 105 Coolnafranky Park, Cookstown, Co. Tyrone, Northern Ireland.
Meetings: Contact Secretary.

Usk Astronomical Society
Secretary: Bob Wright, 'Llwyn Celyn', 75 Woodland Road, Croesyceiliog, Cwmbran NP44 2OX.
Meetings: Usk Community Education Centre, Maryport Street, Usk. Every Thursday during school term, 7 p.m.

Vectis Astronomical Society
Secretary: Rosemary Pears, 1 Rockmount Cottages, Undercliff Drive, St Lawrence, Ventnor, Isle of Wight PO38 1XG.
Website: www.wightskies.fsnet.co.uk/main.html;
Email: may@tatemma.freeserve.co.uk
Meetings: Lord Louis Library Meeting Room, Newport. 4th Friday each month except Dec., 7.30 p.m.

Vigo Astronomical Society
Secretary: Robert Wilson, 43 Admers Wood, Vigo Village, Meopham, Kent DA13 0SP.
Meetings: Vigo Village Hall. As arranged.

Walsall Astronomical Society
Secretary: Bob Cleverley, 40 Mayfield Road, Sutton Coldfield B74 3PZ.
Meetings: Freetrade Inn, Wood Lane, Pelsall North Common. Every Thursday.

Wellingborough District Astronomical Society
Secretary: S.M. Williams, 120 Brickhill Road, Wellingborough, Northamptonshire.
Meetings: Gloucester Hall, Church Street, Wellingborough. 2nd Wednesday each month, 7.30 p.m.

Wessex Astronomical Society
Secretary: Leslie Fry, 14 Hanhum Road, Corfe Mullen, Dorset.
Meetings: Allendale Centre, Wimborne, Dorset. 1st Tuesday of each month.

West Cornwall Astronomical Society
Secretary: Dr R. Waddling, The Pines, Pennance Road, Falmouth, Cornwall TR11 4ED.
Meetings: Helston Football Club, 3rd Thursday each month, and St Michall's Hotel, 1st Wednesday each month, 7.30 p.m.

West of London Astronomical Society
Secretary: Duncan Radbourne, 28 Tavistock Road, Edgware, Middlesex HA8 6DA.
Website: www.wocas.org.uk
Meetings: Monthly, alternately in Uxbridge and North Harrow. 2nd Monday in month, except Aug.

West Midlands Astronomical Association
Secretary: Miss S. Bundy, 93 Greenridge Road, Handsworth Wood, Birmingham.
Meetings: Dr Johnson House, Bull Street, Birmingham. As arranged.

West Yorkshire Astronomical Society
Secretary: Pete Lunn, 21 Crawford Drive, Wakefield, West Yorkshire.
Meetings: Rosse Observatory, Carleton Community Centre, Carleton Road, Pontefract. Each Tuesday, 7.15 p.m.

Whitby and District Astronomical Society
Secretary: Rosemary Bowman, The Cottage, Larpool Drive, Whitby, North Yorkshire YO22 4ND.
Meetings: Whitby Mission, Seafarers' Centre, Haggersgate, Whitby. 1st Tuesday of the month, 7.30 p.m.

Whittington Astronomical Society
Secretary: Peter Williamson, The Observatory, Top Street, Whittington, Shropshire.
Meetings: The Observatory. Every month.

Wiltshire Astronomical Society
Secretary: Simon Barnes, 25 Woodcombe, Melksham, Wiltshire SN12 6HA.
Meetings: St Andrew's Church Hall, Church Lane, off Forest Road, Melksham, Wiltshire.

Wolverhampton Astronomical Society
Secretary: Mr M. Bryce, Iona, 16 Yellowhammer Court, Kidderminster, Worcestershire DY10 4RR.
Website: www.wolvas.org.uk; *Email:* michaelbryce@wolvas.org.uk
Meetings: Beckminster Methodist Church Hall, Birches Barn Road, Wolverhampton. Alternate Mondays, Sept.–Apr., extra dates in summer, 7.30 p.m.

Worcester Astronomical Society
Secretary: Mr S. Bateman, 12 Bozward Street, Worcester WR2 5DE.
Meetings: Room 117, Worcester College of Higher Education, Henwick Grove, Worcester. 2nd Thursday each month, 8 p.m.

Worthing Astronomical Society
Contact: G. Boots, 101 Ardingly Drive, Worthing, West Sussex BN12 4TW.
Website: www.worthingastro.freeserve.co.uk;
Email: gboots@observatory99.freeserve.co.uk
Meetings: Heene Church Rooms, Heene Road, Worthing. 1st Wednesday each month (except Aug.), 7.30 p.m.

Wycombe Astronomical Society

Secretary: Mr P. Treherne, 34 Honeysuckle Road, Widmer End, High Wycombe, Buckinghamshire HP15 6BW.

Meetings: Woodrow High House, Amersham. 3rd Wednesday each month, 7.45 p.m.

The York Astronomical Society

Contact: Hazel Collett, Public Relations Officer

Tel: 07944 751277

Website: www.yorkastro.freeserve.co.uk; *Email:* info@yorkastro.co.uk

Meetings: The Knavesmire Room, York Priory Street Centre, Priory Street, York. 1st and 3rd Friday of each month (except Aug.), 8 p.m.

Any society wishing to be included in this list of local societies or to update details, including any website addresses, is invited to write to the Editor (c/o Pan Macmillan, 20 New Wharf Road, London N1 9RR), so that the relevant information may be included in the next edition of the *Yearbook.*

The William Herschel Society maintains the museum established at 19 New King Street, Bath BA1 2BL – the only surviving Herschel House. It also undertakes activities of various kinds. New members would be welcome; those interested are asked to contact the Membership Secretary at the museum.

The South Downs Planetarium (Kingsham Farm, Kingsham Road, Chichester, West Sussex PO19 8RP) is now fully operational. For further information, visit www.southdowns.org.uk/sdpt or telephone (01243) 774400